PHYSICAL CHEMISTRY
OF THE
HYDROCARBONS

Edited by

ADALBERT FARKAS, PH.D.

VOLUME I

1950

ACADEMIC PRESS INC., PUBLISHERS

NEW YORK

FOREWORD

By HUGH S. TAYLOR, *Princeton, N. J.*

It is a far cry from Drake's well in Bradford, Pennsylvania, in the mid-nineteenth century to the petroleum industry of the mid-twentieth century. The ingredient that has been fed into the industry to produce the astonishing change is fundamental science. The lush period of growth has been the years between two World Wars. The demands of world conflict, the mechanization of armed might, the use of the internal combustion engine for propulsion, on the ground and in the air, provided the urge to develop still better methods of evaluating Nature's provision of oil supplies. Four decades ago it was sufficient to take from the ground what discovery revealed and, with primitive refining methods, produce what the crude oil supplies contained. An inadequate supply of gasoline prompted the first efforts to improve on the natural product. Straight distillation processes yielded to the original cracking processes to increase yields of the valuable gasoline fraction. Thereby was set in motion a whole train of operations designed to modify still further what Nature provided. Science, chemical science, became the handmaiden of the petroleum industry. The operator in the refinery yielded to the scientist and the chemical engineer.

These volumes are a record of how far this intrusion of science into an industry has proceeded. The distillation process is now subordinate to a whole host of chemical processes which take the hydrocarbon molecule from the ground, shatter it to bits and then remold it nearer to the heart's (or the consumer's) desire. That is why he who enters the petroleum or related industries today should enter equipped with the ultimate that modern physico-chemical science can provide. He must know something of the nature of the chemical bond, something of the thermodynamics of hydrocarbon systems. He must know how molecular structure can be explored with the tools of the physicist, with ultraviolet and infrared absorption spectra, for then he can use these properties to follow the change from normal butane to isobutane and hence understand new methods of producing 100-octane fuels. The mass-spectrograph, Aston's device for determining the abundance of isotopes in the ninety-odd elements of the Periodic Table, becomes a tool for the analysis of complex hydrocarbon mixtures defiant of any other tools of analytical measurement. And this is typical; each new advance in fundamental science has relevance to progress in the hydrocarbon industries. Even the lowly Phase Rule, which Nernst once patronized in his *Theoretical Chemistry*, becomes an indispensable tool for the solution of problems of separation by distillation or crystallization.

In brief, the young neophyte who would wish to venture into the petroleum industry today and leave on that industry the mark of his effort must come prepared with a scientific equipment of which his parent never knew or dreamed. Sound, solid scholarship in the fields of chemistry and physics are essential. If he would measure his equipment for the task let him scan these volumes, for they record what is known in this science of hydrocarbons. These are the records of how the industry utilizes science today. If he would write a new chapter it is from these that he will start. Let him also realize that the deeper the understanding of basic science the swifter can one proceed to a desired objective in the applications of science. That fact alone justifies these volumes as a service to hydrocarbon technology.

Preface

The last decade or two has witnessed an unprecedented development and ramification of hydrocarbon technology. The large-scale production of butadiene and styrene; the conversion of petroleum hydrocarbons to isooctane and toluene; the hydrogenation of coal; the synthesis of valuable hydrocarbons from carbon monoxide and hydrogen; the upgrading of gasoline by the judicious application of a number of novel isomerization, condensation, and cracking reactions are typical examples of the development during this period.

The technical progress which proved to be of decisive importance during World War II and has affected many of the products in daily use was made possible by the closest collaboration of science and industry. In the course of this cooperation, the problems of technology were given very close attention in the academic laboratories and conversely, methods and techniques previously reserved for the pure scientists found their way into industrial laboratories.

X-ray diffraction cameras, optical and mass spectrographs, and other complex physical and physicochemical equipment are being used extensively nowadays by the industry, and indeed the demand created by their remarkable usefulness made possible the commercial production of such instruments at a reasonable cost. Fundamental knowledge relating to the different states of aggregation of hydrocarbons; information on the mechanism of chemical reactions involving hydrocarbons; and data on physical properties are being used to great advantage in various separation and conversion processes of hydrocarbons and in their industrial applications.

The purpose of this book is to summarize the physicochemical basis of the new techniques and methods recently adopted by the hydrocarbons industry, and to help the research worker in exploiting these procedures more extensively and more intensively. Although it is fully appreciated that these data have previously been presented dispersed in various journals, monographs, and textbooks, it is felt that the harried researcher might get some benefit from a summary contained in a single book.

This book has been written primarily for the chemist, engineer, or physicist engaged in the petroleum, coal-tar, rubber, or terpene industry, or in some other branch of hydrocarbon technology or research. It is hoped, however, that workers in related fields and academic scientists also will find some useful information in this book to further their work.

In the treatment of the subject matter, emphasis was laid on theory rather than on the experimental side. References to techniques have been included, however, in cases in which this appeared warranted for more complete illustration.

The material covering the physicochemical basis of properties, reactions, separation, and analytical methods relating to hydrocarbons, is treated in two volumes, of which the present book is the first. The second volume will deal with physical properties such as refractive index, density, heat capacity, and viscosity; the chemical kinetics of hydrocarbon reactions; distillation; adsorption and other separation processes.

Since the individual chapters were written independently, there is some overlapping and repetition. It is hoped that this shortcoming will be overlooked in view of the attempt to make each section a self-contained article understandable without the perusal of any other chapter in the book.

If this volume is accorded a favorable reception it will be because of the efforts of the contributors.

Adalbert Farkas
Philadelphia, Pa.

CONTENTS

ix

Optical Methods of Hydrocarbon Analysis

By NORMAN D. COGGESHALL, *Gulf Research and Development Co.,*
Pittsburgh, Pennsylvania

Electrical Properties of Hydrocarbons

By ANDREW GEMANT, *The Detroit Edison Company, Detroit, Michigan*

Solvent Extraction of Hydrocarbons
Solubility Relations between Liquid Hydrocarbons and other Liquids

By ALFRED W. FRANCIS, *Socony-Vacuum Laboratories, Paulsboro, New Jersey*

Solid-Liquid Equilibria of Hydrocarbons

By M. R. CINES, *Phillips Petroleum Company, Research Department, Bartlesville,*
Oklahoma

Chemical Thermodynamic Equilibria among Hydrocarbons

By FREDERICK D. ROSSINI, *National Bureau of Standards, Washington, D. C.*

CHAPTER 1

THE CHEMICAL BOND IN HYDROCARBON MOLECULES

By

G. W. WHELAND

Department of Chemistry, University of Chicago, Chicago, Illinois

CONTENTS

I. HISTORICAL*

The first serious attempt to explain the nature of chemical valence was contained in the so-called *dualistic theory* of Davy and Berzelius. According to this theory, which held the field early in the nineteenth century, atoms in molecules have small electric charges, by virtue of which they attract or repel one another. However, as the information regarding substitution reactions increased, it became evident that an atom of a "negative" element like chlorine may replace an atom of a "positive" element like hydrogen (in a suitably chosen molecule) without causing any marked change in the properties of the compound. The dualistic theory was therefore abandoned, in spite of the vigorous efforts of Berzelius and others to save it. The *substitution theory* which succeeded it was soon replaced by various *type theories*, which in turn gave way (about 1855–1865) to the *structural theory* of Frankland, Couper, and Kekulé. A feature common to all these later theories, and one which distinguishes them from the earlier dualistic theory, is that they do not relate valence to any recognized type of force. Thus, in the structural formulas, for many years considered to be

---

* For further details regarding the early development of the valence theory, see any book on the history of chemistry, cf., for example, reference 1.

the most nearly complete descriptions possible, each valence bond is represented merely as a line. No attempt is made to explain the physical significance of the bond; the line which depicts it indicates merely a special relation (of unstated nature) between the two connected atoms.

The structural theory, in essentially the form in which Kekulé left it, still provides valid interpretations for much of the behavior of many substances. It is, however, not fully satisfactory, for it not only ignores the fundamental problem of the physical nature of valence, but it also fails to deal with some additional features of valence that will be discussed in the following paragraphs. In the course of the last eighty years, the theory has, accordingly, been considerably extended and elaborated, although its basic concepts have not been significantly altered.

The first important extension of the structural theory was made largely by van't Hoff (2) and by Le Bel (3), whose independent, but practically simultaneous, investigations opened the field now known as *stereochemistry*. This elaboration of the theory gave three-dimensional significance to the structural diagrams by assigning directions in space to the various valence bonds (or, more precisely, by assigning values to the angles between the pairs of valence bonds ending in the same multivalent atom). Somewhat later, by Werner's idea of *coordination* (4), the structural theory was extended to a large group of complex (mostly inorganic) substances, the so-called *coordination compounds*, which had not previously been included within the structural scheme. Neither the theory of stereochemistry nor that of coordination, however, shed any further light upon the nature of the valence bond, which remained, as before, an undefined concept, represented by a line. Moreover, the reasons for the empirically observed *quadri*valence of carbon, *uni*valence of hydrogen, and so on, were as mysterious as ever.

With the development of the *electronic theory* of valence (5) the source of the forces responsible for covalent bonds began to become apparent. Although, in a certain sense, this new theory merely replaced each valence line in a structural formula by a pair of dots, it went much further than its predecessor had gone, since it assigned a physical significance to the symbols (i.e., the dots) employed. Thus, the electronic structure I of hydrogen sug-

$$
\begin{array}{cc}
\text{H:H} & \text{H—H} \\
\text{I} & \text{II}
\end{array}
$$

gests, in a way in which its older analog II does not, that a pair of electrons tends, at least on the average, to occupy the region between the two protons, and hence to be *shared* by the two atoms. At one time Lewis proposed that the *magnetic* interaction between the two electrons involved in a covalent bond might be responsible for the valence force. It was soon realized,

however, that such an interaction, although it doubtless exists, is much too
small to account for more than a minute fraction of the total strength of
the bond. Accordingly, an alternative view was accepted; it was concluded
that the *electrostatic* attraction between the two negatively charged valence
electrons and the two positively charged atomic kernels is the major factor
leading to the formation of a stable covalent bond.

That such an interaction does indeed account for the existence of a bond
may be shown in the following way. The potential energy E_1 of electrostatic

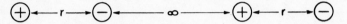

FIG. 1. A model of two isolated atoms with one valence electron each.

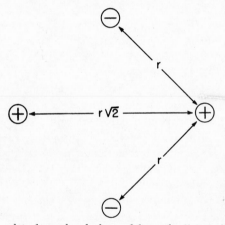

FIG. 2. A model of a molecule formed from the "atoms" of Fig. 1.

interaction between an atomic kernel of charge $+e$ and an electron of charge
$-e$, separated by a distance r, is shown by Coulomb's law to be

$$E_1 = -e^2/r \tag{1}$$

Since the potential energy of a second and exactly similar system is also
E_1, the total potential energy of the two systems, when distant from one
another (as in Fig. 1), is $2E_1$, or $-2e^2/r$. But, if the two systems approach
each other so that they interact, the total potential energy changes. In
particular, if they approach so that the two kernels occupy two diagonal
corners of a square with sides equal to r, and the two electrons occupy the
remaining corners of the square (as in Fig. 2), then the total potential
energy of the united system is decreased to

$$E_2 = -(4e^2/r) + (2e^2/r\sqrt{2}) = -2.586e^2/r \tag{2}$$

Here, the decrease in total potential energy (caused by the interaction of the two original systems) is

$$\Delta E = 2E_1 - E_2 = 0.586e^2/r \qquad (3)$$

If r is assigned the value $1.0\,A$. (1.0 angstrom unit, or 1.0×10^{-8} cm., which is the order of magnitude of atomic and molecular dimensions), then, since e is approximately equal to 4.80×10^{-10} electrostatic units of charge (e.s.u.), ΔE is about 1.35×10^{-11} erg, or about 190 kcal. for a "mole" of the combined systems depicted in Fig. 2. If the independent systems of Fig. 1 are accepted as models of two isolated atoms with one valence electron each, and if the combined system of Fig. 2 is accepted as a model of a molecule formed from these two "atoms," the origin of the "bond" in the "molecule" is evident.

The preceding treatment is, of course, grossly oversimplified since it is based on the certainly incorrect assumption that the electrons can be treated as if they were definitely localized, and since it ignores the *kinetic* energies of the particles involved. Moreover, there is no reason to assume that the distances r in Figs. 1 and 2 must be equal, although these distances are probably of the same order of magnitude. Nevertheless, the calculation is of interest since it shows, though only very crudely, that the electrostatic interactions between the electrons and the atomic kernels *can* lead to the formation of a stable bond if the electrons are concentrated in the region between the kernels (i.e., if they are shared by the atoms). Moreover, it is significant that the calculated "bond energy" ΔE is of the right order of magnitude, for this fact shows the superiority of the electrostatic interpretation over the earlier view that covalent bonds result from the much weaker magnetic interactions. (Actually, the ΔE here calculated is probably more than twice too large, since the energies of most single bonds lie between 50 and 100 kcal. per mole. However, either increase in the "bond length" $r\sqrt{2}$ or inclusion of the neglected kinetic energies, or both, would reduce the calculated value of ΔE.)

The electronic theory of valence not only describes satisfactorily the forces responsible for covalent bonds, but also leads to an understanding of electrovalence and of Werner's coordinate bonds. Moreover, it also accounts for the observed values of the valences of the various elements. Thus, for example, the ionic valence in potassium chloride is formed by the transfer of an electron from the potassium to the chlorine atom. The two resulting ions, each of which has the specially stable electronic "configuration" (see p. 18) of an atom of the rare gas argon, are then attracted to each other by essentially the same sort of electrostatic force postulated in the dualistic theory of Davy and Berzelius. The coordinate bond between the cobalt atom and any one of the nitrogen atoms in the hexamminocobaltic ion

$[Co(NH_3)_6]^{+++}$ is formed by the sharing of two electrons, both of which come from the molecule of ammonia. Finally, the inability of an atom of hydrogen to form more than one covalent bond, and the inability of an atom of any element in the first row of the periodic table to form more than four such bonds, are likewise nicely explained; the reason for these restrictions is that a hydrogen atom completes its valence shell with two electrons (as in the rare gas helium), whereas an atom of any first-row element completes *its* valence shell with eight electrons (as in the rare gas neon). In all these instances, the relative ease with which an atom goes over to the specially stable electronic configuration of a rare gas plays an essential role in compound formation.

The electronic theory thus accounts for the existence of valence forces, correlates the earlier theories mentioned above, and interprets the observed values of the valences of the various elements. It is, however, still not fully satisfactory since it leaves a number of questions unanswered. For instance, although it relates the saturation of valence to the completeness of the valence shells in the rare gases, it does not explain why these shells become complete just when they do, nor even why they should ever become complete at all. Moreover, it adds little, if anything, to the chemists' understanding of stereochemistry, in spite of several ingenious attempts to squeeze stereochemical interpretations out of it. And finally, the picture of the covalent bond which it presents is unsatisfactory in several respects. In particular, although the discussion just given leads to a reasonable *qualitative* interpretation of the covalent forces, it suggests no practical way to calculate *quantitatively* the energies, or any other properties, of covalent bonds. Only with the development of quantum mechanics has this last difficulty been overcome, so that a more satisfactory quantitative treatment of valence is now possible. Although the mathematical complexities of the equations involved in the quantum-mechanical method (cf. the following sections) have so far prevented precise numerical calculations for any molecule larger than that of hydrogen, H_2, the techniques now *in principle* available appear to provide very nearly, if not quite, the complete solution for the problem of valence.

If the single atomic models of Fig. 1 and the molecular model of Fig. 2 were taken as entirely satisfactory descriptions of the respective systems, then both the "atom" and the "molecule" should become more and more stable without limit as r decreases. Each of these systems would therefore collapse to a single point, with r equal to zero, and hence would have a potential energy of $-\infty$. The considerations by which quantum mechanics avoids this "infinity catastrophe" are of sufficient interest to merit a brief description here. For example, as the "molecule" of Fig. 2 becomes smaller, the volume available for each electron (i.e., the region between the two kernels) decreases. According to the so-called *uncertainty principle* (6), this process requires an increase in the *kinetic* energy. Consequently, although the potential energy continues to decrease without limit as the "molecule" shrinks, the system finally reaches a critical size where, with any further contraction, the kinetic energy rises faster than the potential energy falls. This critical size corresponds to the lowest possible value of the still finite *total* energy, and hence represents the true size of the molecule.

The quantum-mechanical interpretation of valence not only shows the way to make valid quantitative calculations of bond energies and bond lengths; it also supplements the electronic theory in still other respects in which the latter is known to be inadequate. For example, it accounts for the saturation of valence and for the stereochemical properties of covalent bonds. Moreover, it leads directly to the *theory of resonance* and thus, by introducing a more general concept of valence, throws light for the first time on several puzzling aspects of chemistry, such as the characteristic and unexpected properties of aromatic substances. The remainder of this chapter will be devoted to discussions of these aspects of quantum mechanics.

II. Principles of Quantum Mechanics (7)

In this section, and in the immediately following ones, the quantum-mechanical treatment of valence will be outlined briefly. Unfortunately, but unavoidably, the discussion will be rather mathematical; in particular, it will involve a large number of more or less complicated equations. However, any reader who does not wish to follow the logical development of the theory, and who is principally interested in the final conclusions reached, may skip these sections and proceed directly to the section entitled *Recapitulation of the Quantum-Mechanical Treatment of Valence* (p. 25).

The quantum-mechanical description of any atom or molecule is contained in its so-called *wave function, proper function,* or *eigenfunction.* (The three expressions are synonymous.) This function is obtainable in principle, though usually not in practice, by the solution of a certain partial differential equation (known as the *wave equation* or *Schrödinger equation*), which assumes a characteristic form for each different kind of atom or molecule. (For more specific descriptions of such wave equations, see below.)

Although the wave equations can rarely be solved *rigorously* by methods now known, *approximate* solutions can frequently be obtained by the aid of suitable simplifying assumptions. The first, and least drastic, of these assumptions is that the complete wave function of any system can be expressed as the product of certain simpler functions, each of which is itself the solution of its own simpler (and usually only approximate) wave equation. One of these simpler functions involves the time as its only variable.

Besides this function, there are four others, of which the first refers to the translational motion of the center of gravity of the system; the second (involved only in systems containing two or more atoms) refers to the rotation of the molecule as a rigid body; the third (likewise involved only in systems containing two or more atoms) refers to the vibrations of the atoms about their positions of minimum potential energy; and the fourth refers to the motions of the electrons in the electromagnetic field produced by the electrons themselves and by the atomic nuclei, here supposed to be *stationary*. When the indicated method of approximating wave functions is adopted, the total energy of the system in question is expressed as the sum of a translational, a rotational, a vibrational, and an electronic energy, related, respectively, to the four types of motion just listed (8).

Although all five (or, in a monatomic system, all three) of the above functions are essential for the complete wave function of the system, only the last one (the so-called *electronic wave function*) is of sufficient importance in the treatment of valence to be discussed here in any detail. If the comparatively minute magnetic interactions and relativistic corrections are ignored (as is usual in discussions of molecular structure), the approximate wave equation satisfied by the electronic wave function is expressed in the general form

$$H\psi \equiv -\frac{h^2}{8\pi^2 m} \sum_j \left(\frac{\partial^2 \psi}{\partial x_j^2} + \frac{\partial^2 \psi}{\partial y_j^2} + \frac{\partial^2 \psi}{\partial z_j^2} \right) + V\psi = W\psi \qquad (4)$$

The symbols here used have the following meanings: H is the *Hamiltonian operator* which (as is indicated by the use, at the left, of the identity sign $\equiv$ instead of the equality sign $=$) is defined in the equation itself; h is *Planck's constant* (approximately equal to 6.6×10^{-27} erg sec.); and m is the mass of an electron. The wave function ψ is a function not only of the three cartesian coordinates x_j, y_j, and z_j of each electron j, but also of the *spin coordinate* σ_j of each electron (see below). The summation over j includes all the electrons in the atom or molecule. Moreover, W is a constant with the dimensions of energy; it is equal to the electronic energy (see the preceding paragraph) of the system described by the function ψ. Finally, V is the potential energy which, in field-free space, assumes the form

$$V = \sum_j \sum_{k<j} e^2/r_{jk} + \sum_A \sum_{B<A} Z_A Z_B e^2/r_{AB} - \sum_j \sum_A Z_A e^2/r_{jA} \qquad (5)$$

In this last equation, e is the magnitude of the electronic charge (approximately 4.80×10^{-10} e.s.u.); Z_A and Z_B are respectively, the atomic numbers of the Ath and Bth atoms; r_{jk} is the distance between the jth and kth electrons; r_{jA} is the distance between the jth electron and the nucleus of the

Ath atom; and r_{AB} is the distance between the nuclei of the Ath and Bth atoms. As stated above, the nuclei are here considered to be stationary and hence precisely located at points in space which are fully defined with respect to one another. Clearly, the first term on the right of equation 5 corresponds to the electrostatic interaction among the electrons; the second corresponds to that among the atomic nuclei; and the third corresponds to that between the electrons and the nuclei.

In equation 4, the Hamiltonian operator, wave function, and energy ought strictly to be designated, respectively, by the symbols H_{elec}, ψ_{elec}, and W_{elec}, where the subscripts indicate that the various quantities refer to the approximate electronic, and not to the complete, wave equation. The simpler expressions H, ψ, and W will be used, however, throughout this chapter, since they cannot here give rise to any confusion.

A wave function ψ, in order that it may have the physical significance assigned to it below, must satisfy certain other mathematical conditions besides the one that it be a solution of the wave equation 4. In the first place, ψ and its first derivative with respect to each of the spatial coordinates x_j, y_j, and z_j must be a *continuous* function of these coordinates. In the second place, ψ must be *single-valued*. In the third place, ψ should remain *finite* for all sets of values of the spatial coordinates; at worst, it may become infinite only for isolated sets of values, and then only provided that certain further conditions (not here described) are satisfied. Finally, ψ must have the correct *symmetry properties* with respect to permutations of the electrons. Thus, in ψ, if all four coordinates of the jth electron (i.e., the three spatial coordinates x_j, y_j, and z_j, and the one spin coordinate σ_j) are replaced by the corresponding coordinates of the kth electron, and vice versa, the resulting function must be identically equal to $-\psi$. This rule, which contains the most general statement of the so-called *Pauli exclusion principle*, is frequently expressed in an equivalent form by the statement that an acceptable wave function must be *completely antisymmetric* with respect to interchanges of the electrons. Later in this chapter, the significance of these rather abstract symmetry considerations will be more fully explained.

In the complete wave function, of which the electronic function discussed here is only one factor, analogous rules apply also to the interchanges of the coordinates of equivalent *atomic nuclei*. These rules turn out, however, to be relatively unimportant in the discussion of valence; hence they need not be stated here.

Investigation of the mathematical form of the wave equation 4 has shown that, in general, this equation can have a solution ψ which satisfies all the conditions stated above, only if the constant W (i.e., the electronic energy) is one of a specified set of values known as the *proper values* or *eigenvalues* of the equation. Consequently, since any atom or molecule must be describable by a wave function ψ which is a solution of equation 4, it follows that the eigenvalues represent the only permissible values for the electronic energy of the system. Accordingly, the lowest eigenvalue is equal to the electronic energy of the atom or molecule in its most stable state. Determining the eigenvalues of any wave equation is essentially equivalent to solving that equation.

The wave function ψ of an atom or molecule in any given state is important not only because of the relation (equation 4) between it and the corresponding eigenvalue, but also because of its direct physical significance; indeed, with its aid, many properties of the system besides the energy can be calculated. For example, if ψ is the wave function of any given atom or molecule, and if ψ^* is the complex conjugate of ψ (i.e., the function obtained from ψ by the replacement of the imaginary unit i, wherever it occurs, by $-i$, and vice versa) the product $\psi^*\psi$, which is a function of the spatial and spin coordinates of all the electrons, is necessarily real; and it must have a nonnegative value no matter how the values of the coordinates are chosen. Moreover, if $\psi^*\psi$ is integrated (or, more precisely, summed) over all the permissible values of the spin coordinates of all the electrons, the resulting function

$$Q \equiv \sum_{\sigma_1} \cdots \sum_{\sigma_p} \psi^*\psi \tag{6}$$

is a function of the spatial coordinates alone and is, like $\psi^*\psi$ itself, real and nonnegative. (In the identity 6, p is the total number of electrons in the system.) The physical significance of Q, and hence also that of the original function ψ, follows from the fundamental postulate that the quantity $Qd\tau$, defined by the identity

$$Qd\tau \equiv Qdx_1 dy_1 dz_1 dx_2 \cdots dy_p dz_p \tag{7}$$

is proportional to the probability that an experiment carried out upon the system in the state described by ψ will find that system in the volume element $d\tau$. In other words, the postulate in question states that $Qd\tau$ is proportional to the probability that the experiment will show the coordinates of the first electron to lie between x_1, y_1, z_1 and $x_1 + dx_1$, $y_1 + dy_1$, $z_1 + dz_1$, respectively; those of the second electron to lie between x_2, y_2, z_2 and $x_2 + dx_2$, $y_2 + dy_2$, $z_2 + dz_2$, respectively; and so on for all p electrons. If the integral

$$I \equiv \int_{x_1=-\infty}^{+\infty} \int_{y_1=-\infty}^{+\infty} \cdots \int_{z_p=-\infty}^{+\infty} Qdx_1 dy_1 dz_1 dx_2 \cdots dy_p dz_p \tag{8}$$

is equal to unity, the original function ψ is said to be *normalized*; then the expression $Qd\tau$ is equal to, and not merely proportional to, the probability referred to above. The wave functions mentioned hereafter will in most instances be considered to be normalized. Analogous, but usually more complicated, mathematical procedures are available for calculating the probability of obtaining a specified result in any further type of experiment, where some property of the system other than the positions of its particles is under investigation.

In the quantum-mechanical treatment of valence the principles just outlined are applied as follows. First, the wave equations for the various individual (i.e., isolated) atoms are solved. The lowest eigenvalue of each equation gives the energy of the corresponding atom in its most stable (i.e., ground) state. Next, the wave equation for the molecule is solved; in this latter step, as has been emphasized above, the various atomic nuclei are considered to be at certain positions, definitely fixed with respect to one another. The lowest eigenvalue found then gives the energy which the molecule in its ground electronic state would have if the nuclei could actually be held in the assumed fixed relative positions. If such a calculation is performed for each of several different sets of nuclear positions, the dependence of the lowest eigenvalue upon these positions can be determined. Obviously, the particular set of nuclear positions for which this lowest eigenvalue is a minimum must correspond (aside from the small effect of the ignored vibrations) to the true size and shape of the molecule in its ground state. The treatment therefore gives the value of each bond length and bond angle. Moreover, the amount of energy liberated when the molecule is formed from isolated atoms (in other words, the sum of the bond energies, when the small effects due to translation, rotation, and vibration are neglected) can be obtained by subtracting the energy of the molecule from the sum of the energies of the isolated atoms.

If a still more precise value of the total energy is desired, the translational, rotational, and vibrational energies can also be computed. Thus, for any gaseous substance, whether its molecules be monatomic or polyatomic, the translational energy is equal to $3RT/2$. (R is the gas constant and T is the absolute temperature.) Moreover, the rotational energy can be taken as zero if the substance is monatomic; as RT if the substance is composed of *linear* molecules; or as $3RT/2$ if it is composed of *nonlinear* molecules. (Some substances, like molecular hydrogen, deviate considerably from this second rule at extremely low temperatures; such deviations are, however, not important for any hydrocarbon.) Finally, the vibrational energy is determined by the force constants for bending and stretching; these constants are themselves determined by the second derivatives of the electronic energies with respect to the coordinates of the nuclei.

In principle, therefore, the problem of valence is solved. *In practice*, however, purely mathematical difficulties have so far prevented the application of the procedure outlined to any except the very simplest molecules. In fact, the most complicated molecule so far treated without the introduction of further and still more drastic simplifications, is that of hydrogen, H_2 (9), and even for this molecule, the simplified wave equation 4 has not been *quite* rigorously solved. Thus, quantum mechanics has not yet fulfilled its promise to provide precise answers to all questions concerning valence and molecular structure. Nevertheless, by the introduction of additional approximations and simplifying assumptions, many of the computations can be so much simplified that they become practicable. The results of such approximate calculations, although *quantitatively* of little, if any, validity, may still be *qualitatively* significant. The remainder of this chapter will accordingly deal largely with such approximate procedures.

III. Central-Field Wave Functions (7)

The first of the more drastic approximations adopted in the treatment of atomic and molecular structure is the replacement of the individual electrostatic interactions between the different pairs of electrons (i.e , the replacement of the term $\sum_{j}\sum_{k<i} e^2/r_{jk}$ of equation 5) by the sum of the *average* interactions between each electron and all the remaining electrons. The relatively rigorous equation 5 is therefore replaced by the much more approximate one

$$V = \sum_{j} V_j(x_j, y_j, z_j) + \sum_{A}\sum_{B<A} Z_A Z_B e^2/r_{AB} - \sum_{j}\sum_{A} Z_A e^2/r_{jA} \quad (9)$$

where $V_j(x_j, y_j, z_j)$ represents the above-mentioned average interaction of the jth electron with all the other electrons. Here, evidently $V_j(x_j, y_j, z_j)$ is a function only of the coordinates of the jth electron. The meaning of this approximation is that each electron is considered to be moving *as if alone* in the potential field $V_j - \sum_{A} Z_A e^2/r_{jA}$. (The second term on the right of equation 9, although an essential part of the *total* potential V, does not *directly* affect the motion of the jth electron.) The finer details of the interelectronic interactions are thus ignored; in particular, no account is taken of the tendency of the electrons, because of their like charges, to remain at considerable distances from one another.

When the system under discussion is a single isolated atom, only a small additional approximation is introduced by the further assumption that the potentials $V_j(x_j, y_j, z_j)$ of equation 9 are of the central-field type (i.e., that they are spherically symmetric and are thus functions only of the distances

r_j of the corresponding electrons from the one nucleus present). The electronic wave equation 4 then assumes the form

$$H\psi \equiv \sum_j \left\{ -\frac{h^2}{8\pi^2 m} \left[\frac{1}{r_j^2} \frac{\partial}{\partial r_j} \left(r_j^2 \frac{\partial \psi}{\partial r_j} \right) + \frac{1}{r_j^2 \sin \theta_j} \frac{\partial}{\partial \theta_j} \left(\sin \theta_j \frac{\partial \psi}{\partial \theta_j} \right) \right. \right.$$
$$\left. \left. + \frac{1}{r_j^2 \sin^2 \theta_j} \frac{\partial^2 \psi}{\partial \phi_j^2} \right] + V_j(r_j)\psi - \frac{Ze^2}{r_j} \psi \right\} = W\psi \tag{10}$$

in which the cartesian coordinates x_j, y_j, and z_j (used heretofore) are transformed into spherical polar coordinates r_j, θ_j, and ϕ_j, with the nucleus at the origin. (The second term on the right of equation 9 does not enter here since there is only one nucleus; the third term reduces to merely $-\sum_j Ze^2/r_j$.) The state of each individual electron in the atom can then be approximately described by some one solution $\psi_{nlm_lm_s}(j)$ of the *one-electron* wave equation

$$H\psi_{nlm_lm_s}(j) \equiv -\frac{h^2}{8\pi^2 m} \left\{ \frac{1}{r_j^2} \frac{\partial}{\partial r_j} \left[r_j^2 \frac{\partial \psi_{nlm_lm_s}(j)}{\partial r_j} \right] \right.$$
$$+ \frac{1}{r_j^2 \sin \theta_j} \frac{\partial}{\partial \theta_j} \left[\sin \theta_j \frac{\partial \psi_{nlm_lm_s}(j)}{\partial \theta_j} \right] + \frac{1}{r_j^2 \sin^2 \theta_j} \frac{\partial^2 \psi_{nlm_lm_s}(j)}{\partial \phi_j^2} \right\} \tag{11}$$
$$+ V_j(r_j)\psi_{nlm_lm_s}(j) - \frac{Ze^2}{r_j} \psi_{nlm_lm_s}(j) = W_{nl}\psi_{nlm_lm_s}(j)$$

Here, the symbol (j) represents the complete set of four coordinates r_j, θ_j, ϕ_j, and σ_j of the jth electron; the significance of the subscripts n, l, m_l, and m_s is explained below.

Since, ordinarily, the explicit form of the potential $V_j(r_j)$ is not known, usually no complete solution of equation 11 can be obtained. Nevertheless, several important properties of all the solutions can be derived from certain general characteristics of the equation. Thus, from the fact that, in this equation, the spin coordinate σ_j occurs only in the solution $\psi_{nlm_lm_s}(j)$ itself, and from the further fact that the potential $V_j(r_j) - Ze^2/r_j$ is spherically symmetric, it follows that the solution can be expressed as the product of four factors

$$\psi_{nlm_lm_s}(j) = R_{nl}(r_j)\Theta_{lm_l}(\theta_j)\Phi_{m_l}(\phi_j)\Omega_{m_s}(\sigma_j) \tag{12}$$

The first of these factors, $R_{nl}(r_j)$, is a function of only the radial coordinate r_j; the second, $\Theta_{lm_l}(\theta_j)$, is a function of only the angular coordinate θ_j; the third, $\Phi_{m_l}(\phi_j)$, is a function of only the remaining angular coordinate ϕ_j; and the fourth, $\Omega_{m_s}(\sigma_j)$ is a function of only the spin coordinate σ_j. The complete function $\psi_{nlm_lm_s}(j)$ depends not only on the four independent *vari-*

ables r_j, θ_j, ϕ_j, and σ_j, but also upon four *constants n, l, m_l*, and *m_s*, which are known, respectively, as the principal, azimuthal, magnetic, and spin *quantum numbers*; these constants are restricted to the following values.

$$n = 1, 2, 3, \cdots \tag{13}$$
$$l = 0, 1, 2, \cdots (n-1) \tag{14}$$
$$m_l = 0, \pm 1, \pm 2, \cdots \pm l \tag{15}$$
$$m_s = \pm (1/2) \tag{16}$$

Since the eigenvalues W_{nl} of equation 11 do not depend upon the quantum numbers m_l and m_s, and since, for any specified pair of values of n and l, several choices of m_l and m_s are usually permitted by equations 13–16, it follows that more than one function $\psi_{nlm_lm_s}(j)$ may correspond to the same energy W_{nl}. Such functions of equal energy are said to be *degenerate*. An important property of the degenerate solutions of equation 11 is that any *linear combination* of these solutions is also a solution. Thus, the most general solution of equation 11 is expressed in the form

$$\psi_{nl}(j) = \sum_{m_l} \sum_{m_s} a_{m_lm_s} \psi_{nlm_lm_s}(j) \tag{17}$$

where the a's are arbitrary constants. (There is here *no* summation over n or l, because functions which differ with respect to n or l are usually not degenerate.)

The spin-free function χ_{nlm_l} of the spatial coordinates of a single electron

$$\chi_{nlm_l} = R_{nl}(r)\Theta_{lm_l}(\theta)\Phi_{m_l}(\phi) \tag{18}$$

is conveniently referred to as an *orbital*. Any such orbital can be specified completely, as shown above, by means of its three quantum numbers n, l, and m_l; or, less completely, by means of its principal quantum number n, together with the letter s, p, d, f, g, $\cdots$ when the value of the azimuthal quantum number l is, respectively, 0, 1, 2, 3, 4, $\cdots$. Thus, a $1s$ orbital is one for which n is èqual to 1 and l is equal to 0; a $3p$ orbital is one for which n is equal to 3 and l is equal to 1; and so on. Orbitals with n equal to 1, 2, 3, $\cdots$ are said to belong, respectively, to the K, L, M, $\cdots$ shells.

Neither the function $R_{nl}(r)$ nor the value of the energy W_{nl} can be determined until the potential $V(r)$ is known. Nevertheless, in any given atom, the values of r for which $R_{nl}(r)$ is of greatest magnitude always increase as either n or l increases. Consequently, in view of the relationship (discussed above) between a wave function and the probability of finding the corresponding electron at any given place, it follows that the smaller the value of n or of l (or of both), the more likely is the electron to be in the region near the nucleus. Since this region is one of relatively low energy, the eigenvalue W_{nl} must increase as n and l increase. The most stable orbital is therefore the $1s$ one, where n and l have their lowest possible values; for the remaining orbitals, the order of decreasing stability is $2s$, $2p$, $3s$, $\cdots$. In hydrocarbons, only the orbitals of the K and L shells are important, and so no reference will be made hereafter to orbitals that lie outside the L shell, where the value of n is greater than 2.

The angular functions $\Theta_{lm_l}(\theta)$ and $\Phi_{m_l}(\phi)$, unlike the radial function $R_{nl}(r)$, can be obtained by solution of wave equation 11. The resulting orbitals of the K and L shells can be put in the following forms.

$$1s: \quad \chi_{100} = R_{10}(r) \tag{19}$$
$$2s: \quad \chi_{200} = R_{20}(r) \tag{20}$$
$$2p: \begin{cases} \chi_{211} = \sqrt{2}/2 R_{21}(r)\sin\theta e^{i\phi} & (21) \\ \chi_{210} = R_{21}(r)\cos\theta & (22) \\ \chi_{21\bar{1}} = \sqrt{2}/2 R_{21}(r)\sin\theta e^{-i\phi} & (23) \end{cases}$$

(In equations 21 and 23, the letter e represents the logarithmic base 2.718..., and not, as heretofore, the magnitude of the electronic charge; the factors $\sqrt{2}/2$ are introduced for purposes of normalization.) In the treatment of most, but not all, problems of molecular structure, it has been found convenient to replace the *complex* functions χ_{211} and $\chi_{21\bar{1}}$ (which contain the imaginary unit i) by *real* linear combinations of them. (The use of the linear combinations is permitted here since χ_{211} and $\chi_{21\bar{1}}$ are degenerate. See above.) The $2p$ functions of equations 21–23 can thus be recast into the forms

$$2p: \begin{cases} \chi_{2px} = \sqrt{2}/2(\chi_{211} + \chi_{21\bar{1}}) = R_{2p}(r)\, r\sin\theta\,\cos\phi & (24) \\ \qquad\quad = R_{2p}(r)\, x & \\ \chi_{2py} = -i\sqrt{2}/2(\chi_{211} - \chi_{21\bar{1}}) = R_{2p}(r)\, r\sin\theta\,\sin\phi & (25) \\ \qquad\quad = R_{2p}(r)\, y & \\ \chi_{2pz} = \chi_{210} = R_{2p}(r)\, r\cos\theta = R_{2p}(r)\, z & (26) \end{cases}$$

where the function $R_{2p}(r)$ is defined by

$$R_{2p}(r) = (1/r)R_{21}(r) \tag{27}$$

The three $2p$ functions χ_{2px}, χ_{2py}, and χ_{2pz} thus become completely equivalent, since the directions corresponding to the x-, y-, and z-axes are themselves equivalent. The further geometrical significance of these various orbitals of the K and L shells will be discussed later. (See pp. 30ff.)

No information about the spin functions $\Omega_{m_s}(\sigma)$ can be obtained from wave equation 11; it is therefore customary to treat the spin in a purely formal manner and to *define* the two possible functions $\alpha(\sigma)$ and $\beta(\sigma)$ by the identities

$$\Omega_{1/2}(\sigma) \equiv \alpha(\sigma) \tag{28}$$
$$\Omega_{-(1/2)}(\sigma) \equiv \beta(\sigma) \tag{29}$$

without enquiring further into the functional dependence of either one upon the coordinate σ. Indeed, the only properties of the spin functions α and β which need be mentioned here are that they satisfy the normalization condition

$$\sum_\sigma \alpha^*\alpha = \sum_\sigma \beta^*\beta = 1 \tag{30}$$

and the so-called *orthogonality* condition

$$\sum_\sigma \alpha^*\beta = \sum_\sigma \alpha\beta^* = 0 \tag{31}$$

An electron for which the spin quantum number m_s is $1/2$, and to which the function α is hence assigned, is said to have *positive* spin; one for which the spin quantum number m_s is $-(1/2)$, and to which the function β is hence assigned, is said to have *negative* spin.

A brief digression into the nature of spin is here in order. The statement that an electron has a spin means that it has an angular momentum of magnitude $h\sqrt{3}/4\pi$ and a magnetic moment of magnitude $eh\sqrt{3}/4\pi mc$ (where c is the velocity of light). A measurement of the component of spin along any arbitrary axis (conventionally taken as the z-axis) leads to one of the only two possible results: either the components of angular momentum and of magnetic moment are found to be $h/4\pi$ and $eh/4\pi mc$, respectively; or else they are found to be $-h/4\pi$ and $-eh/4\pi mc$, respectively. In the former event, the quantum number m_s is equal to $1/2$, the corresponding function is α, and the spin is positive; in the latter event, the quantum number m_s is equal to $-(1/2)$, the corresponding function is β, and the spin is negative. The spin coordinate σ, in terms of which α and β are formally expressed, has no classical analog; consequently, no attempt is here made to describe it more precisely.

IV. Structures of Complex Atoms (7)

When the simplified wave equations 10 and 11 (p. 12) are used, the first approximation ψ' to the wave function of a single *complex* atom (i.e., a single atom containing two or more electrons) can be written

$$\psi' = \prod_j \psi_{k_j}(j) = \prod_j \chi_{k_j}(j)\Omega_{k_j}(j) \tag{32}$$

where the one-electron functions ψ_{k_j} and the orbitals χ_{k_j} are of the central-field type. The subscript k_j represents all the quantum numbers required to specify the particular function (i.e., the kth) associated with the jth electron; (j) represents, as before, all the coordinates of the jth electron that are involved in the corresponding function; and the product over j includes all the electrons present. For example, for an atom containing a $1s$ electron with positive spin and a $2p_z$ electron with negative spin, equation 32 reduces to

$$\psi' = \chi_{1s}(1)\alpha(1)\chi_{2pz}(2)\beta(2) \qquad (33)$$

If each of the one-electron functions χ_{k_j} in equation 32 (or 33) is a solution of the corresponding one-electron wave equation 11, the product ψ' then satisfies the very approximate wave equation 10 for the entire atom; it does not, however, satisfy the more nearly rigorous equation 4 (p. 7).

From the rather qualitative viewpoint here adopted, the most serious defect of the simple product functions ψ' defined by equation 32 is that such functions *cannot* obey the Pauli exclusion principle. Thus, the operation **T** of interchanging the coordinates of the two electrons involved in the function ψ' of equation 33 leads to the function

$$T\psi' = \chi_{1s}(2)\alpha(2)\chi_{2pz}(1)\beta(1) \qquad (34)$$

which is *not* identical with the function $-\psi'$ (cf. equation 33). However, since the functions ψ' and $T\psi'$ are mutually degenerate solutions of the corresponding approximate wave equation 10, any linear combination of them is also a solution of that equation. Moreover, the particular linear combination

$$\psi'' = (1/2)\sqrt{2}[\psi' - T\psi'] = (1/2)\sqrt{2}[\chi_{1s}(1)\alpha(1)\chi_{2pz}(2)\beta(2)$$
$$- \chi_{1s}(2)\alpha(2)\chi_{2pz}(1)\beta(1)] \qquad (35)$$

does satisfy the exclusion principle, since the interchange **T** of the two electrons changes ψ'' into

$$T\psi'' = (1/2)\sqrt{2}T[\chi_{1s}(1)\alpha(1)\chi_{2pz}(2)\beta(2) - \chi_{1s}(2)\alpha(2)\chi_{2pz}(1)\beta(1)] \qquad (36)$$
$$= (1/2)\sqrt{2}[\chi_{1s}(2)\alpha(2)\chi_{2pz}(1)\beta(1) - \chi_{1s}(1)\alpha(1)\chi_{2pz}(2)\beta(2)] = -\psi''$$

Consequently, ψ'' is satisfactory as a second approximation to the correct wave function of the atom.

The procedure by which the antisymmetric function ψ'' of equation 35 was obtained from the simpler function ψ' of equation 33 can be generalized. Thus, the function ψ' of equation 32 can be *antisymmetrized* (i.e., made antisymmetric) by means of the linear combination

$$\psi'' = \frac{1}{\sqrt{p!}} \sum_P (-1)^P P\psi' = \frac{1}{\sqrt{p!}} \sum_P (-1)^P P[\prod_j \psi_{k_j}(j)] \qquad (37)$$

where the summation over **P** includes all of the $p!$ permutations of the p electrons among the one-electron functions ψ_k. The symbol $(-1)^P$ is defined as equal to $+1$ if **P** is an even (or positive) permutation, but equal to

-1 if P is an odd (or negative) permutation. The summation of equation 37 can be written in the form of a determinant with p rows and p columns

$$\psi'' = \frac{1}{\sqrt{p!}} \begin{vmatrix} \psi_1(1) & \psi_1(2) & \cdots & \psi_1(p) \\ \psi_2(1) & \psi_2(2) & \cdots & \psi_2(p) \\ \cdot & \cdot & & \cdot \\ \cdot & \cdot & & \cdot \\ \cdot & \cdot & & \cdot \\ \psi_p(1) & \psi_p(2) & \cdots & \psi_p(p) \end{vmatrix} \tag{38}$$

The function ψ'', defined by either of the two equivalent expressions 37 and 38, is clearly antisymmetric; for example, the interchange in ψ'' of all four coordinates of any one electron with the corresponding four coordinates of any other electron results merely in the interchange of two columns of the determinant 38, and hence merely in the multiplication of ψ'' by -1. Moreover, if any two of the spin-orbit functions ψ_k are identical (i.e., correspond to the same set of four quantum numbers), the determinant has two identical rows and is therefore equal to zero. Since such a vanishing wave function cannot describe any actual atom, it follows that no two electrons in any one atom can have the same set of four quantum numbers. Two electrons can, of course, occupy the same orbital (i.e., have the same values of n, l, and m_l) provided that they have different spins (i.e., have different values of m_s); however, no more than two electrons can, under any conditions, occupy the same orbital, since only the two values $+ (1/2)$ and $- (1/2)$ are possible for m_s. The last two sentences express the Pauli exclusion principle in its simplest and most familiar, although not in its most general, form.

The way in which electrons may be assigned to orbitals in a complex atom will now be discussed. It is convenient first to imagine that all the electrons of the neutral atom are removed, so that only the bare nucleus remains, and then to consider that these electrons are allowed to rejoin the atom one at a time, in such a way as to form in each instance the combined system of least possible energy (i.e., the ground state). The first electron will occupy the $1s$ orbital since, of all the orbitals, this one is the most stable. (See above.) The second electron with spin opposite to that of the first, also enters this most stable orbital. The K shell is now full; hence all further electrons must go into outer, and therefore less stable, shells. The third and fourth electrons, with opposite spins, must accordingly be assigned to the next most stable orbital, $2s$. The fifth to tenth electrons, inclusive (three with positive and three with negative spin), must be assigned to the three different, but degenerate, $2p$ orbitals. Since the L shell is now also full, any remaining electrons must go into still less stable shells. This process of building up the atom continues until all the electrons have been replaced; it leads, in a manner which has often been described (10) to an explanation of the periodic table of the chemical elements.

The way in which the quantum numbers n and l have been assigned to the various electrons in any atom is described by the so-called *configuration* of that atom. (This use of the word "configuration" is, of course, unrelated to that of the same word in *stereochemistry*.) Thus, a hydrogen atom with a single $1s$ electron is said to have the configuration $1s$; a helium atom with two $1s$ electrons is said to have the configuration $1s^2$; a carbon atom in its ground state, with two $1s$ electrons, two $2s$ electrons, and two $2p$ electrons, is said to have the configuration $1s^2\,2s^2\,2p^2$; and so on. It is to be noted that the configuration of an atom does not in general define its state completely. With carbon, for example, there are a number of different ways in which the quantum numbers m_l and m_s can be assigned to the two $2p$ electrons. Each of these assignments gives rise to a different function ψ'' (equations 37 and 38). When the method just described is used, the best approximation ψ to the correct wave function is usually a linear combination of these functions ψ''. However, an account of the procedure by which the correct combination is obtained lies outside the scope of this chapter.

In addition to the *normal* atomic configurations referred to above, *excited* configurations are also possible. Thus, any discussion of the electronic structures of the carbon compounds requires consideration of the less stable configuration $1s^2\,2s\,2p^3$ of the carbon atom, where one of the $2s$ electrons of the normal configuration is raised to the $2p$ level. (See p. 31.)

The energy of a di- or polyelectronic atom cannot be obtained by addition of those eigenvalues of the one-electron wave equation 11 (p. 12) which correspond to the occupied orbitals. Instead, it is computed from the equation

$$
E = \frac{\displaystyle\int_{x_1=-\infty}^{+\infty}\int_{y_1=-\infty}^{+\infty}\cdots\int_{z_p=-\infty}^{+\infty}\sum_{\sigma_1}\sum_{\sigma_2}\cdots\sum_{\sigma_p}\psi^*H\psi\,d\tau}{\displaystyle\int_{x_1=-\infty}^{+\infty}\int_{y_1=-\infty}^{+\infty}\cdots\int_{z_p=-\infty}^{+\infty}\sum_{\sigma_1}\sum_{\sigma_2}\cdots\sum_{\sigma_p}\psi^*\psi\,d\tau} \tag{39}
$$

where E is the *approximate* energy associated with the *approximate* atomic wave function ψ, set up in the manner just outlined. Moreover, ψ^* is, as heretofore, the complex conjugate of ψ; and $H\psi$ is the function which results from the operation of the Hamiltonian operator H (equation 4, p. 7) upon ψ. If the function ψ is normalized (equation 8, p. 9), the denominator of the fraction in equation 39 is equal to unity. Naturally, the nearer ψ is to the correct wave function of the atom, the nearer is E to the correct energy. (It should be obvious that, if ψ is any *correct* solution of the wave equation, the quantity E is the *correct* energy of the atom in the corresponding state.)

V. The Heitler-London Treatment of the Hydrogen Molecule (7, 11, 12)

The concepts developed and the methods described in the above fairly detailed (but still far from complete) discussion of the quantum-mechanical treatment of *atomic* structure can also be applied to the similar treatment of *molecular* structure. The first calculation of the energy of a molecule based upon these concepts and methods was that carried out in 1927 by Heitler and London (11) for the hydrogen molecule, H_2. Most of the further developments in the field of molecular structure may be regarded as elaborations based upon this pioneering calculation. In the following paragraphs, the point of view and the method of approach differ somewhat from the ones adopted by Heitler and London; the underlying principles, however, are the same.

In a system composed of two hydrogen atoms at a considerable distance from one another, each electron occupies a $1s$ orbital about one of the two protons. The configuration can therefore be expressed as $1s_A 1s_B$, where the subscripts A and B serve to distinguish the two different $1s$ orbitals centered, respectively, about the two nuclei A and B. Moreover, it seems reasonable to suppose that the system may still be described, at least approximately, by this same configuration $1s_A 1s_B$, even if the two protons are allowed to approach to the distance that obtains in the actual molecule H_2. Consequently, the configuration in question may be considered valid at all internuclear distances.

In the configuration $1s_A 1s_B$, since the two electrons are not assigned to the same orbital, no restriction is imposed by the exclusion principle upon the spin quantum numbers. Consequently, four simple product-functions ψ'_{++}, ψ'_{+-}, ψ'_{-+}, and ψ'_{--} may be set up.

$$\psi'_{++} = \chi_{1s_A}(1)\alpha(1)\chi_{1s_B}(2)\alpha(2) \tag{40}$$

$$\psi'_{+-} = \chi_{1s_A}(1)\alpha(1)\chi_{1s_B}(2)\beta(2) \tag{41}$$

$$\psi'_{-+} = \chi_{1s_A}(1)\beta(1)\chi_{1s_B}(2)\alpha(2) \tag{42}$$

$$\psi'_{--} = \chi_{1s_A}(1)\beta(1)\chi_{1s_B}(2)\beta(2) \tag{43}$$

(Cf. equations 32 and 33.) When these functions are antisymmetrized (cf. equations 35, 37, and 38), they assume, respectively the forms ψ''_{++}, ψ''_{+-}, ψ''_{-+}, and ψ''_{--}.

$$\psi'_{++} = (\sqrt{2}/2)[\chi_{1s_A}(1)\chi_{1s_B}(2) - \chi_{1s_A}(2)\chi_{1s_B}(1)]\alpha(1)\alpha(2) \tag{44}$$

$$\psi''_{+-} = (\sqrt{2}/2)[\chi_{1s_A}(1)\alpha(1)\chi_{1s_B}(2)\beta(2) - \chi_{1s_A}(2)\alpha(2)\chi_{1s_B}(1)\beta(1)] \tag{45}$$

$$\psi''_{-+} = (\sqrt{2}/2)[\chi_{1s_A}(1)\beta(1)\chi_{1s_B}(2)\alpha(2) - \chi_{1s_A}(2)\beta(2)\chi_{1s_B}(1)\alpha(1)] \tag{46}$$

$$\psi''_{--} = (\sqrt{2}/2)[\chi_{1s_A}(1)\chi_{1s_B}(2) - \chi_{1s_A}(2)\chi_{1s_B}(1)]\beta(1)\beta(2) \tag{47}$$

The correct linear combinations of these last four functions are found to be

$$\psi_{t+} = \psi''_{++} = (\sqrt{2}/2)[\chi_{1sA}(1)\chi_{1sB}(2) - \chi_{1sA}(2)\chi_{1sB}(1)]\alpha(1)\alpha(2) \tag{48}$$

$$\psi_{t0} = (\sqrt{2}/2)[\psi''_{+-} + \psi''_{-+}]$$
$$= (1/2)[\chi_{1sA}(1)\chi_{1sB}(2) - \chi_{1sA}(2)\chi_{1sB}(1)][\alpha(1)\beta(2) + \alpha(2)\beta(1)] \tag{49}$$

$$\psi_{t-} = \psi''_{--} = (\sqrt{2}/2[\chi_{1sA}(1)\chi_{1sB}(2) - \chi_{1sA}(2)\chi_{1sB}(1)]\beta(1)\beta(2) \tag{50}$$

$$\psi_{s} = (\sqrt{2}/2)[\psi''_{+-} - \psi''_{-+}]$$
$$= (1/2)[\chi_{1sA}(1)\chi_{1sB}(2) + \chi_{1sA}(2)\chi_{1sB}(1)][\alpha(1)\beta(2) - \alpha(2)\beta(1)] \tag{51}$$

Since the three functions ψ_{t+}, ψ_{t0}, and ψ_{t-} have the same space factor $[\chi_{1sA}(1)\chi_{1sB}(2) - \chi_{1sA}(2)\chi_{1sB}(1)]$, and differ only in their spin factors, they are more closely related to one another than they are to the fourth function ψ_{s}. Indeed, it can be shown that the first three functions represent the three components of a *triplet* level. In other words, they represent three degenerate states, which differ from one another only with respect to the orientation in space of the resultant spin of the molecule as a whole. The fourth function ψ_{s}, on the other hand, represents the one and only component of a *singlet* level, where the spins of the two electrons are exactly opposed, so that their resultant is zero. Thus, the essential distinction between the triplet and singlet levels is that, in the former, the two electrons have roughly parallel spins (or, in other words, are *unpaired*), whereas, in the latter, the electrons have exactly antiparallel spins (or, in other words, are *paired*).

If the orbitals χ_{1sA} and χ_{1sB} are assumed to have the same form as the $1s$ orbital of an isolated hydrogen atom (for which the wave equation can be rigorously solved), the approximate energies of the triplet and singlet levels can be directly computed. The calculations in question, like the analogous ones for complex atoms, are based upon equation 39, save for the fact that H now represents the Hamiltonian operator (equation 4, p. 7) for the *entire molecule* and not for only a *single atom*. The results of the calculations (11) are shown graphically in Fig. 3, where the calculated energies E of the triplet level (curve 1) and of the singlet level (curve 2) are plotted as functions of the internuclear distance r_{AB}. The horizontal broken line corresponds to the sum of the energies of the two isolated atoms. (For the significance of curve 3, see below.) The triplet curve 1, since it lies entirely above the horizontal broken line, indicates a repulsion between the two atoms at all distances, and does not suggest the formation of a stable molecule; this level has been observed spectroscopically, and has been shown to be indeed "repulsive," as predicted. The singlet curve 2, on the other hand, has a minimum where r_{AB} is equal to 0.80 A., and where E is 73 kcal. per mole less than the energy indicated by the horizontal broken line. This singlet curve, therefore, indicates the formation of a stable molecule with an internuclear distance of 0.80 A. and a *binding energy* of 73 kcal. per mole. (The *bond energy* at 0° absolute is the binding energy minus the "zero-point" vibrational energy.) The agreement between these calculated quantities and the observed values of 0.74 A. and 109 kcal. per mole is as good as can be expected, in view of the approximations made in setting up the function ψ_s. This agreement has been considerably improved by later and more elaborate calculations (13), which differ from the one here outlined in that the orbitals χ_{1sA} and χ_{1sB} are replaced by other and more complicated expressions; moreover, almost complete agreement with experiment has been achieved by a still more complicated procedure (9). The principles underlying this last, most satisfactory calculation are, however, too elaborate to be here de-

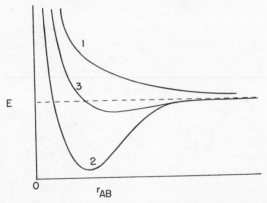

F$_{\text{IG}}$. 3. The calculated approximate energies E of the triplet level (curve 1), of the singlet level (curve 2), and of an imaginary unpolarized state (curve 3) of a system composed of two hydrogen atoms; all energies are given as functions of the internuclear distance r_{AB}.

scribed; moreover, they cannot readily be generalized and applied to molecules more complicated than H_2. Consequently, the earlier and less precise treatment described above will be used instead. This treatment, although less satisfactory, permits qualitative conclusions to be drawn for a wide variety of molecules.

It is instructive to compare the picture given by the quantum-mechanical theory of valence (just described) with the much cruder picture given earlier in this chapter (pp. 3f.). The function ψ_s (equation 51), which describes the approximate average distribution of electronic charge in the normal hydrogen molecule, assumes its greatest magnitude when the spatial coordinates of both electrons correspond to positions in the region between the two nuclei. It follows, therefore (see p. 9), that the electrons are more likely to be found in that region than elsewhere; hence the actual charge distribution in the molecule is at least roughly analogous to the one shown in Fig. 2. (In one sense, Fig. 2 gives a *better* charge distribution than does the approximate function ψ_s; for that figure takes explicit account of the tendency of the like-charged electrons to repel one another, whereas the function ψ_s does not. Indeed, it is just this inadequacy of ψ_s, or of any other approximate function set up in a similar manner, which makes such a function somewhat unsatisfactory. See the preceding paragraph and also Fig. 10 on p. 29.) The triplet functions ψ_{t+}, ψ_{t0}, and ψ_{t-} (equations 48–50), on the other hand, correspond to a charge distribution such that the electrons are *less* likely to be found in the region between the nuclei than they are to be found elsewhere. This distribution (represented schematically by Fig. 4) results in a strong repulsion between the atoms. Moreover, if the two hydrogen atoms in the molecule did not in any way affect each other, so that each electron remained distributed about a single proton, just as it is in an isolated hydrogen atom, an intermediate situation would result; the electrons would be neither concentrated in, nor squeezed out of, the region between the nuclei. The (antisymmetric) wave function would then be one of the

Fig. 4. A model of the repulsive triplet level of the system composed of two hydrogen atoms.

functions ψ''_{+-} and ψ''_{-+} (equations 45 and 46), and the approximate energy E would be that shown in curve 3 of Fig. 3. Consequently, the major factor responsible for the formation of the covalent bond is the redistribution of the average charge, caused by the mutual polarization of the two atoms.

Although, in the last analysis, the existence of a covalent bond in the normal (singlet) level of the hydrogen molecule, and the nonexistence of such a bond in the excited (triplet) level, are the direct results of the respective average distributions of electric charge, it is sometimes convenient to regard the situation from a rather different point of view. As was noted above, the covalent bond in the hydrogen molecule is formed when the two electrons are paired with each other; it is not formed when the electrons are unpaired. The pairing of the electrons is thus a necessary condition for the existence of such a bond. Moreover, since very few molecules, in their normal states, possess net magnetic moments due to spin, it is highly probable that the electrons involved in practically *all* covalent bonds are similarly paired. It is important, however, that covalent bonds in general are *not* due in some mysterious manner to the pairing *per se*, but arise from the concentration of the two electrons in the region between the nuclei—a concentration that can occur only when the electrons in question are paired.

VI. The "Valence-Bond Method" (7, 12)

A rather obvious generalization of Heitler and London's treatment of the hydrogen molecule may be illustrated by an example, chosen to bring out most simply the essential features of the procedure. An atom may be imagined to possess four electrons divided among three central-field orbitals referred to hereafter as a, b, and c; its configuration may therefore be written as a^2bc. Two further atoms may be imagined to possess one electron each; the orbitals occupied will be referred to, respectively, as d and e. The configuration of the entire molecule is then a^2bcde.

The Pauli exclusion principle requires the two electrons occupying the orbital a to have opposite spins, or, in other words, to be paired with each other. These electrons are therefore not available for bond-formation, since they are already paired. The four electrons occupying the orbitals b, c, d, and e, however, can be assigned spins in any desired manner, and so they are available for bond-formation. Two possibilities are immediately suggested: either the electron in b is paired with the one in d, and the one in c is paired with the one in e; or else the electron in b is paired with the one in e, and the one in c is paired with the one in d. (The third possibility, that b and c are paired with one another, and that d and e are also paired with one another, can be ignored; it would not correspond to a single triatomic molecule, but rather to one monatomic and one diatomic molecule.) Equation 51 suggests that

$$\psi'_{bd,\,ce} = (1/4)a(1)\alpha(1)a(2)\beta(2)[b(3)d(4) + b(4)d(3)][\alpha(3)\beta(4) - \alpha(4)\beta(3)]$$
$$\cdot [c(5)e(6) + c(6)e(5)][\alpha(5)\beta(6) - \alpha(6)\beta(5)] \qquad (52)$$

and

$$\psi'_{be,\,cd} = (1/4)a(1)\alpha(1)a(2)\beta(2)[b(3)e(4) + b(4)e(3)][\alpha(3)\beta(4) - \alpha(4)\beta(3)]$$
$$\cdot [c(5)d(6) + c(6)d(5)][\alpha(5)\beta(6) - \alpha(6)\beta(5)] \qquad (53)$$

would be reasonable functions for the representation of the two proposed structures, were it not that they are not completely antisymmetric, and so are not in agreement with the Pauli exclusion principle. They can, however, readily be antisymmetrized. (Cf. equation 37, p. 16.) When thus treated, they become suitable approximations to the wave functions for the stated structures.

By the extension of the method just outlined, an approximate wave function, expressed in terms of the central-field orbitals of the constituent atoms, can be set up for any desired valence-bond structure of any molecule. The corresponding approximate energy of the molecule can then be calculated by the appropriate generalization of equation 39 (p. 18), if explicit forms are assigned to the various atomic orbitals involved. This method of treating molecular structure is commonly referred to as the *valence-bond method*, or as the *Heitler-London-Slater-Pauling (HLSP) method*.

The numerical calculations made for extremely simple molecules by the procedure just described are qualitatively rather satisfactory, though quantitatively unreliable because of the drastic approximations involved. However, even with a molecule as simple as that of methane, CH_4, the mathematical difficulties encountered in evaluating the integrals of equation 39 are so great that no serious attempt has ever been made to obtain quantitative results for this or any other hydrocarbon. Therefore, until more powerful mathematical tools become available, the maximum information obtainable for such molecules by quantum-mechanical methods must remain grossly qualitative and partly empirical. The remainder of this chapter (except for the immediately following section) will accordingly be devoted to such qualitative and empirical considerations.

VII. The "Molecular-Orbital Method" (7, 12, 14)

An alternative method of setting up an approximate wave function for a molecule resembles the treatment of atomic structure discussed on pp. 15*ff.* more closely than it does the one just described. A single example will suffice to illustrate the principles of this second method. The two nuclei of the hydrogen molecule H_2 are supposed to be held at some fixed distance from one another; the two electrons are supposed to be first completely removed and then allowed to return one at a time. The first electron thus to return will occupy an orbital not centered about a single nucleus, but belonging to the molecule as a whole. Such a *molecular orbital* may be represented, at least approximately, by the linear combination of atomic orbitals

$$\chi_{A+B} = (\sqrt{2}/2)[\chi_{1sA} + \chi_{1sB}] \tag{54}$$

The second electron can also go into this same orbital if its spin is opposite to that of the first. The resulting approximate molecular wave function ψ_m, after being antisymmetrized, is of the form

$$\psi_m = (\sqrt{2}/2)\chi_{A+B}(1)\chi_{A+B}(2)[\alpha(1)\beta(2) - \alpha(2)\beta(1)] \tag{55}$$

This function gives a binding energy slightly less satisfactory than the one derived from the function ψ_s (equation 51). The difference, however, is not great. Similarly, approximate wave functions can be obtained for more complex molecules. In general, the *molecular-orbital method*, often referred to also as the *Hund-Mulliken (HM) method*, is about as useful as the valence-bond (HLSP) method for the qualitative treatment of the *normal* states of molecules; it is rather more useful than the valence-bond method for the treatment of the electronically excited states which are of spectroscopic interest. Nevertheless, the following discussion will be restricted to the valence-bond method which can more easily be correlated with the ordinary chemical concepts of valence and of structure.

VIII. RECAPITULATION OF THE QUANTUM-MECHANICAL TREATMENT OF VALENCE

In the preceding sections, the discussion has unavoidably been complicated. It was necessary to start with fundamental principles and to derive,

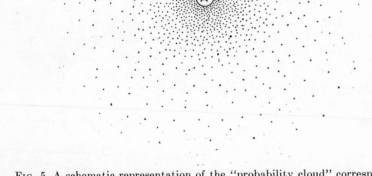

FIG. 5. A schematic representation of the "probability cloud" corresponding to a 1s orbital about an atomic nucleus Ⓐ.

in logical sequence, the intermediate theorems required for the final conclusions. Now, however, it is convenient to summarize the more important of these conclusions and to restate them qualitatively and nonmathematically, without proof.

The electrons in an atom are not located at definite positions; instead, they wander over the entire atom. Nevertheless, any given electron is more likely to be in certain positions than in others. The probability that an electron occupies any one of its possible positions is given by the so-called *orbital* which that electron is said to occupy. Although an electron is commonly regarded as a point-particle, its orbital can be most easily visualized

as a cloud, the density of which at any point is a measure of the probability
that the electron is at that point. (More precisely, the "probability cloud"
represents not the orbital itself, but the square of its absolute magnitude
at any point. Cf. p. 9.) Consequently, if the orbital occupied by each
electron in the atom is known, the average distribution of electronic charge
is determined.

By solution of a suitably simplified, and hence only approximate, Schrödinger equation, the general shapes of the various orbitals are calculated.

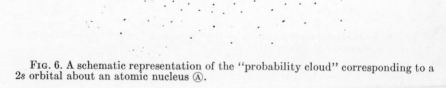

Fig. 6. A schematic representation of the "probability cloud" corresponding to a
2s orbital about an atomic nucleus Ⓐ.

In this way, it is found that all orbitals of the so-called s type are *spherically
symmetric*. In other words, an electron in an s orbital is exactly as likely to
be in any one direction from the nucleus as it is to be in any other. An s
orbital, therefore, does not "project" in any direction. The various s orbitals
of a single atom correspond to different average distances from the nucleus.
An electron in the 1s orbital is, on the average, closer to the nucleus than is
one in the 2s orbital; an electron in the 2s orbital is, on the average, closer
to the nucleus than is one in the 3s orbital; and so on. For this reason, an

electron in an atom is in its most stable state (i.e., has the lowest energy) when it is in the 1s orbital; it is in a less stable state when it is in the 2s orbital; in a still less stable state when it is in the 3s orbital; and so on. Figures 5 and 6 illustrate schematically the respective "probability clouds" of a 1s and a 2s orbital; in each figure, the concentration of the dots in any small region represents the density of the cloud in that region and hence the probability that the electron is in the region in question.

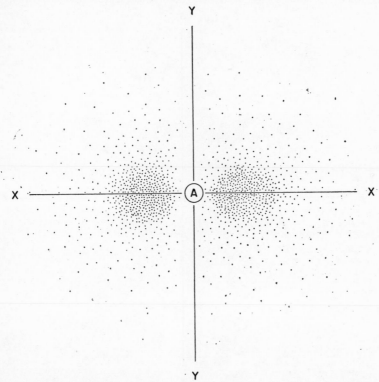

FIG. 7. A schematic representation of the "probability cloud" corresponding to a $2p_x$ orbital about an atomic nucleus Ⓐ.

On the other hand, orbitals of the so-called p type are *not* spherically symmetric. An electron in such an orbital is more likely to be in one of two opposite directions from the nucleus than it is to be in any other direction; in other words, the p orbitals "project" along straight lines running in definite directions through the nucleus. The most stable p orbitals are the three $2p$ orbitals which, although distinct, correspond to the same energy (i.e., are *degenerate*). The $2p$ orbitals in any given atom are less stable than the $2s$ orbitals in that atom, but are more stable than either the $3s$ orbital or the

$3p$ orbitals. It is both permissible and convenient to describe the $2p$ orbitals more precisely as $2p_x$, $2p_y$ and $2p_z$. If the atomic nucleus is assumed to lie at the origin of a set of rectangular cartesian coordinates, the $2p_x$ orbital projects equally in both directions along the x-axis. In other words, an electron occupying the $2p_x$ orbital is most likely to be on the x-axis; it is equally likely to be on either side of the yz-plane, but it *cannot* lie *in* that plane. The $2p_y$ and $2p_z$ orbitals have, respectively, the same relations to the y-axis

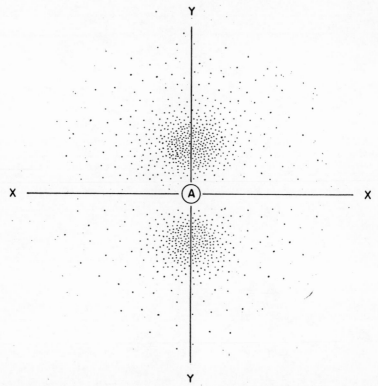

FIG. 8. A schematic representation of the "probability cloud" corresponding to a $2p_y$ orbital about an atomic nucleus Ⓐ.

and xz-plane, and to the z-axis and xy-plane. Figures 7, 8, and 9 illustrate schematically the respective "probability clouds" of a $2p_x$, a $2p_y$, and a $2p_z$ orbital. (In order that the figures may be easily visualized, the z-axis, which in Figures 7 and 8 is *perpendicular to* the plane of the paper, and hence not explicitly represented, is drawn in Figure 9 *in* the plane of the paper.)

Two electrons can be put into the same orbital of the same atom only if they have opposite spins (i.e., are *paired*). An electron in such a doubly

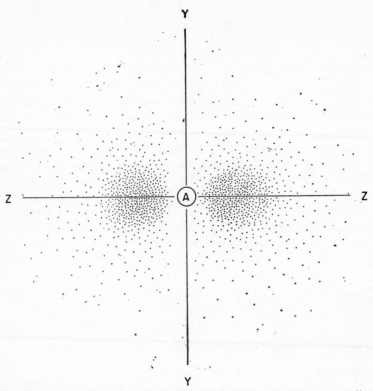

FIG. 9. A schematic representation of the "probability cloud" corresponding to a $2p_z$ orbital about an atomic nucleus Ⓐ.

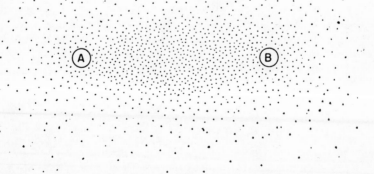

FIG. 10. A schematic representation of the "probability cloud" corresponding to a covalent bond between two atoms Ⓐ and Ⓑ.

occupied orbital of an atom A is unavailable for bond-formation, since it cannot be further paired with another electron from any other atom B. It therefore cannot be *shared* by atoms A and B. Consequently, the only electrons that can participate in covalent bonds are those which, in the isolated atoms, are in *singly* occupied orbitals.

A covalent bond is formed when two electrons tend to come into the region between the nuclei of the atoms concerned (i.e., when the two electrons are shared). If the probability that an electron is in any small volume element is represented by the density of a "cloud" in that volume element, then a covalent bond results when the composite cloud for two electrons (one from each atom) is most dense in the region between the nuclei. A bond thus formed between two atoms A and B is depicted schematically in Fig. 10. (Cf. the still more approximate representation of such a bond in Fig. 2 on p. 3.) In general, the cloud is densest, and hence the corresponding bond is strongest, when the two binding orbitals (one on each atom) *overlap* most effectively. The significance of this last statement will be explained more fully in the following sections.

IX. Bond Angles and the Tetrahedral Carbon Atom (15)

An s orbital, since it is spherically symmetric, does not project in one direction any more than it does in any other direction. (See the preceding section.) Consequently, the overlapping between such an orbital and any orbital on another atom is independent of the direction of the line joining the two nuclei. Hence, a bond formed by an s orbital can have no preferred direction. With a p orbital, however, the situation is different. Such an orbital does project in a definite direction; hence its ability to overlap an orbital on any other atom depends upon the direction of the line joining the nuclei of the two atoms concerned. A bond formed by a p orbital, therefore, does have a preferred direction. This conclusion leads easily to an explanation for the angles found to exist between certain covalent bonds.

In the water molecule, H_2O, for example, the oxygen atom may be considered to have the configuration $1s^2\ 2s^2\ 2p_x^2\ 2p_y\ 2p_z$. (Cf. p. 18.) Since only the electrons in the $2p_y$ and $2p_z$ orbitals can be unpaired, these are the only ones available for the formation of bonds to the two hydrogen atoms. Since, moreover, the $2p_y$ and $2p_z$ orbitals project along the y- and z-axes, respectively, the maximum overlapping between binding orbitals, and hence the strongest bonds, must occur when one hydrogen atom lies on the y-axis and the other on the z-axis. Although, in the absence of an external electric or magnetic field, the directions of these two coordinate axes are completely arbitrary, the *angle* between them is nevertheless uniquely determined. It therefore follows that the angle between the oxygen-hydrogen bonds should be 90°. The discrepancy between this predicted value and the observed one (16) of approximately 105° is probably due to the repulsion between the hydrogen atoms or to hybridization (see below), or to both. In any event, the marked departure of the molecule from linearity is fully explained. Similarly, the nitrogen atom in the ammonia molecule, NH_3, can be considered to have the configuration $1s^2\,2s^2\,2p_x\,2p_y\,2p_z$, so that the three hydrogen atoms should lie on the three coordinate axes. Since the observed angles (16) between the nitrogen-hydrogen bonds are approximately 107°, and not exactly 90° as predicted, the effect of the repulsions between the hydrogen atoms, or of hybridization, or of both, is again evident. The non-planarity of the molecule, however, is again fully explained.

In the attempt to extend to the methane molecule the treatment used in the preceding paragraph, certain complications are encountered. In the first place, the normal configuration of the carbon atom is $1s^2\,2s^2\,2p^2$, where the maximum number of singly occupied orbitals is two. Regardless of which $2p$ orbitals are chosen as the singly occupied ones, the carbon atom, like the oxygen atom, should form only two bonds, and these should be approximately at right angles to each other. Consequently, in order to explain the quadrivalence of carbon, the *excited* configuration $1s^2\,2s\,2p^3$, where four orbitals may be singly occupied, must be taken into account. The latter configuration, although considerably less stable than the normal one, may nevertheless be used, because the energy required to raise the atom to this excited configuration is more than compensated by the energy released in the formation of the two additional bonds.

A second complication arises from the nonequivalence of the four orbitals of the L shell. If the configuration of the carbon atom is taken as $1s^2\,2s\,2p_x$ $2p_y\,2p_z$, three of the bonds formed should be directed along the coordinate axes, but the fourth one, formed by the $2s$ orbital, should be undirected. Three of the hydrogen atoms in the methane molecule should therefore lie on or near the three coordinate axes, whereas the fourth hydrogen atom should take up a position removed as far as possible from the other three, by which it is presumably repelled. The molecule should thus have the shape of a trigonal pyramid. Moreover, the four carbon-hydrogen bonds should not be of the same strength. The three bonds formed by the $2p$ orbitals should be significantly stronger than the one formed by the $2s$ orbital, since the $2p$ orbitals are concentrated along their respective bond axes, and thus more strongly overlap the hydrogen orbitals to which they are bonded than the spherically symmetric $2s$ orbital overlaps the hydrogen orbital to which *it* is bonded.

This nonregularity of the carbon tetrahedron and nonequivalence of the four carbon bonds can be eliminated by assuming that the carbon orbitals which form the bonds in question are not simply the $2s$, $2p_x$, $2p_y$, and $2p_z$ orbitals, but are instead certain linear combinations, or "hybrids," of these.

32 G. W. WHELAND

The 2s and the 2p orbitals are not degenerate (i.e., do not have the same energy), and hence no combination of 2s and 2p orbitals would be permissible in the isolated *atom* (cf. p. 13); nevertheless, the hybridization procedure appears to be permissible in the *molecule*. The formation of the bonds, of course, greatly perturbs the state of the carbon atom, and the energy change brought about by this perturbation is probably much greater than the energy difference between the 2s and 2p levels. Under these circumstances, the *perturbation theory* of quantum mechanics (7) (which cannot here be further discussed) shows that linear combinations of even the nondegenerate 2s and 2p orbitals can, and in fact must, be employed.

The criterion which directs the choice of the proper hybrid orbitals is the principle of maximum overlapping (15). The stability of a molecule is greatest when its interatomic bonds are strongest, that is, when the pairs of orbitals which form the bonds overlap most effectively. Consequently, in any atom, the best orbital for the formation of a bond is the one which overlaps most with the orbital from the other atom. For this reason, as was noted above, a 2p orbital should (other things being equal) form a stronger bond than does a 2s orbital. Even a 2p orbital, however, is not ideally concentrated since it extends equally in *both* directions along its axis. (Cf. Figs. 7–9.) At best, therefore, only one half of such an orbital about an atom A can effectively overlap with a second orbital centered about an atom B; the other half of the 2p orbital about A points off in the wrong direction, and is, so to speak, unavoidably wasted so far as the formation of a covalent bond is concerned. However, certain orbitals more concentrated in single directions than the 2s and 2p orbitals can be obtained as linear combinations or hybrids of the 2s and 2p orbitals. Such hybrid orbitals should form stronger bonds than either the pure 2s or the pure 2p orbitals. Consequently, the best approximation to the wave function of a molecule containing carbon should probably be expressed in terms of hybrid carbon orbitals.

The four independent hybrid orbitals (obtained by combining one 2s and three 2p orbitals), which are most concentrated in definite directions, are

$$\chi_1 = (1/2)(\chi_{2s} + \chi_{2px} + \chi_{2py} + \chi_{2pz}) \tag{54}$$

$$\chi_2 = (1/2)(\chi_{2s} + \chi_{2px} - \chi_{2py} - \chi_{2pz}) \tag{55}$$

$$\chi_3 = (1/2)(\chi_{2s} - \chi_{2px} + \chi_{2py} - \chi_{2pz}) \tag{56}$$

$$\chi_4 = (1/2)(\chi_{2s} - \chi_{2px} - \chi_{2py} + \chi_{2pz}) \tag{57}$$

where χ_{2s}, χ_{2px}, χ_{2py}, and χ_{2pz} are the atomic orbitals of equations 20, 24–26. (Here, and throughout the remainder of this chapter, the reader who has skipped the development of the quantum-mechanical theory on pp. 6–25 need not trouble himself with the mathematical details, which are given only for the sake of completeness.) These hybrid orbitals, χ_1, χ_2, χ_3, and χ_4, are exactly equivalent to one another, as is shown by the fact that any one of them can be transformed into any other merely by a rotation of the coordinate axes. Moreover, the angle between the lines along which any pair of these orbitals project is exactly the tetrahedral angle of 109° 28′. Thus, both of the difficulties encountered with the unhybridized orbitals are eliminated. The concentration of the hybrid orbitals in definite directions

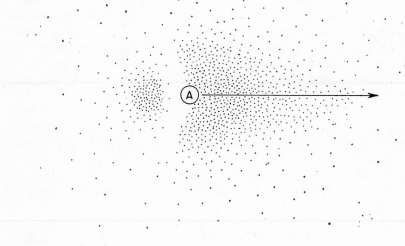

FIG. 11. A schematic representation of the "probability cloud" corresponding to a hybrid orbital on the carbon atom Ⓐ. The bond direction is that shown by the arrow.

is shown schematically in Fig. 11, which gives the "probability cloud" for one such orbital. Although this orbital still projects in both directions from the nucleus, one of its two parts is much smaller than the other; only this comparatively small part is unable effectively to overlap an orbital on another atom.

Although hybridization of the $2s$ and $2p$ orbitals is most clearly evident with the carbon atom, it may occur also to some extent with the oxygen and nitrogen atoms. Consequently, the bonding orbitals of the central atoms in water and in ammonia may not be exactly $2p$, as was assumed above in the discussion of these substances, but may instead have more or less $2s$ character. The *normal* bond angles need not then be exactly 90°, as they must be when pure $2p$ orbitals are used; they may instead be somewhat closer to the 109° 28' observed in methane. Consequently (as was suggested on p. 31), in water and in ammonia, the observed excess of the bond angles over 90° may be due partly to hybridization, and not entirely to the mutual repulsions between the hydrogen atoms.

In most, if not all, compounds of carbon where each carbon atom forms four single bonds, the same type of hybridization used for methane, and hence the same tetrahedral bond angles found for that substance, may be assumed. (For a discussion of unsaturated and highly strained compounds, however, see the following sections.) Thus, in ethane, the six carbon-hydrogen bonds are formed by six tetrahedrally hybridized carbon orbitals and by six $1s$ hydrogen orbitals; similarly, the one carbon-carbon bond is formed by two tetrahedrally hybridized orbitals, one from each atom. The maximum overlapping in this carbon-carbon bond occurs when the bonding orbital on each carbon atom is directed exactly toward the nucleus of the other carbon atom. It may be presumed, therefore, that each of these two orbitals is cylindrically symmetrical about the bond axis, so that the overlapping is not affected by rotation about the bond. Any bond with this characteristic is commonly described as a σ bond. There should be no forces to restrict rotation about such a bond; in other words, the rotation about such a bond should be *free*. (The carbon-hydrogen bonds also are of the σ type, but here, because of the univalence of the hydrogen atoms, the question of free rotation does not arise.)

The predicted complete freedom of rotation about a bond is only an approximation. If the rotation were sufficiently hindered, then many molecules in which two or more multivalent atoms are linked to one another by single bonds should be obtainable in distinct stereoisomeric forms. Such isomers, where the atomic positions differ only with respect to rotation about single bonds, have been observed only among the substituted biphenyls and their stereochemical analogues. In a far larger class of compounds, however, smaller, but definitely detectable, hindrances to free rotation about single bonds have been established. In ethane, for example, the forces restricting rotation about the carbon-carbon bond are such that an energy of about 3 kcal. per mole is required to overcome them (17); and, for several other single carbon-carbon bonds, energies of the same order of magnitude have been found. This small discrepancy between prediction and observation is due to the approximations introduced into the theoretical treatment, more particularly (in ethane) to the neglect of the interactions among the various hydrogen atoms. In any event, however, the *qualitative* prediction that *no large forces* restrict rotation is certainly valid.

In molecules containing bulky atoms or groups, the carbon bond angles may be somewhat distorted from their normal tetrahedral value. Thus, the C—C—C bond angle in propane, $CH_2(CH_3)_2$ (18), and the Cl—C—Cl bond angle in methylene chloride, CH_2Cl_2 (19), are appreciably larger than 109° 28′. These observed distortions can easily be explained; they are due to the mutual repulsions of the large methyl groups and chlorine atoms. Similar explanations apply in all other instances where a valence angle at a saturated carbon atom is found to deviate slightly from the normal tetrahedral value. (Cf., however, *Strain Theory* on pp. 40*ff.*)

X. THE CARBON-CARBON DOUBLE BOND (15, 20)

The treatment of valence in saturated carbon compounds may be extended so that it applies also to molecules containing double bonds. This extension may be illustrated by applying the process to ethylene. Each of the two equivalent carbon atoms in the ethylene molecule has the excited configuration $1s^2\, 2s\, 2p^3$ which was taken as the starting point in the treatment of the saturated molecules. The best hybridization of the $2s$ and the $2p$ orbitals for saturated molecules is, however, not the best for unsaturated ones. For simplicity, the two carbon atoms may be supposed to lie in the xy-plane, and the line joining them may be supposed to be parallel to the x-axis. If the carbon atom with the algebraically smaller value of x is designated by the subscript A, and if the second carbon atom is designated by the subscript B, then a reasonable set of hybridized atomic orbitals is

$$\chi_{1A} = (\sqrt{3}/3)\chi_{2sA} - (\sqrt{6}/6)\chi_{2pxA} + (\sqrt{2}/2)\chi_{2pyA} \tag{58}$$

$$\chi_{2A} = (\sqrt{3}/3)\chi_{2sA} - (\sqrt{6}/6)\chi_{2pxA} - (\sqrt{2}/2)\chi_{2pyA} \tag{59}$$

$$\chi_{\sigma A} = (\sqrt{3}/3)\chi_{2sA} + (\sqrt{6}/3)\chi_{2pxA} \tag{60}$$

$$\chi_{\pi A} = \chi_{2pzA} \tag{61}$$

$$\chi_{1B} = (\sqrt{3}/3)\chi_{2sB} + (\sqrt{6}/6)\chi_{2pxB} + (\sqrt{2}/2)\chi_{2pyB} \tag{62}$$

$$\chi_{2B} = (\sqrt{3}/3)\chi_{2sB} + (\sqrt{6}/6)\chi_{2pxB} - (\sqrt{2}/2)\chi_{2pyB} \tag{63}$$

$$\chi_{\sigma B} = (\sqrt{3}/3)\chi_{2sB} - (\sqrt{6}/3)\chi_{2pxB} \tag{64}$$

$$\chi_{\pi B} = \chi_{2pzB} \tag{65}$$

The three orbitals χ_{1A}, χ_{2A}, and $\chi_{\sigma A}$ about atom A project in the xy-plane in directions which form with one another angles of 120°; moreover, the three orbitals χ_{1B}, χ_{2B}, and $\chi_{\sigma B}$ about atom B likewise project in the xy-plane in directions which form angles of 120° with one another. The situation is illustrated diagrammatically in Fig. 12, where the arrows show the directions in which the various orbitals project most strongly. The six orbitals shown are only slightly less concentrated in the directions indicated than tetrahedral orbitals (equations 54–57) would be; on the other hand, they are much more concentrated than pure $2s$ or pure $2p$ orbitals. In fact, the "probability cloud" corresponding to such a trigonal orbital is hardly distinguishable from one (Fig. 11) corresponding to a tetrahedral orbital. The further orbitals $\chi_{\pi A}$ and $\chi_{\pi B}$, which are not represented in Fig. 12, are unhybridized $2p_z$ orbitals which project equally in the two opposite directions parallel to the z-axis (i.e., perpendicular to the plane of the paper). If these orbitals were shown in Fig. 12, each of them would be represented by *two* arrows perpendicular to the paper and pointing in opposite directions, since the two parts of these orbitals project equally. The justification for the particular hybridized orbitals shown in equations 58–65 should become apparent as the conclusions to which they lead are examined.

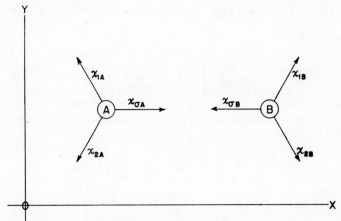

Fig. 12. A diagram showing the directions in which the indicated six orbitals of the ethylene molecule project most strongly in the xy-plane.

The orbitals χ_{1A}, χ_{2A}, χ_{1B}, and χ_{2B} form bonds with the $1s$ orbitals of the four hydrogen atoms. The four carbon-hydrogen bonds, therefore, lie in the xy-plane, so that the molecule is completely planar. The H—C—H and the H—C—C bond angles are all approximately equal to 120°. Similarly, the orbitals $\chi_{\sigma A}$ and $\chi_{\sigma B}$ form a carbon-carbon bond, which, like the carbon-hydrogen bonds just considered, is of the σ type. If this σ bond were the only bond between the two carbon atoms, there should be free (or nearly free) rotation of the two ends of the molecule about the single carbon-carbon bond. Such, however, is not the fact. A second carbon-carbon bond results from the interaction of the orbitals $\chi_{\pi A}$ and $\chi_{\pi B}$. This additional carbon-carbon bond is not even approximately of the σ type, since its average distribution of electric charge is far from cylindrically symmetric about the bond axis. In the region between the two nuclei, the concentration of electronic charge due to this bond is greatest in the plane passing through the carbon nuclei and perpendicular to the paper in Fig. 12. There are two separated regions of greatest charge concentration; one of them lies above, the other below, the plane of the paper. The probability that either of the two electrons (which produce this second component of the double bond) lies in the xy-plane is zero. Such a bond is frequently said to be of the π type. Since the orbitals $\chi_{\pi A}$ and $\chi_{\pi B}$ are not directed toward each other but instead project in parallel directions, they do not overlap as greatly as do the orbitals $\chi_{\sigma A}$ and $\chi_{\sigma B}$. Consequently, the π bond is rather weaker than the σ bond.

The representation just given explains many of the characteristic properties of carbon-carbon double bonds. Thus, although (as noted) the σ component of a double bond should not prevent free rotation, the π component should do so. The π orbitals overlap most strongly when the two doubly bonded carbon atoms and the four other atoms joined to them lie all in the same plane. Any rotation of one half of the molecule about the line joining the carbon nuclei markedly reduces the amount of overlapping, and hence decreases both the strength of the π bond and the stability of the molecule. The minimum overlapping is produced by a relative rotation of 90°, which brings the two halves of the molecule into perpendicular planes; for, after such a rotation, the concentration of the orbital $\chi_{\pi A}$ is greatest just where the concentration of $\chi_{\pi B}$ is least, and vice versa. Were the molecule to assume this latter shape, the π bond would be essentially broken. Consequently, the molecule is normally planar; and it offers a high resistance to any force distorting it from the planar shape. This high resistance accounts for the existence of separable *cis-trans* isomers. To transform a molecule of *cis*-2-butene, for example, into one of the *trans*-isomer by rotation about the carbon-carbon double bond would require enough energy to pass the molecule through a very unstable shape. Since, at room temperature, extremely few molecules can possess so much energy, the rate of spontaneous interconversion under such conditions and by such a mechanism must be, if not actually zero, at least very small.

The spectroscopically determined shape of the ethylene molecule agrees in general with the interpretation just given. The molecule is planar, and the predicted value of approximately 120° for each of the H—C—H and H—C—C bond angles (see above) is in accord with experiment. This last fact is not surprising, since the hybrid orbitals of equations 58–65 were arbitrarily chosen so as to make the angles 120°. If the observed angles had had almost any other values not less than 90°, the hybrid orbitals would have been differently chosen, and equally good agreement would have been obtained. A more significant feature of the quantum-mechanical treatment is that it provides a reasonable qualitative interpretation for the bond length. Since in a double bond *four* electrons are concentrated between the two nuclei, as compared with only *two* similarly situated electrons in a single bond, the nuclei of doubly bonded atoms are more effectively shielded from each other than are the nuclei of singly bonded atoms. In other words, the attraction of the carbon nuclei for the four electrons in the double bond is larger (relative to the repulsion between the nuclei) than is their attraction for the two electrons in a single bond. Inasmuch as attractions shorten, whereas repulsions lengthen, the bonds in which they occur, a double bond may be expected to be somewhat shorter than a single bond. This prediction again agrees with experiment; the observed carbon-carbon distances in ethylene and in ethane are, respectively, about 1.34 and 1.54 A.

Since a π bond leads to a considerable attraction between the bonded atoms, a carbon-carbon double bond is stronger than a carbon-carbon single bond. But, since a π bond is weaker than a σ bond, a carbon-carbon double bond is less than twice as strong as a carbon-carbon single bond. Accordingly, it is easier to break the π component of a double bond (which is thereby converted into a single bond) than it is to break a single bond of the σ type. For this reason, numerous reagents, such as hydrogen, the halogens, the halogen acids, etc., add readily to olefins by rupturing the π components of their double bonds; however, the same reagents do not ordinarily rupture σ bonds and therefore do not react similarly with paraffins, which contain only bonds of this latter type.

Still further characteristics of olefinic compounds may be interpreted by assuming that double bonds consist of strong σ components, essentially equivalent to single bonds, and of weaker π components, which hold the electrons less firmly. Among the phenomena thus interpreted are the relatively high molecular refractions of unsaturated compounds and the closely related displacement (toward longer wave lengths) of the ultraviolet absorption of a hydrocarbon by the introduction of double bonds into the molecule.

XI. THE CARBON-CARBON TRIPLE BOND

The two carbon atoms in a molecule of acetylene, C_2H_2, have the configuration $1s^2 2s 2p^3$ characteristic of the carbon atoms in paraffins and olefins. The hybridization of the carbon orbitals, however, appears to be of still a third type. If the two carbon atoms are thought of as lying along the z-axis, the hybridized orbitals most commonly chosen are

$$\chi_{hA} = (\sqrt{2}/2)\chi_{2sA} - (\sqrt{2}/2)\chi_{2pzA} \qquad (66)$$

$$\chi_{\sigma A} = (\sqrt{2}/2)\chi_{2sA} + (\sqrt{2}/2)\chi_{2pzA} \qquad (67)$$

$$\chi_{+A} = \chi_{211A} \qquad (68)$$

$$\chi_{-A} = \chi_{21\bar{1}A} \qquad (69)$$

$$\chi_{hB} = (\sqrt{2}/2)\chi_{2sB} + (\sqrt{2}/2)\chi_{2p_zB} \qquad (70)$$

$$\chi_{\sigma B} = (\sqrt{2}/2)\chi_{2sB} - (\sqrt{2}/2)\chi_{2p_zB} \qquad (71)$$

$$\chi_{+B} = \chi_{211B} \qquad (72)$$

$$\chi_{-B} = \chi_{21\bar{1}B} \qquad (73)$$

(For the significance of the orbitals defined in equations 68, 69, 72, and 73, see equations 21 and 23 on p. 14). The orbitals χ_{hA} and $\chi_{\sigma A}$ on atom A are equivalent to each other and project in opposite directions along the z-axis; similarly, the orbitals χ_{hB} and $\chi_{\sigma B}$ on the atom B also are equivalent to each other and also project in opposite directions along the z-axis. These four orbitals are only slightly less concentrated than tetrahedral orbitals (equations 54–57) or than trigonal orbitals (equations 58–60, 62–64); presumably, they form strong bonds. The "probability cloud" corresponding to any one of these orbitals would again be scarcely distinguishable from the cloud (Fig. 11) corresponding to a tetrahedral orbital. The two carbon-hydrogen bonds are produced by the carbon orbitals χ_{hA} and χ_{hB}, together with the respective $1s$ orbitals of the hydrogen atoms. The hydrogen atoms must accordingly lie on the z-axis; hence, the molecule is linear. One component of the carbon-carbon triple bond is similarly produced by the two carbon orbitals $\chi_{\sigma A}$ and $\chi_{\sigma B}$, which overlap strongly along the z-axis. This component, like the carbon-hydrogen bonds, is of the σ type. The remaining carbon orbitals χ_{+A}, χ_{-A}, χ_{+B}, and χ_{-B} are unhybridized $2p$ functions in the *complex* forms corresponding to the assignment of the values $+1$ and -1 to the magnetic quantum number m_l. The interactions of χ_{+A} with χ_{+B} and of χ_{-A} with χ_{-B} lead to the two remaining components of the triple bond. Although these further bonds are not exactly like the π components of double bonds (which are formed by *real* $2p$ orbitals) they are usually considered to be of the π type. (In strict usage, the designation π applies *only* to the bonds formed by the complex orbitals χ_{+A}, χ_{+B}, χ_{-A}, and χ_{-B}, since only these orbitals correspond to definite components of angular momentum along the bond axis. The symbol π is, however, usually also applied, as above, to the weaker components of double bonds.)

The foregoing representation of the electronic structure of acetylene leads to several conclusions regarding the properties of that substance. The concentration of *six* electrons in the region between the carbon nuclei means that these nuclei are shielded from each other even more effectively than are the nuclei in ethylene. Accordingly, the length of the triple bond (about 1.20 A.) is still less than that of a double bond. Since π bonds, although effective, are somewhat weaker than σ bonds, the triple bond, although stronger than the double bond, is less than three times as strong as a single bond. To this comparative weakness of the π bonds in acetylene may be attributed such properties of the compound as its ability to add reagents, its high molecular refraction, and its absorption of relatively long-wave ultraviolet light. (Cf. the corresponding discussion of ethylene, above.)

XII. Strain Theory

In cyclopropane, each C—C—C bond angle is 60°. Tetrahedral orbitals on the various carbon atoms cannot, therefore, overlap very effectively; hence, if tetrahedral hybridization prevails in this compound, the carbon-carbon bonds should be relatively weak, and the molecule should be rela-

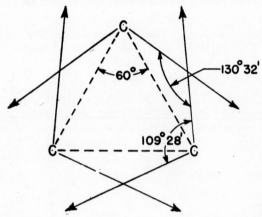

Fig. 13. The overlapping of the carbon orbitals within the cyclopropane ring with tetrahedral quantization.

tively unstable. Such a situation is illustrated schematically in Fig. 13, where the arrows represent the directions in which the bonding orbitals forming the ring project most strongly. (In this figure, the six carbon-hydrogen bonds are ignored.) The two orbitals involved in each carbon-carbon bond project along lines which intersect at an angle of 130° 32'; hence, since the maximum electronic densities associated with each bond lie along a curved line, the bond itself may also be described as curved. If the hybridization in cyclopropane is of this tetrahedral type, each H—C—H bond angle must have the normal tetrahedral value of 109° 28' (or possibly a slightly larger value if the two hydrogen atoms strongly repel one another) (21).

It is, of course, possible that, in cyclopropane, the hybridization is not tetrahedral, but is instead of some other type. However, as long as only the orbitals of the K and L shells are taken into account, the smallest possible angle between carbon orbitals is 90°. The orbitals which lead to this angle are real unhybridized $2p$ orbitals, which are rather poorly concentrated in their respective directions (see p. 32). Since these orbitals (like the tetrahedral ones) point in the wrong directions for maximum overlapping in cyclopropane, the carbon-carbon bonds of this compound would again be somewhat curved if the ring were formed by such real unhybridized $2p$ orbitals. Moreover, if such were the fact, the carbon-hydrogen bonds would be formed by hybrids between the $2s$ and the remaining $2p$ orbitals of the carbon atoms. Since these hybrid orbitals project in exactly opposite directions from their respective carbon atoms (cf. the discussion of the hybridization in acetylene, pp. 38ff.), the H—C—H bond angles in cyclopropane should under these circumstances be 180° (22).

Presumably, the truth lies somewhere between the extremes described in the two preceding paragraphs. By more careful analyses of the cyclopropane problem, Kilpatrick and Spitzer (21) have predicted 121° 58′ for the H—C—H angle; Coulson and Moffitt (21) have predicted 113°. If either calculation is reliable, the hybridization is approximately tetrahedral. The first *experimental* measurement of an exterior valence angle in any cyclopropane derivative was based on the observed dipole moment of 1,2-dichlorocyclopropane; the value 96° thus obtained for the Cl—C—H angle seems unreasonably small, and is probably invalidated by the impurity of the sample used (23). A more recent and doubtless more reliable value of 112° ± 4° for the Cl—C—Cl angle in 1,1-dichlorocyclopropane has been obtained by electron diffraction (24). With cyclopropane itself, an electron diffraction study (25) has led to 116° 24′ for the H—C—H angle. Finally, by the use of a dipole-moment method, the phenyl-C-phenyl angle in 1,1-diphenylcyclopropane has been found to be 116° ± 10° (26). All these experimental values (except the first one cited) are in satisfactory agreement with each other and with the ones predicted (21). It may therefore be concluded that, in accordance with the theoretical calculations, the hybridization in cyclopropane is essentially tetrahedral.

Since, in cyclopropane, the carbon-carbon bonds cannot under any circumstances be strong, the molecule must have a comparatively high energy. The so-called *strain*, thus produced, has characteristic effects upon the properties of the compound (27). For example, it explains the fact that the heat of combustion of cyclopropane is greater, per CH_2 group, than is that of any comparable unstrained compound such as cyclohexane (see below); it also explains partly (and perhaps completely) the relative ease with which the three-membered ring is broken by addition reactions. Similarly, all other molecules containing three-membered rings are likewise strained, and hence likewise unstable.

In four-membered carbon rings (such as that in cyclobutane), the overlapping of tetrahedral orbitals, although still not ideal, is somewhat more effective than it is in three-membered rings; consequently, four-membered rings, although still appreciably strained, are less strained than are three-membered ones. On the other hand, in all five-membered (and still larger) rings, the overlapping of tetrahedral orbitals is nearly, if not quite, as complete as it is in noncyclic compounds; consequently, the phenomena associated with strain are not ordinarily observed in substances containing no rings of less than five members.

XIII. The Theory of resonance (7, 12, 28)

As stated on p. 9, the wave function of any atom or molecule may be regarded as a quantitative description of the average distribution of electronic charge in that atom or molecule; the square of the absolute magnitude of this function is, in fact, the property represented by the "probability clouds" of Figs. 5–11. The wave functions set up (in the ways described above) for specified valence-bond structures are at best only approximations to the correct wave functions of the corresponding molecules. Although such approximations are often good enough for many qualitative purposes, they always lack quantitative accuracy. In fact, not infrequently, such wave functions are not even good enough for the qualitative characterizations of the substances to which they refer. These more serious failures, however, cannot be attributed to the inadequacy of the quantum-mechanical treatment, because they merely reflect the more fundamental inadequacies of the classical structures which the wave functions in question are designed to represent. Some of these inadequacies have long been known. For example, neither of the Kekulé structures III and IV accounts for the characteristic aromatic properties of benzene; nor does either one correctly predict the number of isomeric disubstituted benzenes. Obviously,

III   IV   V

therefore, no wave function set up to represent either of these structures can be a satisfactory approximation to the correct function for the molecule A much less striking example is butadiene, for which the conventional structure V is not entirely adequate, (cf. pp. 47f), and for which, accordingly, the corresponding wave function must be equally unsatisfactory.

Long before quantum-mechanical methods had been applied to the problem of molecular structure, organic chemists had realized these inadequacies of their structural formulas, and they had made considerable efforts to devise more generally satisfactory systems of representation. The innumerable unsuccessful attempts to express the structure of benzene in classical symbols are too well known to require further comment here. The theory of partial valence, which Thiele (29) applied to all conjugated systems, is likewise familiar. During approximately the third decade of the present century, the still more general theories of intermediate stages (30) (Zwischenstufen) and of mesomerism (31) were developed independently in Germany and in England. According to these last two theories (which are equivalent), the true states of certain molecules (e.g., those of benzene and of butadiene) cannot be represented by single structures of the classical type, but must instead be described as intermediate between *imaginary* states which *can* be so represented. If benzene is taken as an example, the Kekulé structure III indicates an average distribution of electric charge, which corresponds to no molecule of that compound; similarly, the second Kekulé structure IV indicates a different average distribution of electric charge, which likewise corresponds to no actual molecule. Neither structure, therefore, is satisfactory. The true distribution of charge in benzene, however, may be regarded as intermediate between the two indicated extremes. In other words, the concentration of the electrons in the region between any two adjacent carbon nuclei is greater than the concentration corresponding to a single bond between those atoms, but less than the concentration corresponding to a double bond between them. Each carbon-carbon bond is therefore regarded as intermediate between a single bond and a double one; and all six such bonds are considered to be equivalent. The structure of the molecule as a whole is thus intermediate between the two Kekulé structures; hence it cannot be represented by any single symbol of the classical type. It is especially to be noted that the molecule is thought of, *not* as constantly undergoing transitions back and forth between the two Kekulé structures, but as having a single structure which cannot be expressed with the classical symbols, and which lies permanently between these two extremes.

With the development of the quantum-mechanical treatment of valence, it became apparent that these concepts of intermediate stages and of mesomerism are simple corollaries of the fundamental mathematical theorems. Thus, if neither the function ψ_{III} set up to represent the Kekulé structure III nor the function ψ_{IV} set up to represent the alternative Kekulé structure IV is satisfactory, it is reasonable to try the linear combination

$$\psi_{III,IV} = a_{III}\psi_{III} + a_{IV}\psi_{IV} \qquad (74)$$

If the numerical coefficients a_{III} and a_{IV} are chosen so that the resulting function $\psi_{III,IV}$ is the best one expressible in the form of equation 74, a considerable improvement may perhaps be achieved. In any event, the *best* function $\psi_{III,IV}$ that can be expressed by equation 74 cannot possibly be any worse that ψ_{III} or ψ_{IV} alone, since the most unfavorable situation which could arise would be that this best $\psi_{III,IV}$ is identical with ψ_{III} or with ψ_{IV}. As a matter of fact, however, since the structures III and IV are equivalent to one another, there is no reason why either of the corresponding equivalent functions ψ_{III} and ψ_{IV} should contribute more to the combination $\psi_{III,IV}$ than does the other. Consequently, the coefficients a_{III} and a_{IV} must be of equal magnitude; and the function $\psi_{III,IV}$ can be described as halfway between ψ_{III} and ψ_{IV}. Hence, just as is assumed in the theories of intermediate stages and of mesomerism, the structure of benzene turns out to be exactly halfway between the two Kekulé structures, and all six carbon-carbon bonds are equivalent. Moreover, since the function $\psi_{III,IV}$ does not, as time passes, change from ψ_{III} to ψ_{IV} and back again, the benzene molecule does not undergo transitions between the structures III and IV. (The structure of butadiene will be taken up later. See pp. 47f.)

The method just used to describe the structure of benzene can be generalized. When the wave function of any molecule is approximated, as in equation 75, by a linear combination ψ_M

$$\psi_M = \sum_i a_i \psi_i \tag{75}$$

of simpler functions ψ_i, each of which represents some particular valence-bond structure, the molecule (and hence the substance) is said to *resonate* among, or better to be a *resonance hybrid* of, all the structures involved. A resonating molecule may also be said (equivalently) to be in an intermediate stage or in a mesomeric state (see above). The individual structures may be said to resonate with one another or to contribute to the state of the molecule.

If the structures among which resonance (i.e., mesomerism) occurs are not equivalent to one another, these structures need not make identical contributions to the molecular state; in other words, the coefficients a_j of equation 75 need not all be of the same magnitude. The general method for determining those values of the coefficients which give the best wave function ψ_M for the *ground state* of the molecule is based upon the so-called *variation principle* of quantum mechanics (7). This principle (a mathematical consequence of the form of the Schrödinger equation) states that the approximate energy E_M calculated for any approximate function ψ_M by means of the equation

$$E_M = \frac{\displaystyle\int_{x,y,z} \sum_\sigma \psi_M^* H \psi_M \, d\tau}{\displaystyle\int_{x,y,z} \sum_\sigma \psi_M^* \psi_M \, d\tau} \tag{76}$$

(cf. also equation 39 on p. 18) is always greater than the correct eigenvalue W. (If ψ_M is the correct eigenfunction of the molecule, then E_M is equal to W; under no circumstances, however, can E_M be less than W.) Since, therefore, the calculated energy is always too high, the lowest value of E_M obtained by any choice of the coefficients a_j is the one nearest to the correct energy W of the molecule in its ground state. That is, the set of coefficients which leads to the lowest possible value of E_M gives the best possible approximation ψ_M to the correct wave function ψ. The closeness of the approximation depends not only upon the forms of the functions ψ_j, but also upon the total number of structures among which resonance is supposed to occur. In fact, it can be shown that an *exactly* correct wave function can be obtained (in the manner described) only as the sum of an infinite number of terms. In other words, an *exactly* correct description of the state of a molecule would require resonance among an infinite number of structures, most of which, of course, could not be represented graphically by any classical symbols.

The remarkable success of the classical structural theory, where a single structure is ascribed to each molecule, shows that highly satisfactory representations of many molecules can be obtained without any consideration of resonance. For example, all hydrocarbons which contain neither aromatic rings nor systems of conjugated multiple bonds can be so represented. Where such is the fact, only the single structure assigned by the organic chemists to the substance under consideration can make any large contribution to the state of the molecule; all other structures must make much smaller (and perhaps even negligible) contributions. That is, the single wave function set up to represent the most important structure is so good an approximation to the correct wave function that, in any purely qualitative treatment, linear combinations of wave functions (cf. equation 75) are unnecessary.

On the other hand, the classical structural theory does not provide satisfactory representations for certain molecules, such as those of the aromatic and conjugated hydrocarbons. With any such substance, therefore, two or more structures must make appreciable contributions to the state of the molecule; hence, the correct wave function is not very close to any function corresponding to a single structure. Here, resonance must be taken into account.

The above statements regarding the relative unimportance of resonance in the different classes of hydrocarbon are based merely upon the relative success of the organic chemists in providing satisfactory single structures for the substances in question. It is of great theoretical significance, therefore, that the quantum-mechanical theory of resonance provides fairly definite and unambiguous rules, by which it may be decided whether or not any important resonance should occur; and that this decision can usually be made without reference to the previously determined properties of the compound in question. Fortunately, these rules have so far always led to the conclusions demanded by the chemical facts; otherwise, grave doubts would be cast upon the validity of the theory.

The most important (but not the only) rules governing the occurrence of resonance are the following. (1) No resonance can occur among structures which differ greatly in the relative positions of their atomic nuclei. For this reason, there is no resonance between the structures VI and VII.

$$CH_3—CH—CH_3$$
$$|$$
$$CH_3—CH_2—CH_2—CH_3 \qquad CH_3$$
$$VI \qquad\qquad\qquad VII$$

(2) No resonance can occur among structures with different numbers of unpaired electrons. For this reason, there is in ethylene no resonance between the structures VIII and IX.

$$H_2C{=}CH_2 \qquad\qquad H_2\overset{\cdot}{C}—\overset{\cdot}{C}H_2$$
(No unpaired electrons)   (Two unpaired electrons)
VIII   IX

(3) When resonance does occur, equivalent structures must make exactly the same contributions, nonequivalent structures usually make different contributions. More particularly, when two resonating structures differ in stability (i.e., in energy), the more stable one (i.e., the one with the lower energy) makes the larger contribution to the ground state of the molecule; the greater the difference in stability between the two structures, the smaller is the relative contribution made by the less stable structure.

These rules clearly show why single structures have proved to be satisfactory for some substances, but unsatisfactory for others. For no *saturated* hydrocarbon is it possible to write two almost equally stable structures, where the first is the classical one and the second has the same number of unpaired electrons and approximately the same relative positions for all the atomic nuclei. Thus, although the two structures X and XI for methane

$$\begin{array}{ccc} H & & H \\ | & & | \\ H—C—H & & H—C:^-H^+ \\ | & & | \\ H & & H \\ X & & XI \end{array}$$

satisfy the first two of the above conditions for resonance, they must certainly differ greatly in internal energy and thus in stability. The second and much less stable one can make only a small contribution to the state of the molecule; hence the first alone is a satisfactory approximation. (The partially ionic structure XI is, however, of interest in connection with the dipole moment of the carbon-hydrogen bond.) Similar situations are encountered in all other saturated hydrocarbons, as well as in all unsaturated ones which contain no aromatic or conjugated systems. For all such substances, therefore, single structures are ordinarily satisfactory, as has long been known by organic chemists.

With benzene, on the other hand, the two Kekulé structures III and IV (p. 42) correspond to relative nuclear positions which differ only slightly; also, they have exactly the same number of unpaired electrons. Consequently, resonance does occur. Since, in addition, the two Kekulé structures are equivalent, they must make identical contributions. No single structure, therefore, can adequately represent benzene. The situation with any other aromatic hydrocarbon is closely similar to that with benzene itself. Thus, resonance between the Kekulé structures must be important in all the homologues of benzene. Moreover, the higher condensed aromatic ring systems permit still more complex resonance. With naphthalene, for example, the *three* structures XII–XIV must be taken into account. Al-

though only the last two of these are equivalent, all three must be of approximately the same stability, and so each of the three must make approximately the same contribution to the state of the molecule. As may readily be verified, *four* structures analogous to XII–XIV can be written for anthracene, *five* can be written for phenanthrene, and so on.

Butadiene is a substance intermediate between the saturated and the aromatic hydrocarbons. For this compound, only one classical structure V can be written. It must be supposed, therefore, that this structure makes a larger contribution to the ground state than does any other presumably

less stable one. Consequently, this single structure V has been found adequate for most purposes. Nevertheless, the characteristic properties of butadiene, which are usually attributed to the *conjugated* pair of double bonds are not satisfactorily accounted for by structure V. The 1,4-addition of hydrogen and of the halogens, for example, is explained more easily by some structure such as XV.

This latter structure has the following significance. The various atomic nuclei occupy the same relative positions in both structures V and XV; the first condition for resonance is therefore satisfied. The dotted line in XV represents a *formal bond*, which is due to the pairing of two electrons located in orbitals on the two atoms thus joined. Since the number of *un*paired electrons in both V and XV is zero, the second condition for resonance is also satisfied. The formal bond of structure XV is sometimes represented by a full line (as in XVI), rather than by a dotted line. Such a symbol, however, easily leads to confusion, since it tends to obscure the important distinction between an actual (or effective) bond joining adjacent atoms and a formal bond joining more distant atoms. An effective bond, since it has considerable strength, markedly increases the stability of the structure in which it occurs; on the other hand, a formal bond, since it has practically zero strength, does not appreciably increase the stability of the structure in which it occurs.

Although there should be resonance between structures V and XV, it should not be very important, since the number of effective bonds in the former structure is one more than the number in the latter; consequently, the former must be considerably the more stable of the two. However, since the effective bond present in structure V but absent in structure XV is of the relatively weak π type, the difference in stability between structures V and XV may not be great enough to prevent XV from making a significant, although small, contribution. Indeed, approximate numerical calculations (32),* which cannot here be further described, have strongly suggested that the resonance in butadiene is not negligible. In fact, although the classical structure V of butadiene (or the analogous structure of any other substance with conjugated multiple bonds) is adequate for most purposes, it is nevertheless not quite as accurate as might be desired for all purposes, since the small contribution of the unstable structure with a formal bond (like XV) exerts an appreciable influence.

If resonance between the structures V and XV is admitted in butadiene, there is no logical reason to ignore the possibility of resonance in propylene

$$CH_2\!-\!CH\!=\!CH_2 \qquad\qquad CH_2\!=\!CH\!-\!CH_2$$
$$\;\;\;|\qquad\qquad\qquad\qquad\qquad\qquad\;\;\vdots$$
$$\;\;H\qquad\qquad\qquad\qquad\qquad H\dots\dots\dots\vdots$$

$$\qquad\text{XVII}\qquad\qquad\qquad\qquad\qquad\text{XVIII}$$

between such structures as XVII and XVIII (33). Here again, the number of effective bonds in the classical structure (XVII) is one greater than the

---

* For analogous calculations from the molecular-orbital point of view, see E. Hückel, reference 14.

number in the less stable structure (XVIII), so that the former must make much the larger contribution, particularly since the bond present in XVII but absent in XVIII is of the relatively strong σ type. Although, with propylene, there is no possibility of 1,4-addition, evidence for a small amount of resonance between structures XVII and XVIII has nevertheless been obtained from thermochemical (see below) and spectroscopic data (33). Such resonance is commonly referred to as *hyperconjugation* or as *no-bond resonance*; it can occur in any alkyl-substituted olefin, acetylene, or aromatic hydrocarbon.

To chemists, the most important effect of resonance is its influence upon the energy of the molecule in which it occurs. For the ground state of the molecule M (see the above discussion of the variation principle), the best linear combination ψ_M of functions ψ_j is the one which leads to the lowest possible value of the calculated energy E_M. Hence, the energy of the resonance hybrid is necessarily lower than that of even the most stable of the contributing structures. The *resonance energy* of the compound is defined as the energy of the most stable structure minus that of the hybrid. Resonance energy is therefore always positive; it thus provides a convenient quantitative measure for the effectiveness of the resonance. In benzene, where two structures, III and IV, make equal and large contributions, the resonance energy should be large; in butadiene, where only one structure, V, makes a large contribution, the resonance energy should be rather small; in methane, where the resonance is negligible, the resonance energy should also be negligible.

A practical experimental method for measuring resonance energies depends on the empirical rule that the heat of combustion of a nonresonating substance can be calculated as the sum of terms corresponding to the various bonds in the molecule. Thus, the heat of combustion of ethane is six times the heat corresponding to a carbon-hydrogen bond plus one times that corresponding to a carbon-carbon single bond. When the bond values which give the most satisfactory results with nonresonating substances are used to calculate the heat of combustion of a resonating substance, the value calculated for the most stable structure is always greater than the observed value. With benzene, for example, a single Kekulé structure (III or IV) leads to a predicted heat of combustion equal to about 829 kcal. per mole (for the *gaseous* substance), whereas the experimental value is only about 788 kcal. per mole (34). The difference between these two quantities (approximately 41 kcal. per mole) represents the excess stability of benzene over the stability which that compound would have if it had either one of the Kekulé structures. In other words, the resonance energy of benzene is approximately 41 kcal. per mole. A slightly different, and doubtless more accurate, value (36 kcal. per mole) has been obtained by a similar treatment of the heat of *hydrogen*ation of benzene (35, 36). With other aromatic systems, the resonance energies, determined in the ways described, are found to be equal approximately to 36 kcal. per mole for each aromatic ring in the molecule (34, 36). That of toluene, like that of benzene itself, is not far from 36 kcal. per mole; that of naphthalene is not far from 2×36, or 72, kcal. per mole; that of either anthracene or phenanthrene is not far from 3×36, or 108, kcal. per mole. On the other hand, with the simple conjugated substances, such as butadiene, the resonance energies (as might be expected) are much smaller. That of butadiene (35, 36), is about 3.5 kcal. per mole; that of cycloheptatriene (36, 37) is about 6.7 kcal. per mole. Even *hyper*conjugation, as it occurs in propylene, seems to lead to an appreciable stabilization which, rather unexpectedly, is approximately as large as that resulting from the ordinary conjugation in butadiene and its analogues.

The exceptionally large resonance energies of benzene and other aromatic hydrocarbons are doubtless the major cause of the characteristic differences in behavior between these substances and the unsaturated aliphatic compounds. For example, in the course of any reaction which benzene undergoes, the resonance in the ring must be more or less disturbed. Since any such interference with the resonance should presumably decrease the resonance energy, and hence also the stability of the system, the relative unreactivity of benzene is thus explained.

The structure of cycloöctatetraene is not yet entirely clear. Although this substance may be presumed to resonate between the two Kekulé-like struc-

XIX   XX

tures XIX and XX, resonance need not here be as effective as it is in benzene. If the molecule is planar, the two structures are equivalent, and hence the resonance energy should be rather large; each structure separately, however, is then made relatively unstable by the strain due to the distortion of the C—C≡C bond angle from its normal value of about 120° to the value of 135° characteristic of a regular plane octagon. Because of this strain, the resonance hybrid may be more stable if the ring is not planar, but puckered (38). Two different puckered forms may be considered. If either of the structures XIX and XX is unstrained, the other must be highly strained by the required rotations about its double bonds (cf. p. 37); under these conditions the resonance energy should be small because the resonating structures differ greatly in energy. A second possibility (preferred by Penney (38)) is that the two puckered structures are equivalent to each other (as are the two planar structures), but that each is somewhat strained by the rotations about its double bonds; this strain would then decrease both the stabilities of the individual structures and the magnitude of the resonance energy. Evidently, no matter which of these alternatives is correct, cyclooctatetraene can hardly have the exceptional stability of an aromatic substance. This expectation is confirmed experimentally by the observation (39) that, in the liquid state, cyclooctatetraene is about 34 kcal. per

$$C_6H_5—CH\!\!=\!\!CH_2$$
XXI

mole less stable than the isomeric styrene XXI. Moreover, from an x-ray study of the crystalline compound (40), it has been concluded that the ring is puckered, and that the lengths of the carbon-carbon bonds are alternately 1.34 and 1.54 A. Since these are just the lengths which would be expected to obtain in a single Kekulé-like structure (XIX or XX), the resonance once more appears to be relatively unimportant. On the other hand, electron-diffraction methods (41) indicate that in cyclooctatetraene all the carbon-carbon bonds are equivalent and that each such bond is only about 2% longer than a ring bond in benzene. These conclusions are inconsistent both with the thermochemical and with the x-ray data.

Resonance, besides decreasing the energies of many compounds, exerts numerous effects upon their other properties (28). For example, the interatomic distances in a resonating molecule are ordinarily intermediate between the distances characteristic of the important contributing structures; and the same is true also of the stretching force-constants. Moreover, important effects of resonance upon dipole moments, ultraviolet and visible absorption spectra, etc. have also been observed. Many of these additional features of the resonance theory are treated in other chapters of this book; to these the reader is referred.

REFERENCES

1. E. v. Meyer, A History of Chemistry. Translated by G. McGowan. Macmillan, London, 1891; F. J. Moore, A History of Chemistry. McGraw-Hill, New York, 2nd ed. revised by W. T. Hall, 1931; T. M. Lowry, Historical Introduction to Chemistry. Macmillan, London, 1936.
2. J. H. van't Hoff, *Bull. soc. chim.* [2] **23**, 295 (1875); The Arrangement of Atoms in Space. 2nd ed. (translated by A. Eiloart). Longmans, Green, and Co., London, 1898.
3. J. A. Le Bel, *Bull. soc. chim.* [2] **22**, 337 (1874).
4. A. Werner, Neuere Anschauungen auf dem Gebiete der anorganischen Chemie. Friedrich Vieweg und Sohn, Braunschweig, 1905.
5. Cf. G. N. Lewis, Valence and the Structure of Atoms and Molecules. Chemical Catalog Company, New York, 1923; N. V. Sidgwick, The Electronic Theory of Valency. Oxford University Press, Oxford, 1927.
6. W. Heisenberg, *Z. Physik* **43**, 172 (1927).

52 G. W. WHELAND

7. Cf., for example, L. Pauling and E. B. Wilson, Jr., Introduction to Quantum Mechanics. McGraw-Hill, New York, 1935; H. Eyring, J. Walter, and G. E. Kimball, Quantum Chemistry. Wiley, New York, 1944; S. Glasstone, Theoretical Chemistry. Van Nostrand, New York, 1944.
8. M. Born and J. R. Oppenheimer, *Ann. Physik* **84**, 457 (1927).
9. H. M. James and A. S. Coolidge, *J. Chem. Phys.* **1**, 825 (1933).
10. See, for example, F. H. Getman and F. Daniels, Outlines of Physical Chemistry. Wiley, New York, 7th Ed. 1943, pp. 6 ff; A. F. Wells, Structural Inorganic Chemistry. Oxford University Press, Oxford, 1945, pp. 27 ff.
11. W. Heitler and F. London, *Z. Physik* **44**, 455 (1927); Y. Sugiura, *ibid.* **45**, 484 (1927).
12. J. H. Van Vleck and A. Sherman, *Revs. Modern Phys.* **7**, 167 (1935).
13. S. C. Wang, *Phys. Rev.* **31**, 579 (1928); N. Rosen, *ibid.* **38**, 2099 (1931); S. Weinbaum, *J. Chem. Phys.* **1**, 593 (1933).
14. E. Hückel, *Z. Elektrochem.* **43**, 752, 827 (1937); C. A. Coulson, *Proc. Roy. Soc. (Edinburgh)* **A61**, 115 (1941).
15. Cf. L. Pauling, The Nature of the Chemical Bond. Cornell University Press, Ithaca, 1st ed. 1939, 2nd ed. 1940, Chapter III.
16. D. M. Dennison, *Revs. Modern Phys.* **12**, 175 (1940).
17. J. D. Kemp and K. S. Pitzer, *J. Am. Chem. Soc.* **59**, 276 (1937).
18. L. Pauling and L. O. Brockway, *J. Am. Chem. Soc.* **59**, 1223 (1937).
19. L. O. Brockway, *J. Phys. Chem.* **41**, 747 (1937).
20. W. G. Penney, *Proc. Roy. Soc. London* **A144**, 166 (1934).
21. Cf. J. E. Kilpatrick and R. Spitzer, *J. Chem. Phys.* **14**, 463 (1946); C. A. Coulson and W. E. Moffitt, *ibid.* **15**, 151 (1947).
22. G. H. Duffey, *J. Chem. Phys.* **14**, 342 (1946).
23. B. I. Spinrad, *J. Am. Chem. Soc.* **68**, 617 (1946); cf. also P. G. Stevens, *ibid.* **68**, 620 (1946).
24. J. M. O'Gorman and V. Schomaker, *J. Am. Chem. Soc.* **68**, 1138 (1946).
25. O. Hassel and H. Viervoll, *Acta Chem. Scand.* **1**, 149 (1947).
26. M. Goldsmith and G. W. Wheland, *J. Am. Chem. Soc.* **70**, 2632 (1948).
27. For a general discussion of the effects of strain upon the properties of substances, see, for example, W. Hückel, Der gegenwärtige Stand der Spannungstheorie. Fortschritte der Chemie, Physik, und physikalischen Chemie, Serie A, Band 19, Heft 4, edited by A. Eucken. Gebrüder Borntraeger, Berlin, 1927.
28. Cf., for example, L. Pauling, The Nature of the Chemical Bond. Cornell University Press, Ithaca, 1st Ed. 1939, 2nd Ed. 1940; G. W. Wheland, The Theory of Resonance. Wiley, New York, 1944.
29. J. Thiele, *Ann.* **306**, 87 (1899).
30. F. Arndt, E. Scholz, and P. Nachtwey, *Ber.* **57**, 1903 (1924); F. Arndt, *ibid.* **63**, 2963 (1930).
31. Cf., for example, R. Robinson, Two Lectures on an "Outline of an Electrochemical (Electronic) Theory of the Course of Organic Reactions," The Institute of Chemistry of Great Britain and Ireland, London, 1932; *J. Soc. Dyers Colourists*, Jubilee Issue **65** (1934); C. K. Ingold, *J. Chem. Soc.* 1120 (1933); *Chem. Revs.* **15**, 225 (1934).
32. Cf. G. W. Wheland, *J. Chem. Phys.* **2**, 474 (1934), and the references to the earlier literature given there.
33. R. S. Mulliken, C. A. Rieke, and W. G. Brown, *J. Am. Chem. Soc.* **63**, 41 (1941); C. L. Deasy, *Chem. Revs.* **36**, 145 (1945). Cf. also G. W. Wheland, reference 32, and J. W. Baker and W. S. Nathan, *J. Chem. Soc.* 1844 (1935).

34. Cf. Table 3.6 of G. W. Wheland, reference 28, and references to the earlier literature given there.

35. G. B. Kistiakowsky, J. R. Ruhoff, H. A. Smith, and W. E. Vaughan, *J. Am. Chem. Soc.* **58,** 146 (1936).

36. Cf. Table 3.2 of G. W. Wheland, reference 28, and references to the earlier literature given there.

37. J. B. Conn, G. B. Kistiakowsky, and E. A. Smith, *J. Am. Chem. Soc.* **61,** 1868 (1939).

38. W. G. Penney, *Proc. Roy. Soc. London* **A146,** 223 (1934).

39. E. J. Prosen, W. H. Johnson, and F. D. Rossini, *J. Am. Chem. Soc.* **69,** 2068 (1947).

40. H. S. Kaufman, I. Fankuchen, and H. Mark, *Nature* **161,** 165 (1948).

41. O. Bastiensen and O. Hassel, *Tids. Kjemi, Bergvesen Met.* **7,** 55 (1947); *Chem. Abstracts* **41,** 5464 (1947).

CHAPTER 2

THE MOLECULAR STRUCTURE OF HYDROCARBONS AS DETERMINED BY SPECTROSCOPY AND ELECTRON AND X-RAY DIFFRACTION

By

M. H. JELLINEK

The Linde Air Products Company, Tonawanda, New York

CONTENTS

INTRODUCTION

In this section the contributions of infrared and Raman spectra will be treated lightly because other sections of the book will go into these two fields in much greater detail. A few of the fundamental concepts and the means of relating actual measurements to molecular structures will be briefly outlined.

The subjects of x-ray and electron diffraction will be reviewed in much greater detail in that the applicable theory will be considered for each individual case, i.e., the diffraction of x-rays by liquids and electrons by gases, etc. The order of presentation was selected because of the fact that the theories of x-ray and electron diffraction by free molecules in the gaseous state are very similar and the development presented for the former could easily be carried over into the latter.

In all cases the emphasis has been on the theoretical bases and the methods of obtaining structural results from them. Experimental methods have not been considered but adequate references are included. The individual results obtained for various compounds have not been considered in detail but rather have been collected into complete tables accompanied by a general discussion elaborating on some of the more outstanding facts presented in the tabulated data.

I. INFRARED ABSORPTION SPECTRA

THEORY

Radiation in the infrared region $(1-200\mu)$ of the spectrum may be absorbed by molecules whose composition and configuration are such that a difference in electric moment exists between various quantum states.

The long wavelength, $40-200\mu$, (far infrared) region of the spectrum yields information about the rotational energy states of the molecule. These energy states are quantized and are designated by the quantum number J. The Schrödinger equation can be interpreted to yield the rotational energy E_J of a diatomic molecule around an axis perpendicular to the line joining the nuclei as

$$E_J = \frac{h^2}{8\pi^2 I} J(J + 1) \tag{1}$$

where h is Planck's constant, and I is the moment of inertia of the molecule. J may be zero or any integer.

Selection rules limit rotational transitions to those where $\Delta J = 1$ or 0. When such a change occurs equation (1) may be written as

$$\Delta E_J = hc\bar{\nu} = \frac{h^2}{8\pi^2 I} 2J \tag{2}$$

or

$$\bar{\nu} = \frac{h}{4\pi^2 c I} J \tag{3}$$

where $\bar{\nu}$ is the frequency of the radiation in wave numbers, and c is the velocity of light. As J assumes successive integers it is obvious that the frequencies of the successive lines in the rotational spectrum are multiples of equation (3) and hence the moment of inertia of the molecule can be estimated. If the atoms comprising the molecule are of known mass then the bond lengths can be computed. These measurements in the far infrared region are experimentally difficult and measurements have been carried out on only a few molecules.

A far more suitable region for experimental work is that of the near infrared $(1-40\mu)$. In this region it is the vibrational spectra of the molecules that govern the frequencies of the lines. These vibrational states are also quantized and designated with the quantum number, v. A characteristic of these vibrational states is that each possesses a fine structure composed of the rotational spectra possible in that vibrational state.

Wave mechanics has provided the equations for this system regarding the vibrations as that of a harmonic oscillator, yielding

$$E_v = (v + \tfrac{1}{2})hc\omega_e \tag{4}$$

where E_v is the energy in state v, and ω_e is the equilibrium frequency of the oscillator. As v changes from 1 to 2, etc. the transition to $v = 0$ produces successively, the fundamental frequency, the first overtone, etc., and these bands have wavelengths in the ratio of 1 to 1/2 to 1/3. By measurement of band position, ω_e can be evaluated. Knowing these values, and the separation of the atoms from rotational spectra or otherwise it is possible to calculate the force constant (restoring force per centimeter displacement) of the bond, and hence have a measure of its strength.

For a more detailed, though short review of this subject, the reader is referred to Glasstone (1) and for more complete details to Herzberg (2).

II. RAMAN SPECTRA

1. THEORY

If a molecule is irradiated with monochromatic light the electrons in the molecule are periodically displaced by the electric vector of the incident radiation, thus inducing a dipole. The dipole moment is proportional to the magnitude of the electric vector and the polarizability (ease of charge deformation) in the molecule. This molecule then emits secondary waves of the same frequency as the incident radiation. Because the atoms or nuclei vibrate along their lines of center, the polarizability may vary with the internuclear distance and the radiation scattered by such a system will consist of the incident radiation of frequency ν, and two new frequencies $\nu \pm \omega$ where ω is a natural vibration frequency of the molecule. $\nu + \omega$ is seldom observed because molecules in excited states are required and these are statistically few in number. A precisely similar situation exists with respect to rotational frequencies although these rotational frequencies are seldom noted.

In polyatomic molecules the mechanical motions are somewhat complicated and the determination of the kinetic and potential energies requires a
"normal coordinate" (3) treatment. The wavelengths of the scattered radiations are determined and the force constants for the various bonds are
computed. In a manner analagous to infrared absorption spectra the
strength of bonds can be evaluated and hence a measure of the chemical
reactivity of that bond is obtained. The significance of such measurements
has been considered by Kronig (4). Reviews, both short and long, by
Murphy (5) and Glockler (6) are available on this subject as well as more
complete treatises by Kohlrausch (7).

2. RESULTS

Only a few compounds will be considered at this point because they have
been more completely treated under diffraction, but they well illustrate
the agreements observed.

Herzberg (2) shows that the structure of tetrahedral methane is completely determined by one distance, namely C-H, and that this may be
computed from the spectral data to be 1.094 A. Assuming this C-H distance
to exist in ethane, the moments of inertia calculated for this molecule allow
the C-C distance to be determined as 1.573 A. and the HCH angle as 112°-
12′. It will be seen that these values are in excellent agreement with those
obtained by the diffraction methods.

Cyclohexane was assigned its possible structural types by the chemists.
These were the "tub" and "chair" (puckered ring) forms. The former required free rotation about the carbon-carbon bonds. The chair model corresponds to a much higher degree of symmetry than the tub. Langseth and
Bak (8) used the Raman effect to study this compound and some of its
deutero-compounds and concluded that hindered rotation around the carbon-carbon bonds favored the puckered ring. As will be shown later, this
conclusion is in complete agreement with results obtained by diffraction
methods.

III. X-RAY DIFFRACTION BY CRYSTALS

1. THEORY OF CRYSTAL DIFFRACTION

X-rays, because they can be produced with wave lengths very nearly the
same as the interatomic distances in crystals, are useful tools in studying
these distances, and because they are scattered by the electron clouds
around individual atoms are useful in determining the density of these electron clouds and their spatial positions. The production of x-rays is adequately discussed in standard treatises by Bragg and Bragg (9), Bunn (10),
and Compton and Allison (11).

After the initial discovery of x-ray diffraction by crystals by Friedrich *et al.* (12) many theoretical and practical advances have made it a most useful device in the study of crystalline materials. The diffraction of x-rays by three dimensional crystals depends fundamentally on Bragg's law (13).

$$n \lambda = 2d \sin \theta \tag{5}$$

where n is an integer, λ the x-ray wavelength, θ the angle between the incident x-ray beam and the atomic planes, and d the interplanar spacing.

One of the simplest applications of this law is powder diffraction of randomly oriented, polycrystalline materials first used by Debye and Scherrer (14). This powder diffraction is mainly useful for identification and, in a few cases, for structural determinations; see (9), (10).

The determination of structures is usually carried out on small single crystals of the material under consideration because the identification and measurement of the reflections can always be uniquely made with single crystal data. Because positions of atoms cannot be observed directly, structures containing them must be determined indirectly. For such an analysis a small crystal is mounted so that a definite predetermined orientation with respect to the x-ray beam is maintained. Techniques of producing single crystal diagrams are discussed in detail by Buerger (15) and Bunn (10).

Thus, if a crystal is mounted so that a collimated beam of monochromatic x-rays passes through it normal to one of its axes and if it is rotated about this axis to satisfy the Bragg relationship (equation 5) with as many crystal planes as possible, a photograph of the diffracted radiation can be obtained which is characterized by spots lying along distinct "layer lines." These layer lines can be used to determine the periodic repeat distance (the edge length of the unit cell) along the rotation axis. By suitable mounting this process can be repeated for each axis. Bragg's law (equation 5) and the geometry of the apparatus supply all the necessary data to determine these cell edges. For the less symmetrical types of crystals complications are introduced requiring more detailed study and the determination of the angles between the axes.

The reflections along the equator or zero layer line are formed by crystal planes that were vertical during the exposure while those above and below this equator represent fixed orientations for various sets of planes.

The procedure of assigning designations to these planes is known as "indexing" and in all except hexagonal crystals three "Miller Indices" uniquely define each set of planes. These indices, h, k, and l, serve to identify every crystal plane by giving the number of equal parts into which each unit cell edge is divided by that set of planes. In this way a plane having indices 310 would cut the a cell edge into three parts, the b edge into units and be parallel to (not cut) the c edge. Complete discussions on indexing can be found in Bragg (9), Bunn (10), and Buerger (15).

It is possible, by a variety of analytical and graphical methods, to assign indices to every diffraction spot on oscillation diagrams and identify the particular crystal plane producing that spot.

The processing of indexing this type of diffraction diagram is greatly facilitated by the use of the "reciprocal lattice" introduced by Ewald (16). This concept simplifies the geometrical problems of diffraction and the direction of x-ray reflections. A condensed treatment is given by Fankuchen (17) and in more detail from the standpoint of theory and method by Bunn (10), Buerger (15), and the International Tables (18).

Even the most precise knowledge of the unit cell dimensions cannot be expected to lead to any definite conclusions regarding the molecular shape, even under such conditions that the molecules are all oriented similarly. However, the knowledge of the cell dimensions can set certain limitations on molecular size and shape.

Up to this point, no mention has been made of the contributions of individual atoms to the amplitude of scattering by the crystal planes. These atoms scatter by virtue of their electron clouds and hence in relationship to their atomic numbers, the atoms of higher atomic number being more powerful scatterers. It is possible to conceive of wave fronts in crystals scattered by planes having different atomic compositions and hence scattering waves of varying amplitudes. Further, depending upon the path of these waves in the crystal their recombination would produce an in-phase condition for only certain particular angles and interplanar spacings. Consequently, the magnitude of these amplitudes and their phasal relationships determine the amplitude of the reflected beams. As the intensities of these rays are proportional to the squares of the amplitudes, consideration of these intensities with respect to the scattering planes producing them can give information about the atoms composing them, and their positions relative to the planes.

This qualitative picture will be treated briefly from a quantitative viewpoint. The atomic structure factor f (scattering form) of each atom increases with the atomic number and decreases with the sine of the angle at which the scatter occurs. Because the dimensions of the electron cloud of an atom are of the order of magnitude of the x-ray wavelength it cannot be considered to be a scattering point. When an x-ray wave front passes through this cloud interferences are formed within it and become more significant as the scattering angle increases (atoms in planes with small spacing). For this reason curves are usually given for f as a function of $(\sin \theta)/\lambda$ having a value of Z (atomic number) at $(\sin \theta)/\lambda = 0$, and diminishing as the parameter increases. These values have been deduced from reflected intensities by James and Brindley (19) and calculated by Hartree (20). Polarization of the scattered radiation introduces another factor proportional to $(1 + \cos^2 2\theta)/2$. This decreases the amplitude up to angles of $2\theta = 90°$ and then increases it. The Lorentz factor, L, is another angle factor depending upon the time the rotating crystal remains in reflecting position. This factor varies with the geometry of the reflections and charts evaluating it are given by Cox and Shaw (21). Other factors relative to thermal vibrations of the atoms and adsorption of the scattered radiation in the crystal itself are fully treated in Bragg (9) and Bunn (10). The complete equation for a single crystal rotation photograph with a crystal of volume, V, completely bathed in radiation is given by

$$\rho = \frac{E\omega}{I_0} = \frac{N^2 e^4 V}{4\pi m^2 c^4} F^2 \lambda^3 \tau p \left(\frac{1 + \cos^2 2\theta}{\sin 2\theta}\right)\left(\frac{\cos\theta}{\sqrt{(\cos^2\phi - \sin^2\theta)}}\right) TA \qquad (6)$$

where ρ is the integrated intensity, E is the total energy in a reflected beam when the specimen has been rotating time, τ, at angular velocity ω, N, the number of unit cells per unit volume, e, the electronic charge, m, the electronic mass, λ, the wavelength, c, the velocity of light, F, the structure amplitude of the beam considered, and p is the multiplicity of the reflecting planes as determined by the symmetry around the axis of rotation. The last trigonometric expression contains the polarization and Lorentz factors, with ϕ the angle between the reflecting plane and the axis of rotation, while T and A are the thermal vibration and absorption factors, respectively.

The situation which we are interested in is the arrangement of the atoms within the crystal and any attempt to discover this arrangement would require a knowledge of its effect upon the scattered intensities. To obtain this information it is necessary to compound all the waves scattered from the different atoms, whatever their locations. This can be done graphically but in practice is usually done analytically as follows:

$$F^2 = A^2 + B^2 \qquad (7)$$

$$A = \sum_n f_n \cos 2\pi(hx_n + ky_n + lz_n) \qquad (8)$$

$$B = \sum_n f_n \sin 2\pi(hx_n + ky_n + lz_n) \qquad (9)$$

where x_n, y_n, z_n are the coordinates of atoms expressed as fractions of the unit cell edges.

In this way, the intensity of each reflection can be computed for a given structure. For complete details and sample calculations see Bunn (10).

2. THE DEDUCTION OF ACTUAL STRUCTURES

a. Trial and Error Method. As has been shown, a knowledge of the atomic positions in a crystal allows the complete computation of the diffracted beam positions and their intensities. Therefore, if it is possible, with the aid of cell dimensions, optical data, etc., to assign a proposed structure to a crystal, a computation using the above formulas allows a check to be made. If agreement is good the structure may usually be presumed to be correct, if agreement is fair the positions of atoms may be shifted and the intensities recomputed in an attempt to locate the correct positions, and if no agreement is obtained a new structure may be tried. Best results are obtained by this method when simple substances are studied or when sufficient evidence about similar structures is available to assist in the assignment of logical possibilities.

In the determination of actual structures the various symmetry elements allow an assignment of the structure to one of the 230 possible space groups. Knowledge of the correct space group, because of these symmetry elements is of considerable assistance in the location of the exact atomic positions. Various short cuts to the intensity calculations have been proposed as well as an optical diffraction method by Bragg (22) which avoids all calculation of amplitudes.

b. Electron Density Diagram. This method of approach is the reverse of the procedure just discussed in that the diffracted intensities are used in an attempt to deduce the structure producing them. This direct method has one major difficulty associated with its application in that it is not generally possible to decide from experiment what are the phase angles of the various diffracted beams with respect to the origin chosen in the unit cell. On occasion, knowledge about the structure from other sources allows the phase angle to be decided upon, or a trial and error method may aid. In such cases a "Fourier Analysis" of the intensity data leads to a direct determination of the electron density as a function of the unit cell coordinates. As the positions of high electron densities are always about atomic nuclei a method of locating atoms is provided. The mathematical expression involved in this analysis is

$$\rho_{xyz} = \frac{1}{V}\left[\sum\sum_{-\infty}^{+\infty}\sum F_{hkl}\cos 2\pi(hx + ky + lz + \alpha_{hkl})\right] \quad (10)$$

where ρ_{xyz} is the electron density at position xyz, V, the volume of the unit cell, F_{hkl} the structure amplitude for the reflection hkl, and α_{hkl} the phase angle of the reflection. The term F_{ooo} represents the structure amplitude of the zero order diffraction and is equivalent to the number of electrons per unit cell.

In this way the electron density at any point in the cell becomes determinable. The effort involved in such a synthesis is enormous except for very simple structures and is seldom carried out. Rather, two dimensional syntheses are the rule allowing the determination of electron density as projected on any chosen plane in the cell. For complete details on Fourier analysis see Robertson (23), and for methods of obtaining phase angles see Bunn (10). An example of this direct determination is that of stilbene (24) whose electron map is shown as Fig. 1.

Therefore, if it is possible by either of the two methods just considered to arrive at the exact positions of the atoms in the crystal, it is possible to measure or compute the atomic radii and bond lengths. Further, in molecular structures the closest approach of molecules can be measured and the spatial configurations of the individual molecules be revealed. Having the

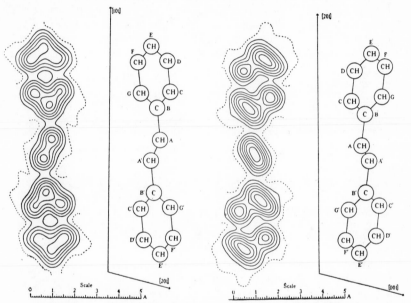

Fig. 1. Stilbene molecule. Electron contour diagram. Two projections shown. (From Robertson and Woodward, *Proc. Roy. Soc. London*, **A162**, 568, 1937.)

actual bond distances allows a calculation as to bond strength by its shortening in particular structures or a determination of the extent of resonance. For a complete discussion of bonds see Pauling (25).

3. THE RESULTS OF X-RAY DIFFRACTION BY CRYSTALS

In this section the various types of hydrocarbons are grouped in Table I and the detailed results for individual members will be given within each group. While the actual crystallographic data on nearly all hydrocarbons have been obtained these data will not be given unless it has some special bearing on the physical properties of the particular compound in the forms usually encountered or on the way it behaves chemically. Most of the data

TABLE I

Compound	Structural data	Reference
1. Aliphatics		
CH_4, Methane	Close-packed, face-centered cubic crystal	28
C_2H_6, Ethane	C—C = 1.55 ± .09 A.; closest intermolecular C—C = 4.46 A.	29
C_7H_{16}, n-Heptane	Crystals form with long chains parallel and molecules close packed	30
n-$C_{29}H_{60}$	Carbons form a plane zig-zag	31
n-$C_{30}H_{62}$	C—C in projection 1.26 ± .04 A. and C—C—C angle 106 ± 4°	32
n-$C_{35}H_{72}$ n-$C_{60}H_{122}$	C—C = 1.52 A.; CH_2 angle 114° C—C = 4.1 A. closest approach between chains	33
n-C_nH_{2n+2} (n = 1000)	Carbon atoms form a plane zig-zag, nonspherical electron clouds in CH_2 group. C—C = 1.53 A., C—C—C angle 112°, closest C—C distance between molecules = 4.13 A.	34
Tolane	Molecule linear and planar. C≡C = 1.19 A.; C— = 1.40 A.	35
2. Cycloparaffins		
C_6H_{12}, Cyclohexane	Ring has a step and not a boat form (puckered ring)	36, 37
C_8H_{16}, Cyclooctatetraene	Puckered ring, all *cis* configuration with alternate single and double bonds, little or no resonance; C—C 1.54 ± .01 A.; C=C 1.34 ± .01 A.; C=C—C angle 125°	57
C_nH_{2n} (n = 12 to 30)	Form double chains that are more closely packed than 4.1 A.	38
3. Aromatics		
C_6H_6, Benzene	Planar rings, all C—C distances equal to 1.42 A., closest C—C between molecules 3.8 A.	39
	C—C 1.41 A.	40
	C—C 1.42 ± .03 A.	41
Durene, 1,2,4,5-tetramethyl benzene	C—C aromatic 1.41 A.; C—C aliphatic 1.56 A., closest C—C between molecules 3.71 A.	42, 43
Hexamethyl benzene	C—C between ring and methane = 1.53 A.	44
	All carbons coplanar, C—C aromatic 1.42 ± .03 A.; C—C between ring and methyl group 1.54 ± .12 A.	45
Diphenyl	Both rings parallel	46
	Coplanar; C—C bond between rings 1.48 A.	47
Stilbene	All carbons coplanar; C—C aromatic 1.39 A. C=C 1.33 A.; C aromatic—C aliphatic 1.45 A.; =C—angle 128°	48, 49

C_8H_8

64

TABLE I—*Continued*

Compound	Structural data	Reference
Dibenzyl	Rings not coplanar but very nearly parallel	50
	C—C aromatic 1.41 A., C—C aliphatic 1.54 A.	51
	C aromatic—C aliphatic 1.47 A., aliphatic bond angle $109\frac{1}{2}°$	52
1,2-diphenyl benzene	Steric hindrance causes the two phenyl groups to be rotated about 50°	53
1,3,5-triphenyl benzene	Molecule almost entirely planar	54
p-Di-diphenyl	All groups coaxial and coplanar; C—C aromatic 1.42 A.;	55
	C—C between rings 1.48 A.	56
4. Condensed rings		
Naphthalene	Flat rings; C—C—C angle 120°	58, 59
Fluorene	C—C aromatic 1.41 A.; C—C between rings 1.48 A.; aliphatic bonds 1.47 A.; molecule not planar, two phenyl groups inclined 20° to the cyclopentane ring	60
Anthracene	C—C all equal at 1.41 A., all carbons coplanar; C—C—C angle 120°	59, 61
Chrysene	All four rings coplanar	60
1,2,5,6-dibenz-anthracene	All five rings coplanar	62

presented will be concerned with intra- and intermolecular distances, bond angles, and spatial configurations. For the crystallographic data on these compounds the reader is referred to the "Structurbericht" (26) and Wyckoff (27).

Study of Table I allows important generalizations to be drawn about hydrocarbons. It is obvious that in truly aliphatic linkages the carbon–carbon distance is unique. Also, the aliphatic double bond (from electron diffraction) and triple bonds have characteristic lengths. The progressive shortening of these bonds is a measure of the greater binding energy involved and x-ray data on halogen compounds and others have proven that free rotation can occur only about true single bonds. The tetrahedral nature of the directed valences of carbon has been unequivocally demonstrated and the zigzag nature of carbon chains has been proven (see Fig. 2). Various properties of compounds containing long hydrocarbon chains are explained by their mode of parallel packing in crystals.

The long-held theory that cyclohexane would have a puckered ring has been adequately substantiated as illustrated in Fig. 3 showing atomic models of cyclohexane and methyl cyclohexane. These models are the result of a careful survey of thermodynamic, spectral, and diffraction data by

Beckett *et al.* (63). Very recent work on cyclooctatetraene has proven it to consist of a puckered ring with alternate single and double bonds and little or no resonance; hence devoid of true aromatic nature (37).

Some of the most valuable contributions have been in the field of aromatic compounds. The planar nature of the benzene ring has been proven time

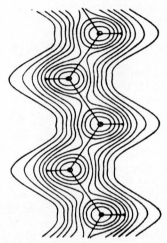

Fig. 2. Electron density diagram illustrating the zigzag character of hydrocarbon chains.
(From Bunn, *Trans. Faraday Soc.*, **35**, 482, 1939.)

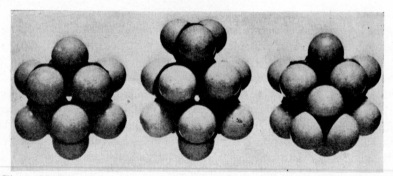

Fig. 3. Models of cyclohexane (left) and methyl cyclohexane (middle and right). (From Beckett, Pitzer, and Spitzer, *J. Am. Chem. Soc.*, **69**, 2488, 1947.)

and again and the dynamic form of the structure conclusively shown on many occasions by the equivalent length of all the bonds, and by the bond value, which is between that of aliphatic single and double bonds (Fig. 1). In this way the contributions of resonance structures are clear. The coplanar nature of diphenyl and *p*-di-diphenyl proves the absence of free rotation around the connecting links, and their shortened length justifies this on the basis of double bond character due to resonance. Orthodiphenyl benzene adequately demonstrates steric hindrance by having the two substituent phenyl groups rotated 50° out of the plane of the parent ring by mutual repulsion while 1,3,5-triphenyl benzene is planar.

The condensed ring systems are generally planar and of constant carbon-carbon distance as would be expected from the dynamic effects of resonance.

Other compounds given in Table I and not specifically considered in the discussion such as stilbene and dibenzyl also illustrate these effects. It can be pointed out that those compounds having marked thermal stability are the more strongly bonded compounds with the more uniform strength of bonds due to resonance effects. The molecular nature of these hydrocarbon crystals is distinctly demonstrated by the fact the intermolecular carbon-carbon distances are between two and three times the intramolecular distances proving that the crystals are bound by "residual forces" and hence have low melting points.

At no point has any mention of the carbon-hydrogen bond length been made because of the fact that the x-ray scatter of the hydrogen nucleus (proton) is essentially zero. Electron diffraction studies on crystalline hydrocarbons have been made by Rigamonti (64) and the carbon-hydrogen distance given as 1.1–1.4 A. For a complete consideration of these effects relative to the chemistry and physical chemistry of compounds of this type, see Pauling (25).

IV. X-RAY DIFFRACTION BY LIQUIDS

1. THEORY OF X-RAY DIFFRACTION BY LIQUIDS

The earliest experiments on the diffraction of x-rays by liquids were carried out by Friedrich (65) in 1913 and due to the contributions to the theory of this scattering by Zernicke and Prins (66) and Debye and Mencke (67) the ability to determine interatomic distances in liquids was realized and hence it was possible to derive data on the structure of the liquid state.

The fact that very distinct interference patterns were obtained from liquids was held to be *prima facie* evidence that a certain regularity existed in the distribution of the component molecules or atoms of the liquid. Due to the strong similarities between the diffraction diagrams of many liquids it was felt that the innermost, and most intense ring must arise from intermolecular interferences rather than interferences arising within the molecules themselves. This "outer effect" was discussed by Debye and Mencke (67), who, because of the complications involved, assumed spherical symmetry of the molecules, thus permitting consideration of the system as though composed of a monatomic gas. Each of these particles would then scatter radiation in directions having amplitude and phase represented by the scatter factor f.

As these molecules can take up all possible positions the only data obtainable refer to the mean intensity scattered in a significant period during which it is easily possible for the molecules to interchange positions. To calculate the intensity theoretically, the probability $W(r)$ of one molecule being within a certain volume element while another is simultaneously within a second at a distance r must be determined. As the molecules are assumed to be impenetrable spheres certain limitations are placed upon their closest approach. Based upon these considerations Debye and Mencke (67) expressed the mean scattered intensity, I_s, as a function of the above probability function

$$I_s = N \frac{1 + \cos^2 \theta}{2} F^2 \left[1 - \frac{\lambda^3}{d^3} \frac{2}{s} \int_0^\infty (1 - W) \sin (2\pi\rho s)\rho d\rho \right] \quad (11)$$

with N being the total number of molecules, $(1 + \cos^2 \theta)/2$ a polarization factor, F the scatter factor for the molecules, λ the wavelength, $d^3 = V/N$ or the volume available to each molecule, s equals $(4\pi \sin \theta)/\lambda$, where θ is half the scatter angle, and ρ is r/λ with r being the intermolecular distance. For large values of r, $W = 1$ because all related positions are equally possible and for very small r, $W = 0$ because the molecules cannot interpenetrate.

Therefore, if the function $W(r)$ were known the intensity of scatter could be calculated. Conversely if I_s as a function of the variable s has been determined experimentally it is possible, by applying a Fourier transform, to determine $W(r)$. For more complete details on this subject see Gingrich (68) and Pirenne (69).

It is beyond the scope of this discussion to consider all the corrections necessary to make this method useful as well as the difficulties involved in determining the structure amplitude, F, of the molecules, the effect of orientation on the above equations or the difficulties involved in applying the Fourier theorem under these circumstances. Suffice to say that these considerations are discussed by Pirenne (69) and that a method of handling these transforms has been given by Warren (70). This latter method is a radial distribution method having the shortcoming that it is difficult to distinguish intra- and intermolecular peaks. More recently Danielson and Lanczos (71) have reported further simplifications in the Fourier analysis of x-ray scatter from liquids. Warren (72) holds that, except for simple cases, liquid diffraction while yielding data on liquid structure, is of small importance to the determination of molecular structures.

2. THE STRUCTURE OF LIQUID HYDROCARBONS FROM X-RAY SCATTERING

Early work in this field by Warren (73) on liquid paraffins allowed a determination of the aliphatic carbon-carbon distance at 1.54 A. The structure in the liquid itself was regarded as consisting of close packing of cylindrical molecules of cross section 21.2 A². Subsequent studies on normal heptane by Pierce (74) deduced a zigzag chain with hexagonal close packing of the chains with their long dimension parallel. The study of cyclohexane and benzene plus the assumption of disc shaped molecules yielded results on the closest approach or "thickness" of the discs. Values of 4.68 A. for benzene and 5.09 A. for cyclohexane were obtained.

These results show that no long term order exists in these liquids but that a definite preferred distance between nearest neighbors predominates. Further, that certain aspects of the crystals of these compounds carry over into the liquid state in that the linear molecules remain parallel and that the disc (flat) molecules behave similarly.

V. X-Ray Diffraction by Gases

1. THEORY

It can be shown (69) that a rigid system of diffracting points will show distinct interferences in the radiation that it scatters despite continuously uncontrolled changes in orientation. Considerations of this sort were the forerunners of the first experiments to show x-ray interferences in a gas by Debye *et al.* (75). When gases scatter x-rays the individual molecules scatter as though they were free or isolated so that there is little if any of the "outer effect" just considered for liquids.

In order to calculate the scattered intensity of a free molecule in space the angular distribution of scattered intensity from a rigid system of Thomson electrons under similar conditions must be known. This equation has been given by Debye (76)

$$I_s = I_0 \frac{A^2_e}{R^2} \frac{1 + \cos^2 \theta}{2} \sum_i \sum_j \frac{\sin x_{ij}}{x_{ij}} \qquad (12)$$

where

$$x_{ij} = 4\pi l_{ij} (\sin \theta/2)/\lambda \qquad (13)$$

and I_s is the scattered intensity, I_o the incident intensity, A_e the classical radius of the electron, R the distance from the scattering center to the point of observation, $(1 + \cos^2 \theta)/2$ the polarization factor, θ the scatter angle*, λ the wavelength and l_{ij} being the distance between the electrons i and j in the system. If I_e is set equal to all the terms before the double summation the equation can be given in its usual form

$$I_s = I_e \sum_i \sum_j \sin x_{ij}/x_{ij} \qquad (14)$$

* It is customary, when considering diffraction by gases to define θ as given. It should be noted that Bragg angle θ is defined as one-half this quantity.

This formula obtained for *diffracting points* can be adapted to a molecule (69) assuming spherical symmetry of the atoms and by considering each atom of the molecule as a *scattering point*. However, as the scattering power of atoms is expressed by the structure amplitude (see section on crystals) this formula is replaced by

$$I_s = I_e \sum_i \sum_j f_i f_j \sin x_{ij}/x_{ij} \qquad (15)$$

where x_{ij} is as given in equation (13) and l_{ij} is the *interatomic distance*.

To here, the electron cloud of each atom in the molecule has been regarded as a *point*, which is clearly an oversimplification. Therefore, if the actual extension of the electronic cloud is considered it turns out that the ratio of this cloud extension to the interatomic distance determines the general shape of the scatter curve. The larger it is the more rapidly I_s decreases with angle; when it is small the curves show maxima and minima tending to become monotonic as it increases and the maxima move to smaller angles. Due to this, any calculation based on the *point* theory would yield interatomic distances that were somewhat too long, especially when diffuse electron clouds were involved.

To carry out exact measurements requires that comparison be made between experiment and a complete theoretical curve including the factor just discussed along with an allowance for incoherent scatter. This incoherently scattered intensity of a molecule is a sum of incoherent intensities scattered by its individual atoms and is devoid of interference effects. This scatter increases as $(\sin \theta/2)/\lambda$ increases. When a molecule is composed of light atoms the incoherent scatter can be very significant. When all these factors are taken into consideration the equation of x-ray scattering by free molecules built up of atoms is given by

$$I_s = I_e \left[\sum_i \sum_j f_i f_j \frac{\sin x_{ij}}{x_{ij}} + Q \sum_i Z_i S_i \right] \qquad (16)$$

The first term in the brackets is the same as given in equation (15) and represents the coherent scatter while the second term covers the incoherent contribution. The new terms in this equation are defined as Z_i, the atomic number of atom i, S_i the incoherent scatter function of atom i, and Q is the relativistic correction for incoherent scatter (Pirenne, 69). One further correction that can be applied to x-ray diffraction by gases is that one due to the thermal vibrations of the atoms and to their zero point energies. This correction is of minor importance, however, and may frequently be ignored.

The foregoing has served to indicate that this method makes it possible to calculate the spatial configurations within a molecule from its diffraction pattern. In general, however, the reverse situation is used whereby a structure is assigned and the scattering curve calculated. A very brief discussion of the actual methods used to obtain these results will be given here because the above theory applies, with minor alterations, to electron scatter by gases which is, as will be discussed and demonstrated in the next section, more suitable in many ways for this type of molecular study.

2. THE RESULTS OF X-RAY SCATTER BY GASES

As has been pointed out in the theoretical section the information that can be gleaned from studies of this type is very important and useful but the experimental difficulties involved in obtaining and accurately measuring the diffraction diagrams are so great that a relatively small amount of work on hydrocarbons has been done in this field. The results from electron diffraction of gases are interpreted in an exactly analogous fashion and the experimental problems are so much less complicated that most of the molecular structures have been studied by this latter method. For the sake of completeness the reader is referred to Table VII in Pirenne (69) wherein all the molecules studied by x-ray diffraction of gases are tabulated with

TABLE II

Molecule	References
CH_4	77, 78
C_2H_2	79
C_6H_6	78, 80, 81

references. Table II contains, in excerpt form, the data from Table VII in Pirenne (69) that are directly applicable to hydrocarbons.

VI. ELECTRON DIFFRACTION BY GASES

1. THEORY

The diffraction of fast electrons by gases was discovered by Mark and Wierl (82) a few years following the proof of the wave nature of such particles. The wavelength associated with such electrons can be obtained from the de Broglie relationship. If the relativistic correction for the variation of mass with velocity is omitted the relationship is $\lambda = h/mv$ where λ is the wavelength, h Planck's constant, m the mass, and v the velocity of the electrons. As was given for x-rays the intensity of an electron beam is equal to the square of the amplitude of the associated wave. If such an electron beam having an associated wave of wavelength λ enters the electrostatic field of an isolated atom, the intensity, I_s, of scattered radiation is

$$I_s = A_s^2 = \frac{I_0}{R^2} \frac{4}{A_H^2} F^2 \tag{17}$$

and F has been given by Bethe (83)

$$F = \frac{Z - f}{[(4\pi \sin \theta/2)/\lambda]^2} \tag{18}$$

A_s being the amplitude, R the distance from the point of observation to the scattering point, A_H the classical radius of the hydrogen atom, F, the structure factor for electron scatter, Z the atomic number, f the scatter factor for x-rays as given previously, and θ the angle of scatter. Therefore, the electron scatter factor F can be obtained directly from a knowledge of f. As is the case for x-rays F is a function of $(\sin \theta/2)/\lambda$. The two terms in this factor are a positive one, Z, due to the plus charge on the nucleus and a negative one, $-f$, due to the screening effect of the electrons on the nucleus. There is one further difference between scattered x-ray and electron waves and that is the absence of a polarization factor in the latter.

Due to these differences the relative ability to be scattered by atoms is of interest and can be evaluated. Assuming $(4\pi \sin \theta/2)/\lambda$ equal to 10, then according to Pirenne (69) I_s/I_0 approximates 10^{-9} f^2/R^2 for x-rays, and I_s/I_0 approximates 10^{-3} $(Z-f)^2/R^2$ for electrons. Since f and $Z-f$ are of the same magnitude it is obvious that electrons interact with matter about 10^6 times more efficiently than do x-rays. This represents one of the important reasons why electrons are more generally used for studying diffraction by gases. Good photographic exposures are made in one second or less using electrons while x-rays require many hours. Nevertheless, the fact that $(4\pi \sin \theta/2)/\lambda$ occurs to the fourth power in the electron scatter equation causes a rapid decrease in intensity with angle and at large angles the scattered intensity diminishes relative to that of x-rays.

Incoherent scatter of electrons occurs as it does for x-rays thereby contributing another factor to the more exact scattering equation

$$I_s = \frac{I_0}{R^2} \frac{4}{A_H^2} \frac{(Z - f^2)}{\left(\dfrac{4\pi \sin \theta/2}{\lambda}\right)^4} + \frac{ZS}{\left(\dfrac{4\pi \sin \theta/2}{\lambda}\right)^4} \tag{19}$$

S in this equation being the same incoherent scattering factor as for x-rays. The incoherent scatter also decreases rapidly with angle due to $[(4\pi \sin \theta/2)/\lambda]^{-4}$. The equations for x-ray and electron scatter show that as $(\sin \theta/2)/\lambda$ increases the incoherent scatter in the former becomes predominant while in the latter the coherent scatter always remains the more important. Therefore, even at angles where electron scatter is no more efficient than x-ray scatter, it is still advantageous to employ the former.

If similar assumptions of spherical symmetry as were used for x-rays be made, equation (19) can be modified to apply to free molecules scattering electrons exactly as was equation (4) for x-rays

$$I_s = \frac{I_0}{R^2} \frac{4}{A_H^2} \frac{1}{\left(\dfrac{4\pi \sin \theta/2}{\lambda}\right)^4} \left[\sum_i \sum_j (Z_i - f_i)(Z_j - f_j) \frac{\sin x_{ij}}{x_{ij}} + \sum_i Z_i S_i \right] \quad (20)$$

The first term in the brackets represents the coherent and the second the incoherent contributions. The fourth power term in the denominator causes such a rapid decrease in intensity with increasing angle that in the general case no maxima and minima are observed in the diagrams but rather points of inflection. Figure 4 shows the theoretical curves for carbon tetrachloride for x-rays and electrons, and serves to illustrate this point [Pirenne (84)]. Debye (85, 86) has been able to counteract the fourth power term in the denominator by using a suitable rotating sector and has obtained electron diffraction curves showing maxima and minima.

One other point that should be mentioned is the ability of electron diffraction to locate light atoms more readily than x-rays, especially hydrogen which x-rays ignore almost completely. For more complete discussions of the theory of electron scatter by gases the reader is referred to review sections by Pirenne (69), Brockway (87), and McMillen (88).

2. DEDUCTION OF STRUCTURES

a. Trial and Error Method. The theory just presented has indicated that the intensity of scatter as a function of angle and wavelength can be related to molecular structure by means of equation (20) wherein the symbol x_{ij} has the same relationship to l_{ij} as indicated in equation (13). Therefore, under suitable conditions it should be possible to determine interatomic distances. As stated in the immediately preceding section the combination of coherent and incoherent scattering produces a rapidly falling background with fluctuations impressed on it due to the coherent scatter. Hence, simple observations of the film are of no use when compared to theoretical maxima and minima scatter curves constructed without taking into account the incoherent scatter. The first attempts to circumvent this difficulty were by Wierl (89, 90), who empirically altered the theoretical curves so that they would appear as did the actual diffraction patterns. Pauling and Brockway (91) justified Wierl's assumptions on the basis of the response of the human eye to such diagrams. These modifications simplified equation (20) by omitting the f_i, $[(4\pi \sin \theta/2)/\lambda]^4$ and the incoherent scatter terms, leaving

$$I_{\text{apparent}} = \sum_i \sum_j Z_i Z_j \frac{\sin x_{ij}}{x_{ij}} \quad (21)$$

In this form the equation lends itself admirably to the trial and error method of assuming a molecular structure and calculating the apparent scatter function and comparing the calculated results obtained in this way with

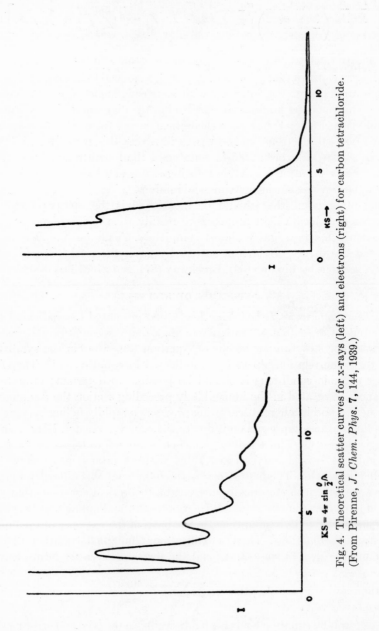

Fig. 4. Theoretical scatter curves for x-rays (left) and electrons (right) for carbon tetrachloride. (From Pirenne, *J. Chem. Phys.* **7**, 144, 1939.)

the empirical diffraction diagram. The method was checked against artificial bromine diagrams and compared with the Br–Br distance obtained from rotational fine structure. Results agreed to 0.008 A. It was concluded that this visual method plus the trial and error system would yield results accurate to $\frac{1}{2}\%$. Despite the fact that various analytical methods and the Debye sector method have been devised, the visual method is still re-

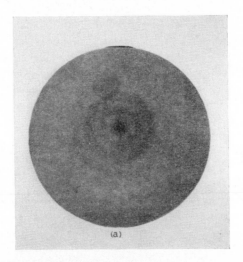

(a)

(b)

Fig. 5.

(a) Electron diffraction pattern of carbon tetrachloride gas.
(b) Microphotometer trace showing the first three apparent maxima in (a) and the first five apparent maxima in (b).
(From Pauling and Brockway, *J. Chem. Phys.* **2,** 867, 1934.)

garded as one of the best methods of determining molecular structures. To illustrate how the human eye sees maxima and minima where none exist, Fig. 5, taken from (91) on carbon tetrachloride, has been included.

b. Radial Distribution Method. Attempts to eliminate the trial and error method for arriving at structures have been made by using the reverse procedure of determining interatomic distances from the observed scattering data. Pauling and Brockway (92) have published such a "radial distribution method." In brief, this method uses electron diffraction curves to calculate a distribution function for scattering power representing the product of scattering powers in volume elements a distance L apart as a function of L. And, because electrons scatter best in the vicinity of nuclei, a maximum in the function indicates the internuclear distance. This method required visual reading of the diffraction diagram but needed no previous model of the molecule. The actual computation is performed by making use of a Fourier inversion to obtain the radial distribution function. The authors conclude that the accuracy is 1 or 2% and that only two or three of the major (most prominent) interatomic distances can be obtained; that in many cases the visual method is better; that this is a straightforward system based on no structural assumptions; and for best results both methods should be used. The radial distribution one serves to eliminate absurd structures and the trial and error arrangement to obtain accuracy.

More recently Beach and Walter (93), by assuming that the shapes of the maxima and minima could be represented by cosine curves, were able to use the radial distribution method and integrate the function rather than approximate it, and were able to calculate the amounts of scattering matter as a function of the interatomic distance.

Sample calculations illustrating these various methods are presented in the papers by Pauling and Brockway (91, 92) and the methods of carrying out the experiments are discussed by Maxwell (94) and Pirenne (69).

3. RESULTS

In general, a great portion of the structural results which have had bearing on hydrocarbons have been done on halogenated compounds because of the influence of the heavy halogen atom on the scattering diagram. Nevertheless, sufficient experiments have been made on pure hydrocarbon materials to allow nearly all the possible conclusions about hydrocarbons to be reached without need of recourse to the data on halogenated materials. Naturally, the interpretation of the experimental results is identical so that the choice is merely a matter of convenience and a desire to confine the discussion to hydrocarbons wherever possible.

As was done for the section on crystals the results of these studies are in tabular form in Table III. This table lists the compounds, the structural results obtained and the sources of the data.

Study of this tabulation shows how similar are the bond lengths and bond angles to those given in Table I. The two methods obviously are measuring the same thing by relatively independent methods. Here too, the constancy of length of single and double bonds is observed and here too it is possible to determine resonance structures by the shortening of the bonds. The tetrahedral angle for singly bonded carbons is amply demonstrated as well as the double bond angle. One quantity frequently measured by

TABLE III

Compound	Structural Data	Reference
Ethane	C—C 1.55 ± .03 A.; C—H 1.09 ± .03 A.	90, 95
Ethylene	C=C 1.34 ± .02 A.; C—H 1.06 ± .03 A.; H—C—H angle 110 ± 5°	90, 95, 96
Propane	C—C 1.54 ± .02 A.; C—H 1.09 ± .02 A.; H—C—H angle 109°28'; C—C—C angle 111°30' ± 3°	90, 95, 97
Allene	C=C 1.34 ± .02 A.; C—H 1.06 ± .04 A.; carbons in linear chain; H—C—H angle 109°28'	90, 95
Butane	C—C 1.51 ± .05 A.	90
i-Butane	C—C 1.54 ± .02 A.; C—C—C angle 111°31' ± 2°	95, 98, 99
Butene-2 *cis* and *trans*	C—C 1.54 ± .03 A.; C=C 1.38 ± .03 A.; C—C=C angle 125°; CH_3—C—H angle 110°	100
i-Butene	C—C 1.54 ± .02 A.	95
Butadiene	Carbon atoms planar; C—C—C angle 124 ± 2° C—C 1.46 ± .03 A.; C=C 1.35 ± .02 A.	90, 101
Pentane	C—C 1.53 ± .05 A.	89, 90
Neopentane	Central carbon tetrahedral; C—C 1.54 ± .02 A.; C—H 1.09 A.	95, 102
Hexane	C—C 1.54 ± .05 A.	89, 90
Tetramethyl ethylene	C—C 1.54 ± .02 A.; C—H 1.09 A.; C—C—C angle 111°30' ± 2°	95
Acetylene	C≡C 1.22 ± .08 A.	86, 90
Methyl acetylene	C≡C 1.20 ± .03 A.; C—C 1.46 ± .02 A.	103
Diacetylene	C—C 1.36 ± .03 A.; C≡C 1.19 ± .02 A., carbons linear	90, 103, 104
Dimethyl acetylene	C—C 1.47 ± .02 A.; carbons linear	103
Dimethyl diacetylene	C—C 1.38 ± .02 A.; C≡C 1.20 ± .02 A.; C—CH_3 1.47 ± .02, all carbons linear	103
Cyclopropane	C—C 1.53 ± .03 A.; H—C—H angle 109°28', C—C—C angle 60°	90, 95
Cyclopentane	C—C 1.52 ± .03 A.; molecule plane pentagon, near trigonal bonding (most recent computations (108) indicate slight pucker in ring)	89, 90, 95, 105, 108
Cyclopentadiene	C—C 1.53 A.; C=C 1.35 A.; C—H 1.09 A., single bond angle 101 ± 4°; double bond angles 109 ± 3, 110 ± 2°	101
Spiropentane	C—C 1.54 A.; C—H 1.08 A.; common carbon in two equilateral triangles both rings perpendicular, C—C—C angle 60°	102
Cyclohexane	C—C 1.54 + .03 A.; puckered ring	89, 95
Benzene	C—C 1.39 ± .02 A.; C—H 1.08 ± .04 A., ring planar	89, 91, 92, 101, 106, 107
Hexamethyl benzene	C—C in ring 1.39 A.; $C_{arom} - C_{aliph}$ 1.54 ± .01 A.; all carbons coplanar	95, 107

these studies and never mentioned under x-ray diffraction is the carbon–hydrogen bond length of about 1.09 A.

It should again be called to mind that many interesting bits of structural information relative to hydrocarbons have been omitted because they were determined on substituted compounds. Some few of these will be briefly mentioned in this discussion. For example, the 1,2 dihalo ethanes exhibit moderately hindered rotation and hence favor a *trans* form.

Resonance in structures like butadiene, benzene and the substituted acetylenes is made obvious by the foreshortening of bonds. Particularly interesting compounds are diacetylene and dimethyl diacetylene because the single bond between the two triple bonds has been shortened by resonance effects until it is as short, or possibly shorter, than a normal double bond. In the latter compound the two bonds to the methyl groups are shortened but not as much as the other single bond.

The structures of the cycloparaffins are also strikingly revealed and excellent agreement with the x-ray crystal methods is obtained. The equilateral nature of the cyclopropane ring; the planar nature of the cyclopentane ring*; the form of the spiropentane structure and the puckered configuration of cyclohexane are all clear. The data on benzene proves again the dynamic, planar structure and the results on hexamethyl benzene show that no resonance with the methyl groups and the aromatic nucleus need to be considered.

Other means of describing these effects exist, one of the most useful being a method whereby the shortening of the bonds due to resonance is quantitatively expressed as percent double bond character. These figures can then be used to calculate heats of dissociation and bond stabilities. For example, in diacetylene the single bond is estimated (103) to have 44% double bond character. For a complete discussion of all such phases regarding chemical bonds see Pauling (25) and the section on the chemical bond (Chapter I).

If the reader is interested in more complete tabulations of structural data on organic compounds he is referred to general review articles on the subject by Maxwell (94) and Robertson (109).

---

*Kilpatrick, Pitzer, and Spitzer, (108) have made a very thorough study of the cyclopentane structure using the puplished data from electron diffraction, Raman and infrared spectra, entropy and specific heat measurements. The results they have deduced are that the ring is slightly puckered; so slightly that it could easily be missed in electron diffraction experiments, and the more striking one that the ring puckering is not of a definite fixed type; but that the angle of maximum puckering rotates around the ring.

REFERENCES

1. S. Glasstone, Physical Chemistry. Van Nostrand, New York, 1940.
2. G. Herzberg, Atomic Spectra and Atomic Structure. Dover Publication, New York, 1944.
   Molecular Spectra and Molecular Structure. Prentice-Hall, New York, 1939.
3. L. Pauling and E. B. Wilson, Introduction to Quantum Mechanics. McGraw Hill, New York, 1935.
4. R. del Kronig, Optical Basis of the Theory of Valency. Cambridge University Press, London, 1935.
5. G. M. Murphy, *J. Optical Soc. Am.* **30**, 396 (1940).
6. G. Glockler, *Revs. Modern Phys.* **15**, 111 (1943).
7. F. Kohlrausch, Der Smekal-Raman-Effekt. J. Springer, Berlin, 1944; Raman-spektren. Becker and Erler, Leipzig, 1943.
8. A. Langseth and B. Bak, *J. Chem. Phys.* **8**, 403 (1940).
9. W. H. Bragg and W. L. Bragg, The Crystalline State. G. Bell and Sons, London, 1939.
10. C. W. Bunn, Chemical Crystallography. Clarendon Press, Oxford, 1945.
11. A. H. Compton and S. K. Allison, X-Rays in Theory and Experiment. Van Nostrand, New York, 1935.
12. W. Friedrich, P. Knipping and M. V. Laue, *Sitzb. Akad. Wiss. München* Vol. 303 (1912).
13. W. L. Bragg, *Proc. Cambridge Phil. Soc.* **17**, 43 (1913).
14. P. Debye and P. Scherrer, *Physik. Z.* **17**, 277 (1916).
15. M. J. Buerger, X-Ray Crystallography. J. Wiley, New York, 1942.
16. P. P. Ewald, *Z. Krist.* **56**, 129 (1921).
17. I. Fankuchen, in Weissberger, Physical Methods of Organic Chemistry, Vol. I. Interscience Publishers, New York, 1945.
18. International Tables for the Determination of Crystal Structures. Gebrüder Borntraeger, Berlin, 1935.
19. R. W. James and G. W. Brindley, *Z. Krist.* **78**, 470 (1931).
20. D. R. Hartree, *Proc. Cambridge Phil. Soc.* **24**, 89, 111 (1928).
21. E. G. Cox and W. F. B. Shaw, *Proc. Roy. Soc. London* **A127**, 71 (1930).
22. W. L. Bragg, *Nature* **154**, 69 (1944).
23. J. M. Robertson, *Repts. Progress Physics* **4**, 332 (1937).
24. J. M. Robertson and I. Woodward, *Proc. Roy. Soc. London* **A162**, 568 (1937).
25. L. Pauling, The Nature of the Chemical Bond. Cornell University Press, Ithaca, 1944.
26. Structurbericht, *Z. Krist.* Vols. 1–7.
27. R. W. G. Wyckoff, The Structure of Crystals. Rheinhold, New York, 1935.
28. J. C. McLennan and W. G. Plummer, *Phil. Mag.* **7**, 761 (1929).
29. H. Mark and E. Pohland, *Z. Krist.* **62**, 103 (1925).
30. S. Katzoff, *J. Chem. Phys.* **2**, 841 (1934).
31. A. Muller, *Proc. Roy. Soc. London* **A120**, 437 (1928).
32. R. Kohlhaas and K. H. Soremba, *Z. Krist.* **A100**, 47 (1938).
33. J. Hengstenberg, *Z. Krist.* **67**, 583 (1928).
34. C. W. Bunn, *Trans. Faraday Soc.* **35**, 482 (1939).
35. J. M. Robertson and I. Woodward, *Proc. Roy. Soc. London* **A164**, 436 (1938).
36. O. Hassel and H. Kringstad, *Tidsk. Kjemi Bergvesen* **10**, 128 (1930).
37. O. Hassel and A. M. Sommerfeld, *Z. physik. Chem.* **B40**, 391 (1938).

38. A. Muller, *Helv. Chim. Acta* **16**, 155 (1933).
39. E. G. Cox, *Proc. Roy. Soc. London* **A135**, 491 (1932).
40. H. de Laszlo, *Proc. Roy. Soc. London* **A146**, 672 (1934).
41. R. Kaiser, *Physik. Z.* **36**, 92 (1935).
42. J. M. Robertson, *Proc. Roy. Soc. London* **A141**, 594 (1933).
43. J. M. Robertson, *Proc. Roy. Soc. London* **A142**, 659 (1933).
44. L. O. Brockway and J. M. Robertson, *J. Chem. Soc.* **1939**, 1324; *Chem. Abstracts* **35**, 9079[5] (1939).
45. K. Lonsdale, *Proc. Roy. Soc. London* **A123**, 494 (1929).
46. J. Hengstenberg and H. Mark, *Z. Krist.* **70**, 283 (1929).
47. J. Dhal, *Indian J. Phys.* **7**, 43 (1932).
48. J. M. Robertson, M. Prasad, and I. Woodward, *Proc. Roy. Soc. London* **A154**, 187 (1936).
49. J. M. Robertson and I. Woodward, *Proc. Roy. Soc. London* **A162**, 568 (1937).
50. J. M. Robertson, *Proc. Roy. Soc. London* **A146**, 473 (1934).
51. J. Dhal, *Indian J. Phys.* **9**, 1 (1934).
52. J. M. Robertson, *Proc. Roy. Soc. London* **A150**, 348 (1935).
53. C. J. B. Clews and K. Lonsdale, *Proc. Roy. Soc. London* **A161**, 493 (1937).
54. B. Orelkin, and K. Lonsdale, *Proc. Roy. Soc. London* **A144**, 630 (1934).
55. E. Hertel and G. Romer, *Z. physik. Chem.* **B23**, 226 (1933).
56. L. W. Pickett, *J. Am. Chem. Soc.* **58**, 2299 (1936).
57. H. S. Kaufman, Thesis, Polytechnic Institute of Brooklyn, 1947.
58. J. M. Robertson, *Proc. Roy. Soc. London* **A125**, 542 (1929).
59. K. Bannerjee, *Indian J. Phys.* **4**, 557 (1930).
60. J. Iball, *Proc. Roy. Soc. London* **A146**, 140 (1934).
61. J. M. Robertson, *Proc. Roy. Soc. London* **A140**, 79 (1933).
62. J. Iball and J. M. Robertson, *Nature* **132**, 750 (1933).
63. C. W. Beckett, K. S. Pitzer, and R. Spitzer, *J. Am. Chem. Soc.* **69**, 2488 (1947).
64. R. Rigamonti, *Gazz. chim. ital.* **66**, 174 (1936).
65. W. Friedrich, *Physik. Z.* **14**, 397 (1913).
66. F. Zernicke and J. Prins, *Z. Physik* **41**, 184 (1927).
67. P. Debye and H. Mencke, *Fortsch. Roentgenforschung* **2**, 1 (1931).
68. N. S. Gingrich, *Revs. Modern Phys.* **15**, 90 (1943).
69. M. H. Pirenne, The Diffraction of X-Rays and Electrons by Free Molecules. Cambridge University Press, London, 1946.
70. B. E. Warren, *J. Applied Phys.* **8**, 645 (1937).
71. G. C. Danielson and C. Lanczos, *J. Franklin Inst.* **233**, 365 (1942).
72. B. E. Warren, *J. Optical Soc. Am.* **30**, 369 (1940).
73. B. E. Warren, *Phys. Rev.* **14**, 969 (1933).
74. W. C. Pierce, *J. Chem. Phys.* **3**, 252 (1935).
75. P. Debye, L. Bewilogua, and F. Ehrhardt, *Ber. Sächs. Akad. Wiss.* **81**, 29 (1929); *Physik. Z.* **30**, 84 (1929).
76. P. Debye, *Ann. phys.* **46**, 809 (1915).
77. H. Richter, *Physik. Z.* **36**, 85 (1935).
78. G. Thomer, *Physik. Z.* **38**, 48 (1937).
79. K. Hoffman, *Physik. Z.* **39**, 695 (1938).
80. R. Kaiser, *Physik. Z.* **36**, 92 (1935).
81. R. Schoppe, *Z. physik. Chem.* **B34**, 461 (1936).
82. H. Mark and R. Wierl, *Naturwissenschaften* **18**, 205 (1930).
83. H. Bethe, *Ann. Physik* **87**, 55 (1928).

84. M. H. Pirenne, *J. Chem. Phys.* **7**, 144 (1939).
85. P. P. Debye, *Physik. Z.* **40**, 66 (1939).
86. P. P. Debye, *Physik. Z.* **40**, 404 (1939).
87. L. O. Brockway, *Revs. Modern Phys.* **8**, 231 (1936).
88. J. H. McMillen, *Revs. Modern Phys.* **11**, 84 (1939).
89. R. Wierl, *Ann. Physik* **8**, 521 (1931).
90. R. Wierl, *Ann. Physik* **13**, 453 (1932).
91. L. Pauling and L. O. Brockway, *J. Chem. Phys.* **2**, 867 (1934).
92. L. Pauling and L. O. Brockway, *J. Am. Chem. Soc.* **57**, 2684 (1935).
93. J. Y. Beach and J. Walter, *J. Chem. Phys.* **8**, 601 (1940).
94. L. R. Maxwell, *J. Optical Soc. Am.* **36**, 374 (1940).
95. L. Pauling and L. O. Brockway, *J. Am. Chem. Soc.* **59**, 1223 (1937).
96. R. W. Dornte, *J. Chem. Phys.* **1**, 566 (1933).
97. S. H. Bauer, *J. Chem. Phys.* **4**, 406 (1936).
98. J. Y. Beach and D. P. Stevenson, *J. Am. Chem. Soc.* **60**, 475 (1938).
99. J. Y. Beach and J. Walter, *J. Chem. Phys.* **8**, 303 (1940).
100. L. O. Brockway and P. C. Cross, *J. Am. Chem. Soc.* **58**, 2407 (1936).
101. V. Schomaker and L. Pauling, *J. Am. Chem. Soc.* **61**, 1769 (1939).
102. F. Rogowski, *Ber.* **72**, 2021 (1939).
103. L. Pauling, H. D. Springall, and K. J. Palmer, *J. Am. Chem. Soc.* **61**, 927 (1939).
104. L. O. Brockway, *Proc. Natl. Acad. Sci. U. S.* **19**, 868 (1933).
105. H. A. Skinner, *Nature* **160**, 902 (1947).
106. L. O. Brockway, *Proc. Natl. Acad. Sci. U. S.* **19**, 303 (1933).
107. P. L. F. Jones, *Trans. Faraday Soc.* **31**, 1036 (1935).
108. J. E. Kilpatrick, K. S. Pitzer, and R. Spitzer, *J. Am. Chem. Soc.* **69**, 2483 (1947).
109. J. M. Robertson, *Chem. Revs.* **16**, 417 (1935).

CHAPTER 3

MASS SPECTROSCOPY IN HYDROCARBON ANALYSIS

By

J. J. MITCHELL

Beacon Laboratories of The Texas Company, Beacon, New York

CONTENTS

I. THE MASS SPECTROMETER

The apparatus which Sir J. J. Thomson (1) developed to analyze canal rays was the precursor of the modern mass spectrometer. In this apparatus a ray of positive ions, issuing from a hole through the cathode of a high-voltage gaseous discharge tube, was caused to pass through crossed electric and magnetic fields. If the direction of the ray is taken to be the z-axis, the direction of deflection due to the electric field X to be the x-axis, and the deflection due to the magnetic field H to be the y-axis, then it can be shown that for small angles of deflection the corresponding deflections for ions in the ray are

$$x = k\,\frac{eX}{mv^2} \qquad \text{and} \qquad y = k'\frac{Hev}{mv^2}.$$

Here k and k' are apparatus constants, m and e are the mass and charge of the positive ions, and v is their velocity. On a photographic plate perpendicular to the z-axis, therefore, all ions of mass to charge ratio m/e will fall on the parabola given by:

$$\frac{y^2}{x} = \frac{e}{m} \cdot \frac{k'^2}{k} \cdot \frac{H^2}{X}.$$

F. W. Aston (2), who gave the mass spectrometer its name, used successive deflections to sort out ions. In his apparatus (3), shown schematically in Fig. 1, first the ions were passed through an electric field X. Only a small range of deflections could then pass through the slit S_5. Those ions which did pass S_5 were then deflected by a magnetic field H. It is a property of this arrangement (4) that, if a photographic plate is properly situated at F, then ions of a given m/e follow paths which bring all of them to the same line on the plate. This property thus produces very sharp lines on the plate and makes it easier to resolve lines which lie very close together. In fact, one use made of the instrument was to show that the difference in mass between H_2 and D was 0.00152 mass unit.

Also in this tradition of high resolution are the instruments due to A. J. Dempster (5), Bainbridge and Jordan (6) and J. Mattauch (7). Fig. 2 shows schematically the arrangement of slits and fields for each of these instruments. In each of these the high resolution is achieved by causing all ions of a given m/e regardless of initial direction and velocity to come to a focus on a photographic plate.

At the same time that these instruments of high resolution were being developed, the refinement of mass spectrometers for the measurement of

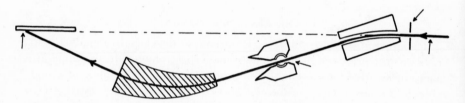

Fig. 1. Schematic diagram of Aston's precision mass spectrograph.

isotopic abundances was under way. Here the emphasis was on measuring the ion currents accurately rather than mass differences. A. J. Dempster (8) constructed an instrument, shown schematically in Fig. 3, which served as a prototype for many which followed. In it ions were formed from gas molecules by bombardment with a beam of electrons. The ions were then all accelerated through the same voltage by means of a slit system which produced a collimated beam of ions all possessing the same energy

$$eV = \tfrac{1}{2}\, mv^2.$$

Here V represents the voltage through which the ions were accelerated, and the other symbols have the same meaning as before. The ion beam then traversed a uniform magnetic field H at right angles to the magnetic lines of force. The original ion beam is thereby broken up into several, their paths being circles given by

$$Hev = \frac{mv^2}{r}$$

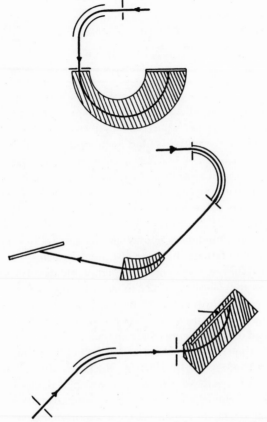

Fig. 2. Schematic diagrams of three precision mass spectrographs.

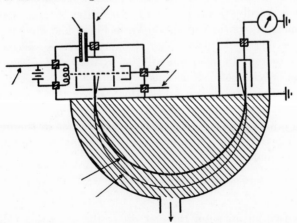

Fig. 3. Schematic diagram of a Dempster-type mass spectrometer.

where now r is the radius of the circle. Since each of the ion beams satisfies both equations, one can eliminate the ion velocity and obtain

$$\frac{m}{e} = \frac{r^2 H^2}{2V}.$$

This relation has often been called "the mass spectrometer equation." While this is an over-simplification, the general prevalence of mass spectrometers derived from Dempster's partially justifies the statement.

A Faraday cylinder situated behind a slit, through which only those ions following a path of radius r can pass, then serves to measure the current due to ions of mass to charge ratio satisfying the equation. By varying either the accelerating voltage V or the magnetic field H one can in turn bring ions of various values of m/e into register with the Faraday cylinder. The assumption, of which more will be said later, that ion currents are proportional to ion abundances allows one to compare isotopic abundances.

Bleakney and Cummings (9), Nier (10), and Brown *et al.* (11) are only a few who have followed the original design with merely minor modifications. Sampson and Bleakney (12), Nier (13), and Tate and Smith (14) changed the means of providing the magnetic field, cobalt steel permanent horseshoe magnets being used in the first case and air-core solenoids in the other two instead of an iron-core electromagnet.

At about this time the exact theory for the double focusing mass spectrograph had been worked out by Herzog, Mattauch, and Hauk (4, 7, 15, 16, 17, 18). One main result of this theory was the demonstration that an electrical field of cylindrical symmetry or a homogeneous magnetic field acted on an ion beam in a manner completely analogous to the way in which a thick, double-convex lens and a prism would act on a light beam. This result is hardly surprising in the Dempster arrangement since the simple geometrical considerations shown in Fig. 3 had already shown that direction focusing took place. Nier designed a mass spectrometer (19) which was based on an independently derived (20, 21) special case of the theory. The special case states that a sector-form magnetic field gives direction focusing. The design takes advantage of this fact to reduce the size of electromagnet necessary to produce the magnetic field. Nier's design, shown schematically in Fig. 4, used a pole shoe in the form of a 60° sector which gave rise to a magnetic field which not only fulfilled the mass spectrometer equation

$$\frac{m}{e} = \frac{r^2 H^2}{2V},$$

but also focused an image of the exit slit of the ionization chamber upon the entrance slit of the current measuring system when the geometry shown in Fig. 4 was fulfilled.

The only two commercial models of mass spectrometers which have been widely sold for hydrocarbon gas analysis (22, 23) are modifications of these two designs. One has 180° deflection with an ionization chamber wholly immersed in the uniform magnetic field. The other uses a sector-type magnet but with a 90° deflection rather than 60°.

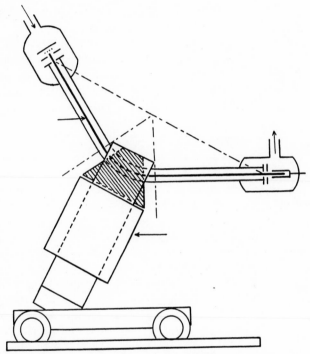

Fig. 4. Schematic diagram of Nier's 60° mass spectrometer.

II. THE PRODUCTION OF IONS FROM GASES

Both of these models use ionization chambers based on the same principles. Figure 5 shows schematic cross-sections of an early type of ionization chamber used in the 180° instrument. A description of this chamber and some of its possible modifications will serve to illustrate the principles involved. Ions are produced in this chamber by the inelastic collision of electrons with gas molecules. The electrons may be emitted from a hot filament such as A in Fig. 5 or they may be emitted from an indirectly heated cathode. Since the ionization chamber shown is immersed in a strong magnetic field, the electrons are accelerated by electrodes B and C in the direction of the magnetic lines of force. This arrangement aids in producing a tightly focused electron beam because the magnetic field then tends to suppress any divergence of the electrons. The holes in the electrodes serve to collimate the electrons passing through them into a beam, and the magnetic field has a focusing action which prevents the beam from spreading. In ionization chambers which are not immersed in a magnetic field, it is advantageous to arrange the electron accelerating electrodes so that they form an electron lens which produces a nondiverging electron beam. The electron beam then passes through a relatively field-free region between the electrodes D and the plate containing the first ion-beam-defining slit and impinges on the electron catcher.

The gas which is to ionized is introduced into the relatively field-free region just mentioned by any one of several means. In the volume in space through which the electron beam passes positive ions are produced by collision of the electrons with the gas molecules. The electrodes D have a small positive voltage on them which serves to repel the ions, hence their

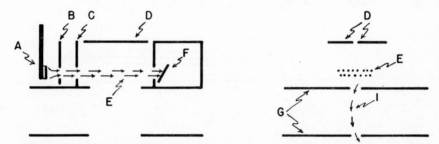

Fig. 5. Schematic cross-sections (at right angles to each other) through a typical ionization chamber. A, Filament supported on heavy legs; B, first electron accelerating plate; C, second electron accelerating plate; D, "pusher" plates to supply small ion ejecting field; E, electron beam; F, electron catcher; G, ion accelerating plates; and I, ion beam.

name of "pushers." In general, the voltages on the two pushers are slightly different. This difference is adjusted so that the drift path of the ions is such that an optimal number strike the first ion beam defining slit rather than the plate containing it. Then between the first and second ion-beam-defining slits there is impressed the potential which accelerates the ions. It has been shown (24) that in instruments where the mass spectrum is scanned by changing the ion accelerating voltage the greatest accuracy in measuring relative ion intensities is reached when the pusher voltages are kept proportional to the ion accelerating voltages.

There are several electrodes which can be added to the ion-accelerating section with profit. An arrangement giving an ion lens producing a nondivergent ion beam increases the resolution of the mass spectrometer. Various deflecting electrodes can be used to line up the beam with the slit in front of the ion current collector and thus increase both resolution and ion current by bettering the efficiency of current collection.

Before going on to the mass spectra produced from hydrocarbons in this way, it will be helpful to consider the ionization process for a simpler gas such as hydrogen. The transfer of energy from electron to molecule during inelastic collision is governed by rules much like those of the absorption of light by the same molecules. The rules which apply are those of quantum mechanics. In particular, one of the most important is the Franck-Condon

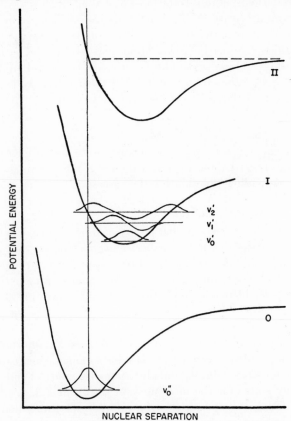

Fig. 6. Franck-Condon transitions to two higher states of a hypothetical diatomic molecule.

(25) principle. Figure 6 shows schematically the basis for this principle. On the figure the internal energy of the molecule against the distance between the nuclei of the two atoms in the molecule has been plotted for an imaginary diatomic molecule. This has been done for the lowest, curve 0, and the first two excited electron energy states, curves I and II. For two of the states a few of the vibrational energy levels have been indicated by horizontal straight lines labeled v', etc. Now, one of the rules of quantum

mechanics is that when energy is absorbed by a molecule only just that discrete amount necessary to go from a lower vibrational energy level to a higher one in the same or in a higher electron state can be absorbed. In this statement the rotational energy levels have been neglected as giving rise only to a second order effect, a fine structure based on the vibrational energy level. The Franck-Condon principle allows one to predict which of the possible discrete energy jumps is the most probable.

Plotted on an arbitrary scale with the horizontal lines representing the vibration levels v_i as abscissae are curves representing the probability density functions Ψ_{v_i} for the given vibrational level in the particular electron energy state. These wave-like functions are derived from quantum mechanics (26) and it is a basic result of the theory that the probability of transition is given by the square of the absolute value of:

$$R_{v_i' v_j''} = R_e \int \Psi_{v_i} \Psi_{v_j''} \, r^2 \, dr.$$

Here double prime refers to the lower electron state and prime to the upper, and the integral is carried out over all values of r, the internuclear distance. R_e is the corresponding function for the transition between the two electronic states in question. A glance at Fig. 6 shows that for this imaginary molecule the Ψ functions for the lowest state v_0'', and for the vibrational level v_2'' will give the largest product of any of those shown. For any higher levels in the *prime* state r will be smaller. Thus one can say that $R_{v_2 v_0''}$ gives the largest probability of transition. Instead of going through quantum mechanical calculations, one can obtain the same result on the grounds that the most probable transition is that vertically upward from the center of the minimum of the lowest electronic state. This is the simplest statement of the Franck-Condon principle.

Transition to electron state I merely produces an internally excited molecule. Transition to electron state II adds so much energy to the molecule that it is no longer stable, and the atoms fly apart. There are higher electron energy states for the molecule, not shown in Fig. 6, which correspond to the flying away of an electron in much the same manner. These can give rise either to positively charged molecules or positively charged atoms depending on their resemblance to state I or state II in Fig. 6.

Bleakney (27) has shown that for hydrogen the results of mass spectrometer ion abundance measurements are in accord with the tenets of this view of the process of ionization. Figure 7 shows a representation similar to his of the theoretically predicted energy states which will lead to ions. Curve *a* represents the normal state of hydrogen molecules. Curve *b* is the corresponding repulsive state leading to neutral hydrogen atoms which cannot be detected by the mass spectrometer and so is not of interest.

Curve c, on the other hand, results in H_2^+ if the transition is made to the lower portion of the curve; in H^+ if transition is made to the upper portion. Curve d, the repulsive state corresponding to curve c, will always lead to H^+ ions, and these will have kinetic energy. Curve e, not shown in Fig. 7, the simple Coulomb repulsion of two H^+ ions, would also give rise to H^+ ions with kinetic energies. From the more exact form of Franck-Condon principle and the location of these curves, Bleakney predicted H_2^+ would

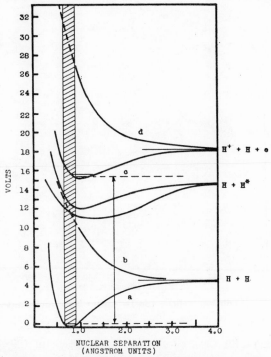

Fig. 7. Potential energy curves for H_2 molecule, after H. D. Smyth (*Revs. Modern Phys.* **3**, 347–91 (1931)). Curves a and b are, respectively, the attractive and repulsive curves for the approach of two neutral H atoms. Curves c and d are the same for the approach of an H^+ ion and a neutral H atom.

first appear at about 15.25 volts and H^+ at 17.9 volts. The shaded area in Fig. 7 shows the basis for these predictions. At about 27 volts one would expect the first appearance of H^+ with kinetic energy. The corresponding values which he found experimentally were 15.4 ± 0.1 volts, 18.0 ± 0.2 volts and 26 ± 1 volts.

Condon (25) has pointed out that the potential energy curves given in Fig. 7 are quite accurately also those for deuterium. However, the width of the shaded band which indicates the region in which transitions favored by the Franck-Condon principle will occur is considerably smaller than for hydrogen because the mass of the atoms is doubled. The doubled mass lowers the zero point energy so that the vibrational levels are lower and hence the Ψ functions sharper. Thus, for bombarding electrons between about 18 and 35 volts, the yield of D^+ relative to D_2^+ should be smaller than that of H^+ relative to H_2^+. For electron energies below 35 electron volts, an approximate theoretical value for the ratio has been developed (28). While the ratio of H^+ to H_2^+ ions calculated did not match well that

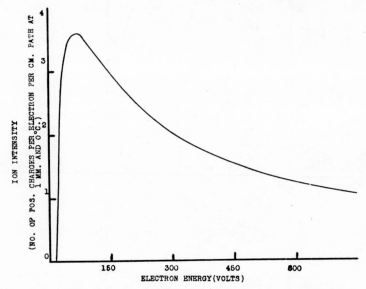

Fig. 8. Ionization efficiency curve for H_2^+, after Tate and Smith (*Phys. Rev.***39**, 270–7 (1932)).

found experimentally (29), the theory was successful (29) in predicting the ratio

$$R = (H^+/H_2^+)/(D^+/D_2^+) = 2.$$

This followed because the difference between transition probabilities for hydrogen and deuterium is only that due to the different masses. For this reason the errors in the relative proportions of monatomic to molecular ions cancel out when hydrogen and deuterium are compared.

Figure 8 shows an actual ionization efficiency curve for H_2^+ from H_2. This is a plot of ion current as a function of the energy of the ionizing electrons. The actual shape of the curve is a function of two factors. One has to do with the transition efficiencies already discussed. The other has to do with the efficiency of the mass spectrometer in recording the ions produced. As has already been pointed out ions formed by transitions of the molecule to very high energy states will have appreciable kinetic energies. It has been shown (30) that the mass spectrometer actually discriminates against such ions. In others words, even if the transition efficiency is high there is still the possibility that the mass spectrometer efficiency is low.

III. Mass Spectra of Hydrocarbons

In practice mass spectrometers use electron energies of from 50 to 100 electron volts. The prediction as to the relative numbers of H^+ and H_2^+

TABLE I

Typical Mass Spectra of n-Butane and Isobutane

m/e	n-Butane	Isobutane	m/e	n-Butane	Isobutane
24	Trace	0	48	0.15	Trace
25	1.61	3.03	49	1.78	4.04
26	47.0	72.7	50	7.62	22.2
27	283	960	51	7.52	23.0
28	241	106	52	2.08	5.45
29	298	215	53	6.66	20.0
30	6.65	5.45	54	1.98	3.23
31	—	—	55	7.42	16.6
			56	6.20	13.9
36	0.25	1.21	57	19.2	110
37	6.71	35.8	58	100.00	100.00
38	14.6	86.8	59	4.35	4.35
39	112	658	60	0.07	0.07
40	15.8	99.8	Sensitivity (chart divisions per mi-		
41	205	1440	cron of sample pressure)		
42	92.5	1210			
43	735	3670		3.86	0.89
44	24.1	119			
45	0.30	1.41			

ions expected from such high energy electrons is complicated by the fact there are between curve c and curve e of Fig. 7 a considerable number of electronic states of H_2^+ which must be taken into consideration.

To add to this confusion imagine the difficulty of visualizing the energy states of a molecule with fourteen atoms instead of two. The prediction of relative ion intensities becomes hopeless. In such a case there is much more sense in looking at the mass spectrum of the molecule to see if correlations exist between the properties of the molecule and the spectrum than there is in an attempt to predict the spectrum from theory. In Table I are given typical mass spectra for n-butane and isobutane (31). Before considering the relation of the values given to molecular properties, a word of explanation regarding the presentation of the spectra is in order. Since it was discovered early that the relative ion intensities remained more nearly constant than did the absolute intensities, it has become customary to base the mass spectrum on one peak as 100.00. Practice varies as to whether the molecule ion or the ion giving the greatest current is chosen as the base. In order that this information may be converted to absolute intensities if desired, the sensitivity, or peak height per unit sample pressure, of the base peak is usually also cited.

This practice is not as arbitrary as it might seem since it is usual experience to find for a given instrument that the relative intensities or "pattern coefficients" for a compound remain constant over periods of time during which the sensitivity varies by several per cent.

In Table I the molecule ion has been chosen as the base peak for both patterns. Ions with a single carbon atom have been omitted solely for convenience. The 50 volt electrons used in producing these mass spectra can be seen to have led to the presence of every conceivable fragment of the original molecule. In fact, at first sight there appear to be more than the conceivable number. The ion intensities for $m/e = 44$ and 45 cannot correspond to $C_3H_7^+$; however, they do correspond to $C^{12}H_2-C^{12}H_2-C^{13}H_3^+$ or $C^{12}H_2-C^{12}H_2-C^{12}H_2D^+$ and to $C^{12}H_2-C^{13}H_2-C^{13}H_3^+$, $C^{12}H_2-C^{12}H_2-C^{13}H_2D^+$, or $C^{12}H_2-C^{12}H_2-C^{12}HD_2^+$, respectively. In the above ions the position of the heavy isotopes is arbitrary, and actually they can occur in any position in the ion. The amounts of contributions due to the rare heavy isotopes will depend on their abundance in nature, 1.1% for carbon thirteen and 0.02% for deuterium (2). It should be appreciated that each ion species $C_nH_m^+$ contributes to the ion intensities of the m/e values next heavier to the m/e corresponding to the ordinary isotopes.

Several features of Table I are of interest in regard to the properties of the two molecules, n-butane and isobutane. First the $m/e = 43$ ion is the most abundant in both spectra. This indicates that breaking of a CH_3 carbon-carbon bond is more probable than either the breaking of a carbon-hydrogen bond or a C_2H_5 carbon-carbon bond. It is interesting to note that the absolute intensities for $m/e = 43$ are 2840 divisions per micron for n-butane and 3270 divisions per micron for isobutane. Thus the difference between primary and secondary carbon-carbon bonds, while in the direction expected from chemical experience is fairly small.

Another obvious point is that in the group of ions having two carbon atoms $m/e = 29$ is most abundant for n-butane and $m/e = 27$ for isobutane. $C_2H_5^+$ is the C_2 ion which is formed by breaking the least number of bonds in n-butane; it cannot be formed from isobutane without internal rearrangement during ionization. $C_2H_4^+$ is the C_2 ion which is formed by breaking the least number of bonds in isobutane.

IV. Use of Mass Spectra in Quantitative Analysis

The property of hydrocarbons which allows one to use mass spectra for the analysis of hydrocarbon mixtures is the possession of an unique pattern by each hydrocarbon. Table II, taken from a paper by Washburn *et al.* (32), gives a concise exposition of their "complete direct method" as applied to a mixture of *n*- and isobutane, propane, ethane, and methane. The "peak height" shown in the column, "M, Mixture Peaks," represents the ion current measured for the ionic fragment having the mass shown and hence is a measure of the abundance of that fragment.

It is evident from the molecular formulas of the compounds in the mixture that only *n*- and isobutane can contribute ionic fragments of mass 57 and 58. Therefore, the percentage of these two compounds can be computed from the simultaneous equations (1) and (2) shown at the bottom of Table II. The italic coefficients were determined in pure gas calibration measurements not shown in the table. The second and third columns show the contributions of *n*- and isobutane to the mixture peak heights as calculated from their percentages and the patterns of the pure gases. Now if one subtracts these contributions from the mass 44 peak, the remainder is due only to propane. Its percentage is calculated from this remainder value as shown at the bottom of Table II. By proceeding in the same manner with the remaining compounds, one may calculate the percentage of the other components.

As the mixtures grow more complex, occasions arise where a large number of simultaneous linear equations must be solved. This computational difficulty has turned out to be the most time-consuming part of carrying out analyses by means of the mass spectrometer. Matrix algebra is of considerable help if most of the mixtures analyzed have the same components. In such a case the labor of computing the inverse of the matrix of the coefficients of the equations is more than repaid by the fact that each new mixture calls only for a change in the constant terms of the equations and hence the inverse matrix allows very rapid solution of each new set of equations.

Another labor saving device is an electrical simultaneous linear equation calculator. There is one now on the market (33) which will solve twelve equations in twelve unknowns as accurately as is necessary for carrying out mass spectrometric analyses.

The difference between the sum of the calculated contributions to each mass and the actual peak height in the mixture spectrum, shown in Table II in the column called "Residuals," is a valuable check on the accuracy of the analysis. Of course, the method of calculation used made the residuals for masses 16, 30, 44, 57, and 58 exactly equal to zero, but this does not carry over to the other masses. In general, if the analysis is to be good, all

TABLE II
ANALYSIS OF DEPROPANIZER OVERHEAD

Mass	M, Mixture Peaks	n-Butane	Isobutane	Propane	Ethane	Methane	Σ, sum of component peaks	M − Σ, residuals
15	167.3	1.0	1.6	30.4	23.0	110.3	166.3	+1.0
16	*134.4*	*0.0*	*0.0*	*0.9*	*0.8*	132.7	134.4	0.0
26	146.1	1.6	0.9	37.6	106.4		146.5	−0.4
27	361.6	10.8	12.1	183.0	158.0		363.9	−2.3
28	777.8	9.3	1.2	275.3	494.4		780.2	−2.4
29	593.1	12.5	2.6	467.8	105.6		588.5	+2.4
30	*130.0*	*0.3*	*0.0*	*10.0*	119.7		130	0.0
31	2.4				2.5		2.5	−0.1
38	24.0	0.5	1.2	21.9			23.6	+0.4
39	98.0	4.3	8.7	84.6			97.6	+0.4
40	14.7	0.6	1.3	13 0			14.9	−0.2
41	94.1	9.0	18.9	65.8			93.7	+0.4
42	49.9	3.9	15.6	30.2			49.7	+0.2
43	207.4	32.2	49.8	124.5			206.5	+0.9
44	*145.3*	*1.0*	*1.6*	142.7			145.3	0.0
45	4.6	0.0		4.6			4.6	0.0
50	0.6	0.3	0.3				0.6	0.0
51	0.5	0.3	0.3				0.6	−0.1
52	0.1	0.1	0.1				0.2	−0.1
53	0.6	0.3	0.3				0.6	0.0
54	0.1	0.1	0.0				0.1	0.0
55	0.7	0.3	0.2				0.5	+0.2
56	0.5	0.3	0.2				0.5	0.0
57	*2.5*	0.9	1.6				2.5	0.0
58	*5.0*	3.8	1.2				5.0	0.0
59	0.2	0.2	0.0				0.2	0.0

Mole per cent

n-Butane		=	1.8
Isobutane		=	2.4
Propane	(145.3 − 1.0 − 1.60) *0.269*	=	38.4
Ethane	(130.0 − 0.3 − 0 − 10.0) *0.3175*	=	38.0
Methane	(134.4 − 0 − 0 − 0.9 − 0.8) *0.146*	=	19.4

Computation of per cent of n- and isobutane:

(1) From peak 57:

$0.503 \, p_n + 0.654 \, p_i = 2.5$

(2) From peak 58:

$2.10 \, p_n + 0.498 \, p_i = 5.0$

where p_n = per cent of n-butane

and p_i = per cent of isobutane

Italic coefficients are obtained from calibration mass spectra of pure compounds.

of those residuals not identically zero should be less in value than 1% of the corresponding mixture peak.

Often if only one unexpected compound is present, say air, its mass spectrum can be recognized in the residuals by an experienced computer. If a calibration pattern for the unexpected compound can be obtained, its percentage in the mixture can then also be computed. In other cases large residuals indicate only the presence of a disturbing compound or compounds, and other means have to be used to discover their identities.

If the reader wishes a more detailed explanation together with the specific computations for an actual test mixture, he is referred to a paper (31) published by the National Bureau of Standards.

From the above description of the complete direct method of computation, it is apparent that, if one does not care to check one's accuracy by means of residuals, a short cut may be taken. This "partial direct method" consists of measuring only those peak heights necessary for the calculation of the composition of the mixture. Using these peak heights in the same manner as in the complete direct method, one saves the time needed to make the parallel computations for the fragments neglected.

Washburn *et al.* (32) also describe a more rapid method of analysis to be used where one analyzes only samples of nearly identical composition such as would be encountered in many practical cases. This method is called the "comparison method" because it is based on the use of a known gas mixture, of composition closely approximating that of the unknown mixtures, whose mass spectrum is compared with that of the unknown mixture. The small differences between the peak heights in the two spectra can then be used to calculate the exact composition of the unknown mixture. This method of analysis, whenever it can be used, offers several advantages over the direct method. First, calibration of the mass spectrometer with the pure gases in the mixture need be made only about once a month, whereas experience has shown that with the direct method once weekly is usually necessary. These periodic calibrations must be made because instrument conditions change gradually with time. Second, in the comparison method all the data necessary for an analysis are taken, but if inspection of the record shows no or a very small change from the spectrum of the standard sample, one need not make a calculation in order to obtain the analysis of the unknown sample. Third, the actual process of computation for the comparison method takes less time. In Table III is shown experience (30) with the time in man-hours necessary to analyze three typical gas mixtures by the direct method and by the comparison method. It illustrates the time saving to be expected when the comparison method can be used. If the unknown and control samples are very nearly the same, the time required for analysis will be much shorter than that shown. If, on the other hand, they differ widely the necessary time will be of the order of that for the direct method.

In both the direct and comparison methods, the partial pressure of a given compound present is calculated from the sensitivity in divisions per unit sample pressure and the necessary peak height contribution. Thus, in order to obtain the mole per cent, one needs also to measure the total pressure of the mixture. The fact that the sum of all the partial pressures should equal this is a valuable check if all components are determined.

If one is willing to run in addition a mass spectrum of a mixture containing known amounts of each component, one can do away with the necessity for measuring sample pressures (34). The simplest way to illustrate the use of this method is to run through the analysis of a two component mixture using both schemes. In the direct method one measures the peak heights, A and B, for two peaks for the pure compounds at known pressures P. One can then compute a sensitivity for each peak $S_A = A/P$,

TABLE III

TIME REQUIRED FOR GAS ANALYSIS
(MAN-HOURS)

Type of mixture	Complete direct method	Comparison method
Synthetic C_1 to C_4 paraffin-olefin mixture....................	3.25	2
Typical feed stocks for catalytic polymerization and acid alkylation (C_3 to C_5 paraffin-olefin mixture)..............	3.5	2
Synthetic C_4 paraffin-olefin-diolefin mixture.................	2.5	1.5

etc. Next one measures the heights of the same two peaks in the unknown mixture M. The partial pressures p_1 and p_2 of the two components are then given by the equations:

$$S_{A_1} p_1 + S_{A_2} p_2 = A_M$$
$$S_{B_1} p_1 + S_{B_2} p_2 = B_M.$$

If one does not wish to measure the sample pressures and has at hand a known mixture of the two components, one measures two peak heights A and B for both pure components and for the known mixture. The ratio $R = A/B$ gives the ratio of the sensitivities $R = S_A/S_B$ directly since the pressure factors out. The peak heights for the known mixture M_0 are given by

$$A_{M_0} = p_1 S_{A_1} + p_2 S_{A_2}$$
$$B_{M_0} = p_1 S_{B_1} + p_2 S_{B_2}.$$

Since this is a known mixture, the mole ratio $F_{M_0} = p_1/p_2$ is known. Using these relations one can write:

$$\frac{S_{B_2}}{S_{B_1}} = \frac{R_{M_0} - R_1}{R_2 - R_{M_0}} F_{M_0}.$$

Exactly the same reasoning leads to the expression for the unknown mixture:

$$F_{M_u} = \frac{R_2 - R_{M_u}}{R_{M_u} - R_1} \cdot \frac{S_{B_2}}{S_{B_1}}.$$

In other words, the mole ratio in the unknown mixture is given by:

$$F_{M_u} = F_{M_0} \frac{R_{M_0} - R_1}{R_2 - R_{M_0}} \cdot \frac{R_2 - R_{M_u}}{R_{M_u} - R_1}.$$

If one writes the solution to the equations for the direct method in the same form one has:

$$F_{M_u} = \frac{P_1}{P_2} \cdot \frac{A_M B_2 - A_2 B_M}{A_1 B_M - A_M B_1}.$$

The relative accuracies of the two methods depend on how accurate a known mixture one can prepare or procure in the one case or on how accurately one can measure sample pressures in the other case.

A successful extension of the idea of using a mass spectrum to identify a compound has been developed (35). The method comprises using the mass spectra of decomposition products of rubbers, plastics, or other solids not suitable for direct introduction to the mass spectrometer to identify the original materials. The procedure is simply to heat a 0.01 g. sample in an evacuated ampoule to 400°C. for 10 minutes and to admit the resulting pyrolysis products to the mass spectrometer. In this manner many of the constituents of the solid sample can be detected and their amounts measured. The method has been used to identify the source of a scrap of paper by analyzing the sizing in the paper and to identify the manufacturer of a piece of photographic film from the film's analysis.

In the methods for analysis described above, the electrons that break the sample molecules into ions are given sufficient energy to give rise to all possible ionic fragments. In many cases the ions from one molecule are identical in mass with ions from other molecules. In the example given in Table II, this was true for n- and isobutane. A patent has been granted to D. D. Taylor of the Consolidated Engineering Corporation (36) for a method of analysis which in some cases simplifies the computations by reducing the number of masses common to more than one constituent of a mixture. The method is based on reducing the energy of the bombarding electrons to the point where only a few of the possible fragments are produced from each molecule. In the patent, it is pointed out that, for instance, a mixture of CO and CO_2 will give rise only to CO^+ ions from CO and CO_2^+ ions from CO_2 when bombarded by electrons with energy between 14.4 and 20.4 electron volts. If the energy of the electrons were higher, CO_2 would also give rise to CO^+ ions. Thus, by reducing the electron energy, one can obtain the ratio of CO to CO_2 by measuring the ratio of CO^+ to CO_2^+, whereas if the energy were higher this would not be possible.

The appearance potentials of ions from the hydrocarbons are almost all in the range from 10 to 15 electron volts. Therefore this method is not generally useful. However, there has been one case in which it has been used with great success. The appearance potentials of ions from free radicals are quite a bit lower than for the corresponding hydrocarbons (37). Thus the electron energy can be adjusted so that ions are produced from free radicals present in a hydrocarbon mixture with no production of ions from the hydrocarbons themselves. Very interesting results have been obtained by determining concentrations of free radicals in hydrocarbon mixtures in this way under various experimental conditions (38, 39).

It would appear from the foregoing that if one wishes to determine the concentration of only one hydrocarbon in a complex mixture by means of the mass spectrometer, first, the mixture must not contain compounds which cannot be introduced to the mass spectrometer and, second, the concentration of a large proportion of the compounds present in the mixture must be determined in order to find the desired one. The "isotopic dilution method" (40, 41, 42, 43) allows one to avoid these difficulties. In this method, for which the mass spectrometer is used only to measure heavy carbon percentages, reliance is placed on the chemical similarity of the carbon isotopes. In one way of using this method to determine the concentration of a hydrocarbon in a complex mixture one adds to a measured amount M of the mixture a known amount W of that hydrocarbon, in which the heavy carbon percentage is greater than that naturally occurring. Now if one chemically separates a pure sample of the hydrocarbon from this new mixture and measures its heavy carbon percentage, one is in a position to calculate the amount W' of the hydrocarbon present in the original mixture. It has been shown (42) that W' is given by

$$W' = \frac{X - X'}{X'} W$$

where X is the amount the heavy carbon percentage was in excess of the natural value in the added hydrocarbon and X' is the excess percentage after the hydrocarbon was added to the mixture and a pure sample isolated. The concentration W' per M is then directly calculable.

It will be seen that the accuracy of the method depends on the degree to which the natural and heavy hydrocarbons are identical with regard to the separation process. Its accuracy of course depends on the accuracy of measurement of X, X', M, and W and on how effectively the hydrocarbon has been purified after separation, but it does not depend on the completeness of the removal of the hydrocarbon from the mixture. It is the latter property which makes this method important. It is easy to remove all of a given compound in an impure state or part of it in a pure state from many complex chemical mixtures, but it is almost impossible to remove all of the compound in a pure state. If the latter were easy, one would simply measure the amount removed to obtain the concentration of the hydrocarbon in the mixture. Addition of a known amount of a hydrocarbon enriched in heavy carbon and measurement of the isotopic dilution due to the unknown amount of the natural compound in the mixture allows one to take advantage of the fact that it is easy to separate part of the hydrocarbon from the mixture in the pure state.

The present day situation with regard to isotope concentration makes a word of caution necessary. Strictly speaking, the equation for W should have been

$$W = W' \frac{X - X'}{X} \frac{M}{M'}$$

where M is the molecular weight of the natural compound and M' that of the heavy analogue (44). Thus, if one is analyzing for butane and adds butane containing 20 atom $\%$ heavy carbon, $M/M' = 0.986$. If this were neglected, one would be in error by 1.4% with regard to W.

V. FACTORS CONTROLLING ANALYTICAL ACCURACY

This question of accuracy is, of course, one of great importance in analytical work. Before going on to actual experience in the use of the mass spectrometer in hydrocarbon analysis, it will be well to consider the factors controlling analytical accuracy. In the descriptions given above, it has been tacitly assumed that for each compound there is a unique pattern which is always the same and the intensity of which is directly proportional to the concentration of that compound in any mixture. None of these assumptions is exactly true. Yet, if conditions are chosen properly, they can be near enough true so that the limiting factor in analytical accuracy will be the accuracy with which one can read the peak heights in the experimental mass spectrum.

The assumption of uniqueness of pattern is the one that in many cases is the least well fulfilled. For instance, as shown in Table IV, the spectra of the cis and trans isomers of butylene-2 are very similar (45). The result of this similarity is that the simultaneous linear equations which one must solve in order to obtain an analysis form an almost singular system. The fact that this means that the mass spectra must be determined with unusual accuracy in order that one may obtain solutions which are only reasonably accurate for these equations has led to the practice of lumping structural isomers or other compounds which give very similar spectra and reporting only the total concentration of the lumped group. If accurate analysis of the separate compounds in the group is desired, it is necessary to separate the groups by some means, such as low temperature fractional distillation, from the rest of the mixture. When this is done and mass spectrometer analysis is applied, one can obtain satisfactory accuracy. Table V shows an analysis done with a Westinghouse mass spectrometer on a

TABLE IV

MASS SPECTRA OF THE BUTYLENE-2'S

(Electron Energy 50 Electron Volts)

m/e	cis-Butylene-2	trans-Butylene-2	m/e	cis-Butylene-2	trans-Butylene-2
56	100	100	29	26.7	32.3
55	38.6	40.0	28	57.7	56.3
54	7.3	6.8	27	62.6	59.1
53	13.7	14.5	26	20.0	18.1
52	3.5	3.6			
51	10.4	10.2	15	9.9	9.0
50	10.3	10.0	14	1.8	1.6
42	6.0	5.9			
41	187	194			
40	13.2	12.3			
39	69.2	65.7			

mixture of butylene-1, 1,3-butadiene, and the *cis*- and *trans*-butylene-2's (46). The indicated accuracy is 2.5% of the actual value or better.

If one is satisfied with a less accurate analysis, one can proceed with the straightforward analytical scheme. While the sum of the percentages found still give an accurate lumped concentration, because of the similarity of all the butylene spectra the individual values can easily be in error by 20% of the value measured.

The assumption of constancy of pattern is more complicated, but on the other hand it can be satisfied with considerable success. One vital factor in maintaining constancy of pattern is instrumental stability. The amplifier that magnifies the ion current so that it may be measured more accurately must have an amplification factor which does not change appreciably while a mass spectrum is being measured. The same must be true of the ionizing electron current since ion production is directly proportional to the number of bombarding electrons. Another vital factor is the behavior of the ionization chamber. It goes without saying that the energy of the bombarding electrons should remain constant. If it does not, the mass spectrum shifts because new points on the ionization efficiency curves for the different ions are reached each time a measurement is made. However, although in this case instrument stability is necessary, it is not sufficient. As various samples are run through the mass spectrometer, the surfaces of the electrodes in the ionization chamber will collect and lose contaminants depending on the nature of the samples. The net result is that the contact potentials between electrodes change. Thus, even though the voltage placed on the electrodes may be maintained constant, potentials between them need not stay constant. In hydrocarbon analysis this effect is usually minimized by the fact that all hydrocarbons have essentially the same action on the electrode surfaces. However, if other types of compounds are present in the mix-

TABLE V

ANALYSIS OF A MIXTURE OF C_4 OLEFINS

Compound	Amounts present in synthetic mixture	Mass spectrometer analysis
	%	%
Butylene-1..	3.7	4.1
cis-Butylene-2..	18.3	20
trans-Butylene-2......................................	31.1	28.6
1,3-Butadiene...	46.9	47.3

ture, general practice has been to "condition" the spectrometer for various periods with a pure hydrocarbon.

If insulating layers are built up on the electrode surfaces, charges can be formed on them which will shift the position of the electron beam. This in turn will shift in space the volume in which ions are being produced, and the efficiency with which ions are collected by the first ion beam collecting slit will change. By the time an ionization chamber has reached this condition, it is so dirty that it should be removed for cleaning.

There are also other factors that affect the location of the volume in space from which ions are collected to form the ion beam (24). As has already been mentioned, it is good practice to have the voltage, V_d, that draws the ions toward the first ion beam defining slit proportional to the ion accelerating voltage. This follows from the fact that the mass spectrometer equation

$$\frac{m}{e} = \frac{r^2 H^2}{2V}$$

is followed in the ionization chamber just as well as elsewhere. Thus,

$$r_d^2 = m \frac{2V_d}{H^2 e}$$

for a constant V_d would require r to be proportional to $\sqrt{m}$ and ions of each mass would come from different parts of the ionization region. If

$$V_d = kV,$$

then

$$r_d^2 = kr^2$$

which, because of the geometry of the mass spectrometer, is a constant. Thus, all of the ions will come from the same place. It has been shown (24) that even this arrangement does not ensure that the volume in space from which the ions come will be the same for the different ions, and that better representation will be obtained if the ion accelerating voltages are held constant and the magnetic field is varied to obtain the mass spectrum.

In the above it was assumed that ions are formed completely at rest. This is not so (47). For instance, from n-butane the $C_2H_5^+$ ions are formed with 0.08 e.v. initial energy whereas the $C_4H_{10}^+$ ions have 0.04 e.v. Thus, different ions will have different velocities in the ionization region in a way that depends on the molecule being ionized as well as on the ionization chamber conditions. The volume in space from which ions are collected will differ from ion to ion in spite of adjustment of ionization chamber conditions as described.

These effects, which are of considerable importance if one wishes to measure absolute values of the relative abundances of ions, are not of much importance in hydrocarbon analysis (45). In other words, in analytical work if a pattern is characteristic of a compound, its detailed origin is not important.

A more subtle factor in the effect of the ionization chamber on constancy of pattern is the chamber temperature. It has been shown that the molecule ion peaks for isobutane, n-butane and 2,2,3-trimethylpentane change very rapidly with temperature whereas the other peaks change more slowly (48). For instance, for isobutane at 70°C. the $C_4H_{10}^+$ ion is about twice as abundant as the $C_4H_9^+$ ion, but at 180°C. the two ions are equally abundant. In ordinary mass spectrometer operation this temperature effect can be brought under control by keeping the ambient temperature constant and operating the mass spectrometer under normal conditions for about an hour before undertaking analyses. The latest model Consolidated mass spectrometer (20) has a temperature compensating device which keeps the ionization chamber temperature constant.

In spite of all the care that may be taken, the patterns do change. For this reason, the mass spectra of the pure compounds must be measured periodically at intervals depending on the rate of pattern change in the mass spectrometer being used.

R. E. Honig (49) has presented an excellent analysis of the conditions under which the intensity of a pattern is directly proportional to the amount of the corresponding compound in the sample being measured. The basis for this proportionality is the fact that the current $I_a{}^+$ due to an ion I^+ from a given pure gas a is directly proportional to the electron current I^-, as already stated, to the concentration p_a of the gas in the ionizing region, and to the pattern coefficient $P_a(I^+)$ characteristic of gas a:

$$I_a{}^+ = k\ I^-\ p_a\ P_a\ (I^+)$$

If p_a can be regarded as directly proportional to the concentration of gas a in the unknown mixture and the other factors are kept constant, this pattern intensity is directly proportional to compound concentration. Honig has shown that this will be true if each gas behaves as if the other gases were not present, a situation which obtains when the gas flow through the mass spectrometer obeys the conditions of "molecular flow." He points out that this occurs when pressures are kept low, below 10^{-2} mm. Hg, and when any orifices through which the gases must flow have a diameter $\frac{1}{20}$ or less of the mean free path of the molecules in the gas.

One condition which Honig has declared is necessary can be neglected if a proper alternative is taken. This condition is that the pressure in the sample container must remain substantially constant during the time a mass spectrum is being measured. If this is done, the whole pattern will relate to the original sample pressure and will be a proper measure of concentration. The alternative is to take exactly the same time interval for each corresponding operation in determining different mass spectra. Then if the sample is flowing out of a closed reservoir through a small orifice into the mass spectrometer the per cent pressure decay will be the same for each pure gas spectrum and for each mixture spectrum. If the gases in the mixture are mutually independent, then the spectra of the components will be as truly representative of the initial pressures of the components present in the mixture as though the pressures had remained constant. In other words the ion current will have an additional term $exp\ [-R_a t(I^+)]$ where R_a is a leak rate or pressure decay rate and $t(I^+)$ is the time after starting the sample into the mass spectrometer at which one measures I^+. The necessary and sufficient condition for

$$I_a^+ = k\ I^-\ p_a\ P_a\ (I^+)\ exp\ [-R_a t(I^+)]$$

to be exactly comparable for a pure compound alone and for the same compound in a mixture is that $t(I^+)$ must be a constant. This follows since, under conditions where molecular flow occurs, R_a is a constant not depending on the initial sample pressure or on the other gases present.

A final factor in the assumption that the pattern intensity is proportional to compound concentration is one which is common to any method of hydrocarbon analysis. Great care must be taken in sampling mixtures that are partially liquefied. Otherwise the sample taken may not have the same concentration as the original mixture. One procedure that has been found satisfactory in such cases is to chill the mixture so that it all liquefies, take a small portion of the liquid, and vaporize the whole small sample by expanding it into a large volume (50).

There is another condition that does not apply to hydrocarbon analysis as such, but which can be quite important if other related compounds, such as alcohols, are present. Some compounds such as these adsorb strongly on glass. Unless the mass spectrometer is pretreated with a strongly adsorbed compound, the first analyses of a mixture containing it can be quite incorrect because that compound will be partially removed from the mixture by adsorption on the way to the ionization chamber (51). The same is true in reverse for subsequent analyses of other mixtures since the adsorbed compound is released slowly and will appear to be present in small concentrations in mixtures where it is really absent. A sufficiently long pumping interval between unlike samples will remove this difficulty. Heating of the glass surfaces will, of course, shorten pumping times and minimize adsorption difficulties.

VI. PRACTICAL USE OF THE MASS SPECTROMETER IN HYDROCARBON ANALYSIS

Now that the conditions and methods for hydrocarbon gas analysis by means of the mass spectrometer have been presented, it will be of interest to see the range of usefulness and accuracy of the mass spectrometer in this regard. The Consolidated Engineering Corporation has published extensively with regard to the success of its instrument (32, 52, 53, 54, 55). These papers report the extension of mass spectrometer analysis (32) to gas mixtures with as many as thirteen components and, in some cases, with compounds as high in molecular weight as the C_8's. The accuracy given was well within 1 mole % in most cases. The largest error mentioned was 3.7 mole % for lumped butylene-2's in a C_4 paraffin-olefin mixture containing all of the C_4 olefins. This, of course, is in line with the fact that, while total butylenes can be determined accurately, analysis for one butylene will not be as accurate.

Of considerable interest in regard to accuracy is the success (32) with which small amounts of diethylbenzene (presumably a mixture of the three isomers) can be measured in ethylbenzene. Table VI shows analyses of eight mixtures of varied diethylbenzene concentration as shown in the column labeled "Synthetic." It will be noted that the difference between the true and observed values is in general about 10% of the true value even when that value is as small as 0.036 mole %.

Other hydrocarbon mixtures for which successful mass spectrometer analyses were reported were a C_7 mixture containing nine components (55) and a C_8 mixture of six components (55). In view of the increasing similarity of spectra for compounds in higher mass ranges, analyses of such mixtures is an even greater success than those of thirteen component mixtures of low molecular weight compounds. In the case of the C_7 mixture, the largest expected error (the average error of a number of determinations) is 3.0 mole % for 3-methylhexane; in the C_8 mixture, 1.7 mole % for 2,2,4-trimethylpentane. Ability to analyze such a C_8 mixture is of direct interest to the petroleum industry, for it means that, by use of the mass spectrometer in conjunction with the new electrical simultaneous linear equation calculator (33) routine analysis of alkylates is now practical.

TABLE VI

ANALYSIS FOR SMALL AMOUNT OF DIETHYLBENZENE IN NEARLY PURE ETHYLBENZENE

Mixture	Synthetic (added impurity mole %)	Mass spectrometer mole %	Difference
1	0.036	0.033	−0.003
2	0.071	0.066	−0.005
3	0.235	0.22	−0.02
4	0.479	0.44	−0.04
5	0.789	0.76	−0.03
6	2.41	2.2	−0.2
7	4.02	3.6	−0.4
8	7.97	8.0	0

A more complete picture of the accuracy of analysis can be gained from Table VII which is a resumé of a large number of analyses of a nine-component test mixture (50). Since 90% of the errors were below 1.4 mole % even in the worst case, it can be seen that mass spectrometric analysis is indeed an accurate means of determining hydrocarbon concentrations.

It will be appreciated that all of the above work was undoubtedly done under optimum conditions by persons highly skilled in mass spectrometer operations. To determine how the mass spectrometer rates as an analytical tool in the field, one must turn to the experience of mass spectrometer users. Some of the earlier reports (56, 57) are not useful in this regard since they use only data supplied by Consolidated. However, there are later descriptions (58, 59, 60) which in the main confirm Consolidated's statements.

The report of the General Petroleum Corporation (59), based on 3 months of routine operation of the mass spectrometer at their Torrance refinery, gives a good picture of the all-around behavior of the instrument as a means for hydrocarbon analysis. In this report several interesting comments were made. First, while isopentane, n-pentane, total pentylenes, and C_6 traces (0.1 to 1%) are determined regularly by means of the mass spectrometer, large amounts of C_6 or heavier compounds require the use of low temperature fractional distillation for their analysis. Second, carbon dioxide interferes seriously with analysis and should be removed beforehand. Third, water cannot be determined, probably because of its adsorption on the walls of the apparatus. Fourth, on the credit side, the presence of oxygen and nitrogen can be determined quantitatively, and hydrogen and methane can be split accurately where low temperature fractional distilla-

TABLE VII

ERRORS IN MASS SPECTROMETER ANALYSES

Components	Composition (mole %)	No. of determinations	Average error (mole %)	90% of errors less than
Methane..................................	15 ⎫			
Ethane..................................	20 ⎪			
Propane..................................	20 ⎬	215	0.2	0.4
Isobutane..................................	10 ⎪			
n-Butane..................................	8 ⎭			
Propylene..................................	10	43	0.2	0.5
Isobutylene..................................	7	43	0.4	0.7
Butylene-1..................................	5 ⎫	86	0.7	1.4
Butylene-2's..................................	5 ⎭			
Total Butylenes..................................	17	43	0.4	0.8

tion can give only an approximate split between methane and the permanent gases.

Initial tests run by General Petroleum showed excellent agreement between mass spectrometer and fractionation plus acid absorption analyses of such actual mixtures as cracking unit absorber release gas and cracking unit stabilizer release gas. In many instances calculations can be done by inspection, especially in the case of small amounts (up to 5%) of undesirable heavy constituents caused by improper operation of refinery equipment.

The partial direct method of analysis has proved useless in the case of liquid stream analyses because refinery operators demand results in liquid volume per cent. Since the mass spectrometer yields results in mole per cent, a complete analysis must be run before the liquid volume per cent can be calculated.

The time required by General Petroleum for an analysis in routine operation compares favorably with that presented in Table III. The shortest time required is 25 minutes for the determination of isobutane by inspection in depropanizer overhead while a complete analysis of a cracked gas containing no pentanes required 95 minutes. It was determined that if half of the samples are calculated by inspection, two operators and one calculator can turn out an average of fourteen refinery samples in an eight-hour day or, 1.72 man-hours are required per sample. If the samples are to be calculated accurately through the C_4's, another person is needed, and 2.28 man-hours are required per sample. In the above routine operation, a complete calibration was run once every two weeks and a monitoring spec-

TABLE VIII

ACCURACY OF ANALYSIS OF A NATURAL GAS SAMPLE

Compound	Average of all determinations (%)	Total range (%)	Mean of laboratory averages (%)
Methane..............................	77.7	4.6	77.5 ± 0.6
Ethane...............................	14.9	2.3	14.8 ± 0.2[a]
Carbon dioxide........................	0.94	0.7	1.00 ± 0.03
Ethylene.............................	0.26	0.6	[b]
Propylene............................	0.2	0.3	0.2 ± 0.03
Propane..............................	2.7	1.2	2.8 ± 0.1[c]
Nitrogen.............................	3.4	3.3	3.5 ± 0.5

Approximately 10% of the 118 analyses made included carbon monoxide, oxygen, hydrogen, butylenes, or butanes. Only carbon monoxide and oxygen were reported in quantities greater than 0.1% In four cases it seems self-evident carbon monoxide was confused with nitrogen.

[a] Two extreme values discarded.
[b] Reported by only half the laboratories.
[c] Two low values discarded.

trum of n-butane was made once daily. The samples being analyzed included all of the gas plant samples and about two-thirds of the samples from the alkylation unit in a process where butylenes and pentylenes were being alkylated together. It is interesting to note that where low temperature fractional distillation and acid absorption were used for analysis, the time required was sometimes as much as ten times greater than the time for mass spectrometric analysis.

A report has been issued (60) on a cooperative analysis made, under the auspices of the American Society for Testing Materials, by twenty laboratories on portions of a single sample of natural gas. Both Westinghouse and Consolidated mass spectrometers were used. Table VIII shows the accuracies obtained. A comparison with Table VII shows that, except for methane, analyses made in the field are of an accuracy comparable to that found in the makers' own laboratory.

The traces of gases reported where these gases are known not to be present in the sample should not be ascribed to a failure of the mass spectrometer. They are the result either of improper sample transfer or of impatience in not allowing previous samples to be pumped completely out of the mass spectrometer.

In conclusion it can be said that for hydrocarbons ranging up to C_8's, the mass spectrometer is an accurate and versatile analytical tool.

REFERENCES

1. J. J. Thomson, Rays of Positive Electricity. Longmans, Green, London, 1913.
2. F. W. Aston, Mass Spectra and Isotopes. Second edition, Edward Arnold and Company, London, 1942.
3. F. W. Aston, *Proc. Roy. Soc. London* **A163**, 391 (1937).
4. J. Mattauch, *Physik. Z.* **35**, 568 (1934).
5. A. J. Dempster, *Phys. Rev.* **51**, 67 (1937).
6. K. T. Bainbridge and E. B. Jordan, *Phys. Rev.* **50**, 282 (1936).
7. J. Mattauch, *Phys. Rev.* **50**, 617 (1936).
8. A. J. Dempster, *Phys. Rev.* **11**, 316 (1918).
9. W. Bleakney and C. S. Cummings, *Phys. Rev.* **57**, 1072 (1940).
10. A. O. Nier, *Phys. Rev.* **52**, 933 (1937).
11. H. S. Brown, J. J. Mitchell, and R. D. Fowler, *Rev. Sci. Instruments* **12**, 435 (1941).
12. M. B. Sampson and W. Bleakney, *Phys. Rev.* **50**, 456 (1936).
13. A. O. Nier, *Phys. Rev.* **50**, 1041 (1936).
14. J. T. Tate and P. T. Smith, *Phys. Rev.* **50**, 773 (1936).
15. R. Herzog, *Z. Physik* **89**, 447 (1934).
16. J. Mattauch and R. Herzog, *Z. Physik* **89**, 786–795 (1934).
17. R. Herzog and V. Hauk, *Z. Physik* **108**, 609–634 (1938).
18. R. Herzog and V. Hauk, *Ann. Physik* **33**, 89–106 (1938).
19. A. O. Nier, *Rev. Sci. Instruments* **11**, 212 (1940).
20. N. F. Barber, *Proc. Leeds Phil. Soc.* **2**, 427 (1933).
21. W. E. Stephens and A. L. Hughes, *Phys. Rev.* **45**, 123 (1934).
22. Consolidated Engineering Corporation, 620 North Lake Avenue, Pasadena 4, California (Bulletin No. C.E.C. 21102).
23. Westinghouse Electric and Manufacturing Co., Research Products Dept., Radio Division, Baltimore, Maryland (Technical Data 85–940, November 1941).
24. N. D. Coggeshall, *J. Chem. Phys.* **12**, 19–23 (1944).
25. E. U. Condon, *Am. J. Physics* **15**, 365–74 (1947).
26. L. Pauling and E. B. Wilson, Introduction to Quantum Mechanics. McGraw-Hill, New York, 1935.
27. W. Bleakney, *Phys. Rev.* **35**, 1180–6 (1930).
28. D. P. Stevenson, *J. Chem. Phys.* **15**, 409–411 (1947).
29. N. Bauer and J. Y. Beach, *J. Chem. Phys.* **15**, 150–1 (1947).
30. H. W. Washburn and C. E. Berry, *Phys. Rev.* **70**, 559 (1946).
31. A. K. Brewer and V. H. Dibeler, *J. Res. Natl. Bur. Stand.* **35**, 125–139 (1945).
32. H. W. Washburn, H. F. Wiley, and S. M. Rock, *Ind. Eng. Chem., Anal. Ed.* **15**, 541–7 (1943).

33. C. E. Berry, D. E. Wilcox, S. M. Rock and H. W. Washburn, A Computer for Solving Linear Simultaneous Equations. Consolidated Engineering Corporation, Pasadena, California, 1945.

34. E. J. Johnsen, *Anal. Chem.* **19**, 305–6 (1947).

35. A. K. Brewer, Domestic Commerce, 10-11 (June 1945); also Letter Circular LC-791, May 3, 1945, National Bureau of Standards, U. S. Department of Commerce, Washington 25, D.C.

36. Consolidated Engineering Corporation, Assignee of D. D. Taylor, U. S. Patent No. 2,373,151 (April 10, 1945) (filed July 29, 1942).

37. J. A. Hipple and D. P. Stevenson, *Phys. Rev.* **63**, 121–6 (1943).

38. G. C. Eltenton, *J. Chem. Phys.* **10**, 403 (1942).

39. G. C. Eltenton, *J. Chem. Phys.* **15**, 455–481 (1947).

40. A. V. Grosse, A. D. Kirshenbaum, and S. G. Hindin, *Science* **105**, 100–101 (1947).

41. F. C. Henriques, Jr. and C. Margnetti, *Ind. Eng. Chem., Anal. Ed.* **18**, 476–478 (1946).

42. D. Rittenberg and G. L. Foster, *J. Biol. Chem.* **133**, 737–744 (1940).

43. D. Rittenberg, *J. Applied Phys.* **13**, 561–569 (1942).

44. N. S. Radin, *Nucleonics* **1**, (No. 2), 48–59 (Oct. 1947).

45. V. H. Dibeler, *J. Research Natl. Bureau Standards* **38**, 329–36 (1947).

46. J. A. Hipple and H. E. Dralle, *Petroleum Refiner* **22**, 425–426 (1943); *Electronics* **16**, (11), 120–124 (1943).

47. H. W. Washburn and C. E. Berry, *Phys. Rev.* **70**, 559 (1946).

48. R. E. Fox and J. A. Hipple, *J. Chem. Phys.* **15**, 208 (1947).

49. R. E. Honig, *J. Applied Phys.* **16**, 646–54 (1945).

50. V. H. Dibeler and F. L. Mohler, *J. Research Natl. Bur. Standards* **39**, 149–54 (1947).

51. R. C. Taylor, R. A. Brown, W. S. Young, and C. E. Headington, Paper No. 13, Division of Petroleum Chemistry, 111 Meeting, American Chemical Society (April 1947).

52. H. Hoover and H. W. Washburn, *Am. Inst. Mining Engrs., Engrs. Tech. Pub.* No. **1205**, 7 (1940).

53. H. W. Washburn, D. D. Taylor, E. E. Hoskins. and R. V. Langmuir, *Proc. Calif. Natl. Gas Assoc.* **15**, (11), 7–9 (1940).

54. H. Hoover and H. W. Washburn, *Calif. Oil World* **34**, (22), 21–2 (1941).

55. H. W. Washburn, H. F. Wiley, S. M. Rock, and C. E. Berry, *Ind. Eng. Chem., Anal. Ed.* **17**, 74–81 (1945).

56. O. L. Roberts, *Petroleum Engr.* **14**, (8), 109 (1943).

57. O. L. Roberts, *Petroleum Refiner* **22**, (5), 145–51 (1943).

58. R. A. Brown, R. C. Taylor, F. W. Melpolder, and W. S. Young, Paper No. 14, Division of Petroleum Chemistry, 111 Meeting, American Chemical Society (April 1947).

59. J. G. Schaafsma, *Oil Gas J.* **42**, (48), 57, 59, 60, 63 (1944); *Calif. Oil World* **37**, (8), 13, 15–16, 25, 27 (1944); *Natl. Petroleum News* **36**, R196–200 (1944); *Petroleum Refiner* **23**, (4) 123–7 (1944).

60. M. Shepherd, *J. Research Natl. Bur. Standards* **38**, 491–8 (1947).

CHAPTER 4

OPTICAL PROPERTIES OF HYDROCARBONS; INFRARED ABSORPTION, RAMAN, AND ULTRAVIOLET ABSORPTION SPECTROSCOPY

By

NORMAN D. COGGESHALL

Gulf Research and Development Company
Pittsburgh, Pennsylvania

CONTENTS

In the past few years optical properties have become very important in the study of hydrocarbons and in various phases of the petroleum and allied industries. These properties are now being extensively studied and quite wide-spread application is being made of them for analytical purposes, for molecular structure determination, and for the determination of fundamental information such as is necessary for thermodynamic calculations.

In the following sections a brief introduction is given to infrared, Raman, and ultraviolet spectroscopy. Restriction of the material exclusively to a consideration of hydrocarbons has not been attempted there since, as a class, they are one of many that can be studied by these means. Any discussion restricted to them specifically would detract from the generality of the material.

In the material to follow a uniform convention with regard to wavelengths and wave numbers has not been used. This has been done deliberately since the literature contains both usages. Various individuals and groups have lamented the dual usage and have attempted standardization. However, the average reader has no choice at this time but to become acquainted with both conventions. In the discussion of infrared spectra the unit of wavelength is the μ (1 $\mu = 10^{-4}$ cm.). Often the frequencies are specified in wave numbers. The wave number for a frequency is the reciprocal of the wavelength. Its units are cm.$^{-1}$ and it represents the number of vibrations per centimeter. In Raman spectroscopy it is customary to give the absolute location of a line in Angstrom units (1 A. = 10^{-8} cm.) and the line displacements in wave numbers. In the discussion of ultraviolet absorption the wavelengths are given in terms of mμ (1 m$\mu = 10^{-3}$ $\mu = 10^{-7}$ cm.), in A. and in wave numbers.

With regard to references, the aim has been to give a sufficient number that the reader may profitably supplement the present material. However, there has been no attempt at completeness and the question of priority of publication has been given a second place to that of convenience to the reader.

The section dealing with infrared is more extensive than the others since here some discussion of quantum conditions and modes of vibration, which also apply to the later sections, has been included.

I. INFRARED ABSORPTION

The infrared region of the spectrum is that portion which lies between the approximate wavelength limits of 0.8 μ and 300 μ. The absorption or emission of radiation in this region is accompanied by changes in molecular vibrations and/or rotations.

A molecule is not a rigid structure. The atoms of the component groups are held together by valence forces which have their origin in the sharing of electrons or in the coulombic attraction between ionic forms. Due to these valence forces the atoms are maintained in average equilibrium positions and with definite angles between the valence bonds. The restraints that maintain the atoms in their relative positions are not, however, sufficiently strong to maintain rigidity, and in all molecules the atoms are constantly vibrating about their equilibrium positions. Such vibrations are determined by the geometry of the molecules, the masses of the atoms, and the nature of the valence forces. A vibrating molecule will possess definite energy levels in accordance with the rules of quantum mechanics, and when a transition occurs from one energy level to another a photon of radiation may be absorbed or emitted. The energy differences between the levels are of such an order of magnitude that the frequency of the associated radiation falls in the infrared region.

In addition to the molecular vibrations a molecule may be free to rotate. The amount of energy associated with the rotation will depend upon the moments of inertia and the angular frequency. It may not assume any value but will take on discrete values as imposed by the quantum conditions. Transitions between the rotational states may be accompanied by the absorption or emission of photons of such a frequency range as to also fall in the infrared region as defined above.

Transitions between the electronic configurations which involve the disposition of the bonding electrons give rise to absorption or emission of radiation in the ultraviolet and visible portion of the spectrum. Thus the infrared data for a molecular species may be interpreted in terms of the dynamics of the molecule. Conversely the structure of an unknown material may be determined from a study of the infrared data obtained for it. The study of infrared data for these purposes has enormously increased the knowledge and understanding of molecules and molecular structure.

1. EXPERIMENTAL METHODS

The infrared region may be broken down into three parts which differ both in experimental approach and in the type of data furnished. The near infrared or photographic region extends from about 0.8 to 1.3 μ, and in it are found the overtone and combination frequencies. A fundamental frequency refers to a transition between the lowest energy level and the first excited one while an overtone frequency refers to a transition from the lowest level to the second excited state. A combination frequency is that which results when simultaneous transitions occur for two different modes of vibration. The prism region, or region of fundamental vibrations, lies between the approximate limits 1 and 25 μ. Here are found the absorption bands corresponding to the fundamental vibrational frequencies for all but the most massive molecules. The far infrared region, between 30 and 300 μ is the region wherein the rotational frequencies are found. These are due to transitions wherein the energy of the photons is transformed into rotational energy of the molecules.

In the near infrared or photographic region the detection of the radiation is by photographic plates and the long wavelength limit of this region is that imposed by the sensitivity of the plates. Studies here can be carried out on spectrographs and gratings used for the ultraviolet and visible regions. In that respect the technique is simple and high dispersion is attainable. Since the data obtained for this region are for the overtone and combination frequencies it is necessary to use greater thicknesses of absorption cells or tubes, i.e., impose more of the material being studied in the radiation beam, than for the region of fundamental vibrations. This is because transitions involving overtone or combination frequencies are generally much less frequent than those involving a transition from the ground level to the first excited one.

The photographic region has several advantages and disadvantages. Of the latter the most serious one is that it can yield only a restricted amount of information. In order for an observable overtone frequency to lie in this region it is necessary that the corresponding fundamental frequency be not much less than about 3000 cm.$^{-1}$ However, only molecules containing hydrogen possess fundamentals in this range. Other disadvantages are the long sample containers necessary and the fact that the data are harder to interpret since they are for overtone and combination frequencies. On the other hand, the methods are simple and valuable information, not otherwise attainable, about the potential energy curves for the molecules can be deduced from the data.

In the region of fundamental vibrations the data are best obtained by the use of prism or grating spectrometers equipped with some sort of a heat-responsive radiation detector. A diagram of a prism instrument showing the relative disposition of components may be seen in Fig. 1. Here R represents a source of continuous radiation and the mirrors M_1 and M_2 serve to send a converging beam through the sample cell L to the entrance slit S_1 of the monochromator. From S_1 the light passes to the collimating mirror C from whence it proceeds to the prism P. By the arrangement of prism and mirror M_3 the light is returned through the prism for a second refraction. Part of the returning light will intercept the collimating mirror C and be sent to the mirror M_4 which reflects it so that an image of the entrance slit will fall in the plane of the exit slit S_2. The diverging beam leaving the exit slit is intercepted by the mirror M_5 and focused onto a radiation detector T. With narrow slit settings, the radiation striking T will be nearly monochromatic. Its wavelength may be changed by rotation of the mirror M_3.

Light of these wavelengths and longer will not pass through glass. Consequently special optical materials must be used (1). As a prism material NaCl is the most versatile, giving satisfactory spectra out to about 15 μ. Its dispersion is poor in the lower wavelength regions and here prisms of LiF and CaF_2 are very useful. As defined above the prism region includes the section between 1 and 2.5 μ where overtone rather than fundamental frequencies are actually observed. For this region quartz and some varieties of optical glass may be used while for the wavelengths in the fundamental region beyond 15 μ the prism material must be of KI, KBr, or KCl. Of course, all windows on the instrument and the sample cell must be of optical material suitable for the region being studied. The mirrors are of the first-surface metallized type.

For the wavelengths beyond the photographic region some sort of heat-sensitive radiation detector must be used. This is because of the low energy per photon for these wavelengths. Probably the most commonly used detector is the vacuum thermocouple (2) in which the radiation raises the temperature of a blackened strip onto which it falls and onto which is fastened a sensitive thermocouple junction. The rise in temperature creates a small voltage in the thermocouple due to the thermoelectric effect. The

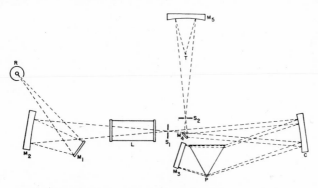

FIG. 1. Optical diagram of an infrared spectrometer.

source of radiation must necessarily be some sort of a small hot body. For that either a Nernst glower or a small rod of Carborundum, called a Globar heater, is used. Both are heated by the passage of electricity.

Figure 2 shows an infrared absorption spectrum in a portion of this region for the hydrocarbon styrene as obtained with a small prism instrument. Such resolution as may be seen here is sufficient to bring out the main vibrational bands but is not sufficient to resolve the fine structure which is due to the combination of vibrational and rotational frequencies. For high resolution, spectrometers are built to incorporate both prisms and gratings (3). In these it is customary to pass the radiation through a prism monochromator and from there to a grating. From the grating the diffracted radiation passes to suitable mirrors and is focused onto a radiation receiver. With the combination of fore-prism and grating tremendous improvements in resolution are possible. The use of a grating alone as a dispersion device is attended with difficulties due to the overlapping of orders wherein the first order spectrum for one wavelength coincides with the second order spectrum of a second wavelength, etc.

In the far infrared region, 30 to 300 μ, the experimental difficulties are very serious. The only source of continuous radiation for the infrared is the black-body radiator, and the radiation from it falls off very rapidly in the far infrared. This means that the energy in any spectral region is low and that there is generally considerable scattered energy of shorter wavelengths. Further difficulties lie in the lack of suitable materials for making windows for the absorption cells and for the spectrometer. Also efficient radiation receiving devices for this region are difficult to fabricate. The isolation of wavelengths may be done by utilizing the Reststrahlen phenomena (4). However, this only allows a study over definite portions of

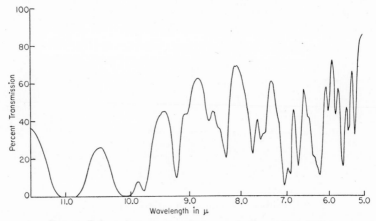

Fig. 2. Infrared spectrum of styrene between 5 and 11μ.

the spectrum, dependent on the nature of the crystalline material used for the Reststrahlen plates. However, more flexibility is allowed when gratings are used. These may be either reflecting or transmitting (5), of which the latter type consists of wires stretched tightly on a frame. In this spectral region are observed the purely rotational frequencies.

More details on experimental methods and techniques in the 1 to 25 μ region will be provided in a later chapter describing the application of infrared spectroscopy to the analysis of mixtures of hydrocarbons.

2. ENERGY LEVELS, THE SCHROEDINGER EQUATION

As stated above, the total energy of a molecule, i.e., kinetic plus potential energy, cannot be equal to any arbitrary value but will be one of a number of discrete values in accordance with the laws of quantum mechanics. These energy values, called eigenvalues, may be computed from the Schroedinger equation which is basic to quantum mechanics (6). For the stationary states of a molecule, i.e., those associated with the various energy levels, the Schroedinger equation is:

$$\sum_k \frac{1}{m_k}\left(\frac{\partial^2 \Psi}{\partial x_k^2} + \frac{\partial^2 \Psi}{\partial y_k^2} + \frac{\partial^2 \Psi}{\partial z_k^2}\right) + \frac{8\pi^2}{h^2}(E - V)\Psi = 0 \tag{1}$$

where m_k and x_k, y_k, z_k are the mass and coordinates respectively of the kth particle, h is Planck's constant, E is the total energy, and V is the potential energy of the system expressed as a function of the particle coordinates. Ψ is known as the probability amplitude function and can only assume certain forms in accordance with the conditions given below. These allowable forms are known as eigenfunctions.

To be a physically acceptable solution of equation 1 an eigenfunction Ψ must be finite for all allowable values of the coordinates. It must also be continuous, be single valued, and vanish at infinity. It is found in general that equation 1 possesses solutions satisfying these conditions only for definite values of E. These are known as the eigenvalues of E and are the definite energy values the system may possess. The physical interpretation of the probability amplitude equation is as follows: the quantity Ψ (x_1, y_1, z_1, ...) Ψ^* (x_1, y_1, z_1, ...)$d\tau$ (where Ψ^* is the complex conjugate of Ψ and $d\tau = dx_1$, dy_1, dz_1 ...) gives the probability of finding the physical system with coordinates x_1, y_1, z_1, ... and in the volume element $d\tau$. Therefore, $\Psi\Psi^*$ is the probability distribution function for the system. These eigenfunctions are customarily denoted as Ψ_1, Ψ_2, Ψ_3 ... in 1 to 1 correspondence with the energy levels of the system.

As stated above, it would be necessary in setting up equation 1 in its most general form for a molecule to consider all particles, i.e., electrons and atomic nuclei. However, it has been shown (7) that the nuclear and electronic motions may be considered separately. Hence, in the application of equation 1 to the vibrational and rotational states it is only necessary to consider the nuclear coordinates. Actually, the application of equation 1 to definite molecules is a very complex procedure and satisfactory solutions can only be obtained for the simpler molecules. Further discussion of this will be given later.

A more detailed consideration of quantum mechanics than is possible here leads to methods of calculating the transition probabilities from the eigenfunctions (6). The probability coefficient for the spontaneous transition from a state characterized by Ψ_n to one characterized by Ψ_m will be proportional to the quantity:

$$\{ (R_x^{nm})^2 + (R_y^{nm})^2 + (R_z^{nm})^2 \}$$

where the terms $R_x{}^{nm}$, $R_y{}^{nm}$, and $R_z{}^{nm}$ are given by

$$\left. \begin{aligned} R_x{}^{nm} &= \int \Psi_n (\Sigma e_i x_i) \Psi_m{}^* \, d\tau \\ R_y{}^{nm} &= \int \Psi_n (\Sigma e_i y_i) \Psi_m{}^* \, d\tau \\ R_z{}^{nm} &= \int \Psi_n (\Sigma e_i z_i) \Psi_m{}^* \, d\tau \end{aligned} \right\} \tag{2}$$

and are known as the matrix elements of the electric moments for the transitions. Here e_i represents the unbalanced charge on the ith atom. It may be predicted from equation's 2 that in certain cases there will be no transitions and no corresponding absorption spectra. If $\Sigma e_i x_i$, $\Sigma e_i y_i$, and $\Sigma e_i z_i$ are all zero for a particular vibration there will be no corresponding infrared activity. An example of such a vibration is for a symmetrical diatomic molecule such as N_2, O_2, or H_2. Other cases wherein these terms are zero due to symmetry will be discussed later. In general, a rule of classical electrodynamics may be used to determine whether or not a vibration is infrared active. This rule is that any motion of an atomic configuration that gives rise to a change of its dipole moment will be capable of the absorption or emission of radiation.

3. VIBRATIONAL LEVELS OF A DIATOMIC MOLECULE

Although no diatomic hydrocarbon molecules exist a consideration of this simplest type of molecule serves as an excellent introduction to molecular energy levels. We know that the two atoms in such a molecule will oscillate about an equilibrium separation distance. It is a reasonable assumption, therefore, that the restoring force on each atom will, at any instant, be proportional to the difference between their instantaneous separation and the equilibrium separation. This leads to the two equations:

$$\left. \begin{aligned} m_1 \frac{dr_1^2}{dt^2} &= -k \, (r_1 + r_2 - r_e) \\ m_2 \frac{dr_2^2}{dt^2} &= -k \, (r_1 + r_2 - r_e) \end{aligned} \right\} \tag{3}$$

where the subscripts refer to the two atoms, r_e is the equilibrium distance, and r_1 and r_2 are the distances of the two atoms from the center of mass of the system. To reduce equations 3 to a single equation we use a new variable $x = r_1 + r_2 - r_e$, which is the difference between the interatomic distance and the equilibrium separation. We also use the relations resulting from measuring r_1 and r_2 from the center of gravity, which are

$$r_1 = (rm_2)/(m_1 + m_2), \; r_2 = (rm_1)/(m_1 + m_2), \text{ and } r = r_1 + r_2 \tag{4}$$

With the combination of equations 3 and 4 we obtain:

$$\mu \frac{d^2 x}{dt^2} = -kx \tag{5}$$

where $\mu = (m_1 m_2)/(m_1 + m_2)$ and is called the reduced mass of the system. Equation 5 may be recognized as the equation of motion for a simple harmonic oscillator which would, in the classical theory, possess a vibration frequency ν_0 given by

$$\nu_0 = (1/2\pi)\left(\sqrt{k/\mu}\right) \tag{6}$$

The simplification of above wherein the vibrational motion of a diatomic molecule was shown to be equivalent to the motion of a simple harmonic oscillator allows the Schroedinger equation for the same system to be expressed in terms of one variable. This is

$$\frac{1}{\mu}\frac{d^2 \Psi}{dx^2} + \frac{8\pi^2}{h^2}\left(E - \frac{1}{2}kx^2\right)\Psi = 0 \tag{7}$$

When solved, this equation is found to possess a series of allowable solutions, or eigenfunctions, which are finite for all values of x, are single valued, are continuous, and which vanish at infinity (6). These are given by

$$\Psi_n = N_n e^{-v^2/2} H_n(v^2) \tag{8}$$

where $v = \sqrt{ax}$, $a = (2\pi \sqrt{\mu k})/h$, and

$$N_n = \left\{\sqrt{\frac{a}{\pi}}\frac{1}{2^n n!}\right\}^{1/2}$$

$$H_n(v) = (-1)^n e^{v^2} \frac{d^n e^{-v^2}}{dv^n}$$

the latter functions being known as the Hermite polynomials.

It is found that for each eigenfunction there is a definite value of the energy E. The series of energy values is given by

$$E_n = (n + \tfrac{1}{2})h(1/2\pi)(\sqrt{k/\mu}),\ n = 0,1,2\cdots \tag{9}$$

In applying equation 2 to calculate the transition probabilities for the harmonic oscillator we have, except for a constant factor, the integral $\int x\Psi_n\Psi_m{}^* dx$. Evaluation of it, using the above functions for Ψ_n, shows it to be zero for all cases wherein $n \neq m$, except for

$$\Delta n = \pm 1 \tag{10}$$

This then means that the permitted transitions for a diatomic molecule are only those between adjacent energy levels. To calculate the frequency ν of the absorbed radiation for such a transition we use the equation

$$\Delta E = h\nu$$

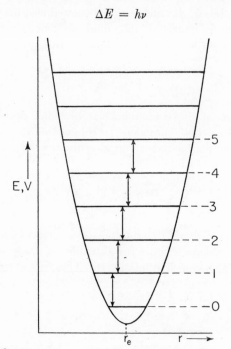

FIG. 3. Potential energy curve, energy levels, and allowable transitions for a simple harmonic oscillator.

which gives the relation between the absorbed energy and the frequency of the radiation. This gives

$$\nu = \frac{\Delta E}{h} = (E_{n+1} - E_n) = (1/2\,\pi)\left(\sqrt{k/\mu}\right) \tag{11}$$

which we recognize as the same as ν_0 in equation 6. Thus, the frequency of the light absorbed by a harmonic oscillator in quantum mechanics is the same as the fundamental resonance frequency in classical mechanics. In fact, qualitatively correct conclusions concerning the absorption frequencies may in general be deduced from an intuitive consideration of the classical mechanics of a molecule.

In Fig. 3 may be seen a diagram showing the potential energy curve, energy levels, and allowable transitions for a harmonic oscillator. In this figure the parabolic curve is a plot of the potential energy as a function of the internuclear separation. The solid lines inside the curve represent the energy levels and the corresponding values of the vibrational quantum number n may be seen to the right. The allowable transitions, either by emission or absorption are represented by the lines with arrows between the adjacent levels.

In a diatomic molecule the use of a parabolic potential energy function is accurate only for internuclear distances close to the equilibrium separation. That it cannot be accurate for large distances can be seen from a consideration of the finite energy needed for dissociation. A true potential energy curve must therefore be one that rises rapidly for internuclear distances smaller than the equilibrium separation and which approaches an

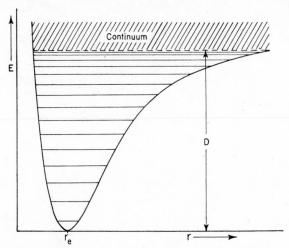

Fig. 4. Potential energy curve and energy levels for a diatomic molecule.

asymptote for large separations. Such a curve may be seen in Fig. 4. Here the separation D between the asymptote and the minimum of the curve is the dissociation energy of the molecule. Such a potential energy curve has been found to be represented by the Morse function (8) which is amenable to mathematical treatment. This function is

$$V(r) = D\{1 - e^{-\beta(r-r_e)}\}^2 \tag{12}$$

where D has the value of above and β may be calculated from a knowledge of D and the fundamental absorption frequency.

The anharmonicity of an actual potential energy curve renders two of the results obtained for the harmonic oscillator inexact for diatomic molecules. The equal spacing of the harmonic oscillator energy levels as shown by equation 11 does not hold for molecules. Rather, the spacing between successive levels progressively decreases as may be seen in Fig. 4. Also, the selection rule of equation 10 which says transitions can only occur between adjacent levels does not hold. Excitation by absorption whereby a transition from the ground state to the second or third energy levels occurs is possible. The corresponding absorption frequencies are called the first and second overtones respectively. Although they may be observed, the intensity of the first overtone absorption is much less than for the fundamental and there is a corresponding drop in intensity in passing from the first to the second overtone. Higher overtones are very difficult to detect because of their low intensity.

The progressive decrease of energy level spacing for the anharmonic oscillator accounts for the observed fact that the first overtone frequency is less than twice the fundamental frequency. In Fig. 4 the region above the dissociation energy is marked continuum as the two atoms are independent of each other and their total energy may assume any value in this range.

4. ABSORPTION FREQUENCIES FOR DIATOMIC GROUPS

In a polyatomic molecule we no longer have the simple condition wherein a vibrational frequency depends only on one force constant and one reduced mass. Rather, the molecule will possess a number of modes of vibration and in calculating them the molecule must be considered as a whole. To a first approximation, however, the force constant for a specific diatomic group will be independent of the remainder of the molecule. This, together with the fact that the vibrations of a specific diatomic group may in many cases be considered, to a first approximation, as independent of the remainder of the molecule, leads to the expectation that similar groups would exhibit approximately equal characteristic vibrational frequencies in different compounds. This has been experimentally confirmed by observations on many compounds. All compounds containing C—H groups, for example, show an absorption band around 2910 cm.$^{-1}$ (3.4 μ), which is known to be due to a stretching vibration along the valence bond joining the carbon and hydrogen atoms. They also exhibit another absorption band around 1450 cm.$^{-1}$ (6.9 μ), which is due to a bending vibration of the valence bond.

Similar studies have been made of other diatomic groups and it is found that as a general rule the same type of group will absorb at approximately the same frequency in different molecules (9). In Table I are tabulated a number of such groups and the approximate frequency values for their fundamental stretching vibrations. It is to be observed that in progressing through a series involving the same two atoms but different valences, as for C—C, C=C, and C≡C that the greater the valence bond order, the higher the absorption frequency. This is consistent with the greater bond strengths of the higher bond valences and the smaller interatomic distances. These indicate larger force constants which, when used in equation 6, result in higher frequencies.

In an interesting study of a series of hydrocarbons Fox and Martin (10) found that the C—H stretching frequency depends upon the manner in which the remaining valences in the carbon are fulfilled. They considered the groups: $=CH_2$, $=CH$, $-CH$, CH_2, and $-CH_3$. It was found that:

(a) In ethylene and higher olefins the $=CH_2$ groups give rise to two frequencies with mean values 3079 and 2978 cm.$^{-1}$

(b) In olefins the $=CH$ groups usually give a frequency at approximately 3019 cm.$^{-1}$

TABLE I

FUNDAMENTAL STRETCHING VIBRATION FREQUENCIES FOR VARIOUS DIATOMIC GROUPS

Group	Frequency (cm.$^{-1}$)	Wavelength (μ)	Group	Frequency (cm.$^{-1}$)	Wavelength (μ)
O—H	3680	2.7	C—O	1030	9.7
N—H	3350	3.0	C=O	1740	5.7
C—H	2920	3.4	C—N	1050	9.5
C—C	990	10.1	C=N	1650	6.0
C=C	1620	6.2	C≡N	2090	4.8
C≡C	1970	5.1	S—H	2600	3.8

(c) Normally the CH_2 groups give rise to two frequencies with mean values of 2926 and 2853 cm.$^{-1}$

(d) In saturated compounds a $-CH$ group gives rise to a frequency of about 2890 cm.$^{-1}$

(e) In general $-CH_3$ groups show two main frequencies, one at about 2962 and one at about 2872 cm.$^{-1}$

In addition to these general conclusions the groups at times show additional bands and in some cases the frequencies above split into doublets. The physical basis of the multiplicity of frequencies will be discussed later. In Fig. 5 may be seen the C—H fine structure obtained for 2,4,4-trimethylpentene-1.

The empirical results such as those above for the C—H frequencies and as tabulated for other groups in Table I are of great importance in the application of infrared absorption spectroscopy to the determination of molecular structure for unknown compounds.

As seen in equation 11, the vibrational frequency of a diatomic group depends upon the reduced mass of the two atoms. There will therefore be an isotope effect as the substitution of an isotopic species will change the reduced mass. The change of frequency accompanying the substitution of an isotopic species will be given by the formula

$$\Delta\nu = \nu_1 \left(1 - \sqrt{\frac{\mu_1}{\mu_2}} \right) \tag{13}$$

which may readily be derived from equation 11. The substitution of deuterium for hydrogen in a diatomic group containing the latter shifts the

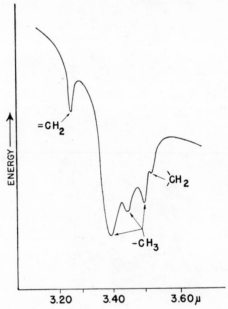

FIG. 5. Structure of the C—H valence bond vibration absorption band for 2,4,4-trimethylpentene-1.

absorption frequency to approximately one half of its original value. With the present low cost of deuterium this isotope effect can be readily utilized in the determination of force constants, the determination of molecular structure, and in studies utilizing isotopic tracers.

In some cases the absorption frequencies of a diatomic group may be altered due to external effects. One of the most familar examples of this is the lowering of the stretching frequency of an O—H group when hydrogen bonding occurs. The large difference of electronegativity between oxygen and hydrogen is responsible for a strong displacement of charge and a resultant large dipole moment in the hydroxyl group. Because of this, hydroxylated molecules tend to combine into complexes held together by the electrostatic and dipole effects of the O—H groups (11). When such a hydroxylated compound is examined in a solution dilute enough that these complexes are not present the normal O—H frequency is observed. However, as the strength of the solution is increased this normal or "free" O—H frequency disappears and a new one of lower value appears. In phenol, for example, the O—H fundamental frequency which appears in dilute solutions at approximately 3600 cm.$^{-1}$ (2.77 μ) shifts to approximately 3400 cm.$^{-1}$ (2.95 μ) in concentrated solutions (12). The interpretation is that the effective force constant for the O—H group is reduced when a hydrogen bond forms due to the close proximity of the dipolar hydroxyl groups. This effect also occurs for intramolecular hydrogen bonding and is found for other structural groups.

5. ROTATIONAL ENERGY LEVELS

The simplest model that may be considered for its rotational energy levels is the rigid rotator. Although no molecule is directly analogous to this simple model a consideration of it is illuminating in pointing out some of the general aspects of rotational spectra. We may take for our rotator a dumbbell model, i.e., two atoms of masses m_1 and m_2 rigidly held a fixed distance, r, apart. The moment of inertia for this system will be

$$I = m_1 r_1^2 + m_2 r_2^2$$

where r_1 and r_2 are the distances of the respective atoms from the center of mass of the system. Using the relationships given in equations 4 and the previous definition of μ, the equivalent mass, we find that the moment of inertia may be expressed as

$$I = \mu r^2 \tag{14}$$

From equation 14 we see that the rotation of the dumbbell rotator is equivalent to the motion of a single mass μ constrained to move at a fixed distance r from a center of rotation. For such a system we may write the Schroedinger equation as

$$\frac{1}{r^2 \sin^2 \theta} \frac{\partial^2 \Psi}{\partial \varphi^2} + \frac{1}{r^2 \sin \theta} \frac{\partial}{\partial \theta} \left(\sin \theta \frac{\partial \Psi}{\partial \theta} \right) + \frac{8\pi^2 \mu}{h^2} E\Psi = 0 \tag{15}$$

wherein the Cartesian coordinates of equation 1 have been transformed into polar coordinates. Equation 15 may be solved by the method of separation of variables to give the eigenfunctions (6)

$$\Psi_{j,m} = K_{j,m} P_j^{|m|}(\cos \theta) e^{im\varphi}, \tag{16}$$

Here $K_{j,m}$ is a constant depending upon the quantum numbers j and m. The quantum number j which specifies the rotational state may take any one of the values $0, 1, 2 \cdots$ etc. and for any value of j, m can take the values

$$m = j, j - 1, j - 2 \cdots , -j$$

The values of E that allow the acceptable eigenfunctions of equation 16 are given by

$$E_j = \frac{h^2 j(j + 1)}{8\pi^2 \mu r^2} = \frac{h^2 j(j + 1)}{8\pi^2 I} \tag{17}$$

It is to be noted that in equation 17 that only the quantum number j is effective in specifying the energy. The fact that there can exist a multiplicity of states, as evidenced by the $2j + 1$ possible choices of m for a given value of j, is known as degeneracy.

When transition probabilities are calculated, using equation 2 it is found that transitions occur only for $\Delta j = \pm 1$, i.e., between adjacent levels. The energy difference between the jth and $(j + 1)$th levels would then be

$$\Delta E = \frac{2h^2}{8\pi^2 I} (j + 1) \tag{18}$$

This leads to a series of rotational lines of wave numbers given by

$$\nu = \frac{2h}{8\pi^2 cI} (j + 1), \qquad j = 0, 1, 2, 3 \cdots \tag{19}$$

From equation (19) the spacing between lines, $\Delta\nu$, may be calculated.

$$\Delta\nu = \frac{2h}{8\pi^2 cI} \tag{20}$$

Thus the pure rotation spectra for a rigid rotator would consist of a series of equally spaced lines. Actually, for reasons to be discussed below no molecule behaves exactly as a rigid rotator. However, the results for the rigid rotator may be applied as a first approximation. As an example of this some of the far infrared rotational lines for HCl are given in Table II. Note here that although $\Delta\nu$ is not constant, as predicted by equation (20), it is approximately so.

Since the potential energy of a diatomic molecule varies rather slowly with internuclear separation near the equilibrium value the model of a rigid rotator is necessarily only approximate. We must use instead a model wherein the two masses are connected by a massless spring. The internuclear distance can then change due to the centrifugal force of rotation. This allows an increase of moment of inertia with increase of rotation. A quantum mechanical study of this case yields the results that the energy levels are given by (14)

$$E_j = \frac{h^2}{8\pi^2 I} (1 - aj(j + 1))j(j + 1)$$

where a is a constant very small compared to unity. In comparison with the rigid rotator energy levels the effect is to depress each one an amount depending on j. This leads to the slight decrease of $\Delta \nu$ with increase of j which may be observed in Table II.

It is interesting to note that the observable frequencies, given by equation 19, vary inversely with the moment of inertia of the system. Thus an increase in moment of inertia shifts the frequencies to the red. Actually

TABLE II

Rotational Lines and Line Spacings for HCl in the Far Infrared (13)

cm.$^{-1}$	$\Delta\nu$ cm.$^{-1}$
124.30	
	20.73
145.03	
	20.48
165.51	
	20.35
185.86	
	20.52
206.38	
	20.12
226.50	

the moments of inertia of most polar molecules are so large that the pure rotational spectra lie outside the regions studied to date.

6. NORMAL VIBRATIONS OF POLYATOMIC MOLECULES

In the above discussion we have restricted ourselves to the simple cases of diatomic molecules or groups. The extension of these considerations to polyatomic molecules is attended by considerable mathematical complexity. It is neither within the intention nor scope of this chapter to present more than a general idea of the treatment of polyatomic molecules and some of the qualitative results. In two review articles (15, 16) Dennison has covered in some detail the theoretical approach to the energy levels of polyatomic molecules. Those interested in further detail than is possible here should consult them and the references cited therein. Actually, comprehensive correlations between theoretical frequencies and observed bands have been been made for only a relatively few molecules up to the present.

The Schroedinger equation for a complicated system such as a polyatomic molecule may be readily set up if the Hamiltonian is available (6). The Hamiltonian for a system is the sum of the kinetic energy T and the potential energy V expressed as functions of the coordinates of the component particles. In general, these may be expressed as

$$T = \tfrac{1}{2}(a_{11}\dot{q}_1{}^2 + a_{22}\dot{q}_2{}^2 + \cdots + a_{nn}\dot{q}_n{}^2 + 2a_{12}\dot{q}_1\dot{q}_2 + \cdots)$$

$$V = \tfrac{1}{2}(b_{11}q^2 + b_{22}q_2{}^2 + \cdots + b_{nn}q_n{}^2 + 2b_{12}q_1q_2 + \cdots)$$

where the a_{ij}'s and b_{ij}'s are constants and $q_1, q_3 \cdots, q_n$ are the coordinates specifying the displacement of the particles from their equilibrium positions. In this form the equations are very difficult to solve due to the presence of the cross-terms, i.e., terms involving the product of two coordinates or their velocities. Such a restriction may be removed by a transformation to new coordinates such that the cross-terms disappear in the expressions for T and V. These coordinates we shall specify as $x_1, x_2 \cdots x_n$ and they are known as normal coordinates. They are related to the original coordinates through equations such as

$$q_i = \sum_{j=1}^{n} c_{ij}x_j \tag{21}$$

where the c_{ij}'s are constants and may be determined algebraically (17). With these coordinates T and V are expressed in the simple forms

$$\left.\begin{aligned}T &= \tfrac{1}{2}(\dot{x}_1{}^2 + \dot{x}_2{}^2 + \cdots + \dot{x}_n{}^2)\\ V &= \tfrac{1}{2}(\lambda_1 x_1{}^2 + \lambda_2 x_2{}^2 + \cdots + \lambda_n x_n{}^2)\end{aligned}\right\} \tag{22}$$

where the λ_i's are constants depending on the a_{ij}'s and b_{ij}'s.

It is clear on examining the new expressions for T and V that they are the same as obtained for a set of n independent oscillators. This allows the quantum mechanical investigation of the system to be reduced to a consideration of n individual oscillators whose energy levels depend upon the λ_i's. This may be done by the means described in Section 1. The energy value for the molecule for any particular state is the sum of the energy values of the n oscillators and the eigenfunction is a product of the individual oscillator eigenfunctions. Thus, we have

$$\begin{aligned}\Psi^{V_1, V_2 \cdots V_n} &= \Psi^{V_1}(x_1)\Psi^{V_2}(x_2) \cdots \Psi^{V_n}(x_n)\\ E^{V_1, V_2 \cdots V_n} &= E^{V_1} + E^{V_2} + \cdots E^{V_n}\end{aligned} \tag{23}$$

Since linear relationships as given in equation 21 exist between the normal coordinates x_i and the displacement coordinates q_i it is possible to calculate the terms of equation 2, which are necessary for the evaluation of the transition probabilities. When this is done it is found that only those transitions are allowed in which the quantum numbers for all the oscillators are unchanged but one. Furthermore, the changes in quantum numbers for the one oscillator are restricted to ± 1. This means then that only fundamental frequencies are allowed.

From equation 23 are obtained the various allowable energy levels for the molecule. However, the above treatment is valid only for small displacements of the atoms from their equilibrium positions. Thus, we expect the above results to apply primarily to the lower levels and that some modifications would apply to the higher ones wherein increasing anharmonicity of the potential energy function would be felt. One of these is that overtone and combination frequencies are allowable. By combination frequencies is meant the frequencies arising when a transition occurs wherein the quantum numbers change for two or more of the normal coordinate oscillators. Further modifications are necessary since the energies of these oscillators are not correctly given by expressions such as equation 9 but need additional correction terms.

It must be remembered that the normal coordinate oscillators are not physically real in the sense of the molecule actually containing n individual and independent oscillators. They afford a mathematical simplification whereby the energy levels of the actual molecule are obtained. If there are S atoms in the molecule the necessary number of normal coordinates and hence the number of fundamental frequencies will be given by $n = 3S—6$ except in the case of a linear molecule for which it will be $n = 3S—5$. This is a result of the fact that for an assembly of S particles it requires $3S$ coordinates to completely specify its configuration and position in space. For a linear and nonlinear assembly respectively 5 and 6 of these coordinates will suffice to locate the centers of gravity and the angular orientations. In some cases there will be degeneracy in the sense of two or more of the individual oscillators possessing the same energy levels. Also all the fundamental frequencies may not be infrared active as they may not involve a change of dipole moment of the molecule. Thus, in general, there will be less than n fundamental frequencies observed.

From the above material some readers may be misled in regarding the calculation of energy levels of a polyatomic molecule as a fairly simple process. Although the general theory as given above may be set down in simple equations the actual computation for a particular molecule is generally long and complex. This results from the large number of coordinates involved and the difficulties of choosing an appropriate set of variables and force constants.

To obtain a qualitative description of the physical nature of the normal vibrations of a molecule Dennison's method of extreme force fields (15) is very valuable. In this some of the valence bond forces are assumed to be extremely weak compared to others, and thus the molecule is divided into a number of simpler units for which the normal modes are known. It is then possible to proceed to the case of the intermediate or normal force fields and consider this as a perturbation of the extreme field case. This allows the deduction of some of the physical characteristics of the normal modes of the intermediate case. This procedure does not replace the theoretical normal coordinate treatment which is capable of numerical answers but provides some of the properties that are dependent on the geometry of the molecule. It is an interesting result that many of the properties depend primarily on the geometric symmetry of the molecule and are

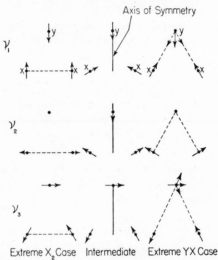

FIG. 6. The modes of vibration for a YX_2 type of molecule.

independent of the force fields assumed. We shall consider a few simple cases here by this method.

a. *The YX_2 Molecule.* The type of molecule we wish to consider here is the kinked type such as H_2O, SO_2, H_2S, etc., wherein the three atoms lie at the corners of an isosceles triangle. Following Sutherland (4) we may consider this molecule in either of two ways. It may be considered to be constructed of a tightly bound X_2 diatomic molecule to which the Y atom is weakly held. We shall designate this as the X_2 case. Alternatively, the molecule may be considered as one Y atom to which two X atoms are tightly bound with very weak interaction between the latter. This case we designate as the YX case. These are illustrated in Fig. 6 as well as the intermediate case.

With reference to Fig. 6 we see that for the extreme X_2 case there are three possible modes of vibration: ν_1 wherein the X_2 group moves as a rigid bar towards and away from the Y atom, ν_2 wherein the X_2 group itself vibrates longitudinally with the Y atom essentially at rest, and ν_3 wherein the X_2 group tilts back and forth relative to the Y atom. As we allow the forces between the Y atom and the X atoms to increase these extreme modes of motion will pass to the actual intermediate case. Thus ν_1 goes over to a breathing type frequency as seen wherein the Y atom vibrates along the line of symmetry. In the case of ν_2 the passage to the intermediate situation produces another vibration such that the Y atom again vibrates along the line of symmetry. In both these cases the change of dipole moment will be along the axis of symmetry. For ν_3 the passage to the intermediate case will produce a motion such that the Y atom vibrates perpendicular to the symmetry axis with an attendant change of dipole moment in the same direction.

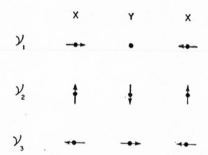

FIG. 7. Modes of vibration for a linear YX_2 molecule.

The other YX extreme cases may also be seen in Fig. 6 and similar considerations for them lead to the same types of vibrations for the intermediate forces. It is important to note that the character of the vibrations are therefore independent of the initial assumption concerning the force fields but depend rather on the symmetry. Note also that for this case $n = 3$ which agrees with the formula $n = 3S-6$ given above.

For the case of the linear YX_2 such as CO_2 molecule the situation is simple enough that extreme force considerations are unnecessary. A little thought will show that the three types of vibration seen in Fig. 7 are the only ones possible. Here ν_1 will not be infrared active as it gives no change in dipole moment. The other two are, however, active, ν_3 being a "parallel" frequency, i.e., giving a dipole moment change parallel to the symmetry axis and ν_2 being a "perpendicular" frequency, i.e., giving a dipole moment change perpendicular to the symmetry axis. The frequency ν_2 is really degenerate as such a mode of motion may be resolved into two motions one in the plane of the figure and one perpendicular to it. Thus counting two for ν_2 we see that the number of normal vibrational modes is four which agrees with $M = 3S—5$ which applies for linear molecules.

b. The YX₃ Molecule. We shall here consider the type of YX_3 molecule wherein the three X atoms are at three corners of an equilateral triangle and with the Y atom displaced from the center of the triangle and in a direction perpendicular to the plane defined by the X atoms. An example of such a molecule is NH_3. As an extreme force approach we may assume the X_3 group to be tightly bound and loosely coupled with the Y atom. This allows us then to utilize the results obtained above for the YX_2 molecule. In the present case ν_2 and ν_3 are no longer distinct due to the equivalence of the three X atoms. However, ν_1 retains its uniqueness and is now

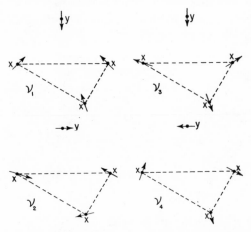

FIG. 8. Modes of vibration for a YX_3 type of molecule.

a completely symmetrical frequency. In applying the extreme force field method we may then consider the X_3 group to be executing a ν_1 type of motion independent of the Y atom. As we allow the interaction forces along the YX bonds to increase the motion of the X_3 group will induce a motion of the Y atom. For the actual intermediate case we then have a motion such as is indicated by ν_1 in Fig. 8. It is clear that this mode of motion will result in a parallel type of frequency with the dipole varying along the symmetry axis. As this motion is not isotropic it will not be degenerate.

We may next consider the X_3 group to be executing a motion of the ν_2 type (now degenerate) and consider the motion induced in the Y atom as the interaction forces are increased. This gives the motion designated by ν_2 in Fig. 8. For this case the motion of the Y atom will be in a plane perpendicular to the symmetry axis and will be isotropic in two dimensions. Because of this latter fact ν_2 for the YX_3 case is doubly degenerate and thus the degeneracy is carried over from the X_3 portion of the model. This frequency will be of the perpendicular type with the dipole moment changing in a direction perpendicular to the symmetry axis.

Another mode of motion may be deduced by considering the X_3 group to be oscillating with respect to the Y atom and in such a manner as to be always parallel to itself. As the YX bond forces are allowed to increase there will result the motion designated by ν_3 in Fig. 8. This will also be a parallel frequency and will be nondegenerate. The last remaining modes may be deduced by considering the extreme case of a tipping motion of the X_3 group relative to the Y atom. Passage to the intermediate case yields a motion such as designated by ν_4 in Fig. 8. This is a perpendicular frequency and is doubly degenerate as the motion of the Y atom is isotropic in a plane perpendicular to the symmetry axis. We see now that with ν_1 and ν_3 nondegenerate, and with ν_2 and ν_4 both doubly degenerate we have a

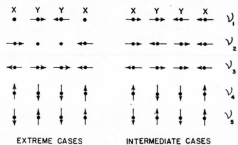

EXTREME CASES   INTERMEDIATE CASES
FIG. 9. Vibrational modes of a linear Y_2X_2 molecule.

total of six fundamental modes of vibration, which satisfies the value for n in the equation $n = 3S - 6$ when $S = 4$.

c. *The Collinear Y_2X_2 Molecule.* This last model, which turns out to be rather simple, has an example in the highly unsaturated hydrocarbon acetylene, C_2H_2. The extreme and intermediate force conditions are shown in Fig. 9. In these a constant set of force conditions are not assumed. Rather to obtain ν_1 the Y_2 group is allowed to oscillate independent of the X atoms and to obtain ν_2 the X_2 group is allowed to oscillate independent of the Y atoms. Passage to intermediate forces produces the types of oscillations shown but these are infrared inactive as they produce no change of dipole moment. In the next instance a rigid Y_2 group is allowed to oscillate relative to a rigid X_2 group and the intermediate case results in ν_3 which is a nondegenerate parallel type frequency which will result in a dipole change. For ν_4 and ν_5 the figure is virtually self-explanatory. Each of these frequencies will be of the perpendicular type and both will be doubly degenerate as they are isotropic in a plane perpendicular to the axis of the molecule. The latter frequency ν_5 will be infrared inactive.

7. VIBRATION-ROTATION SPECTRA FOR POLYATOMIC MOLECULES

In Fig. 2 it may be observed that there is no fine structure in the bands shown. This is due to two reasons: the data were obtained on an instrument of medium resolving power and the sample was in the liquid phase. When gases are examined in an instrument of high resolving power the absorption bands are seen to consist of many closely spaced fine structure lines. An example of such data may be seen in Fig. 10 which shows the fine structure for methane in the 3.3 μ region. These individual lines correspond to transitions which involve simultaneous changes in both vibrational and rotational energy. As the energy differences between the rotational levels are very much smaller than between the vibrational levels each transition between vibrational levels may be accompanied by any one of a large number of rotational energy transitions.

The mathematical treatment of the molecular dynamics is of course complicated by the coexistence of both vibrational and rotational motion.

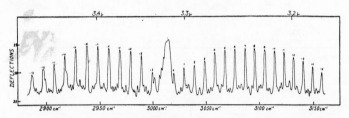

FIG. 10. Fine structure in a vibration-rotation band of methane (from reference 18).

However, it is fortunate that to a good approximation the two motions with their energy levels can be considered separately and the results then combined to explain the observed bands. This separate treatment is a consequence of the rotational energies being small enough as to not appreciably alter the interatomic forces responsible for the vibrational levels. Some of the results of the mathematical investigations will be given below but none of the details of obtaining them. For those the reader should consult Dennison's articles (15, 16).

In terms of its principal moments of inertia A, B, and C a molecule will fall into one of four classes. These are:

(a) Linear molecules. In this case $A = B$ and $C = 0$.

(b) Symmetrical top molecules. In this instance $A = B$ and $C \neq 0$.

(c) Spherical molecules. For these $A = B = C$.

(d) Asymmetrical top molecules. For these $A \neq B \neq C$.

It is found that the fine structure for the vibration-rotation bands is different for the different classes. Furthermore, it is found that the structure will be different for parallel and perpendicular type frequencies.

For the case of linear molecules of which CO_2, CS_2, SCO, HCN, and C_2H_2 are examples, we may combine the results of equations 9 and 17 to obtain the vibration-rotation energy levels with a particular vibrational frequency ν. We then have

$$E_{n,j} = (n + \tfrac{1}{2})h\nu_0 + \frac{h^2 j(j+1)}{8\pi^2 I}. \tag{24}$$

In determining the selection rules it is found for the parallel frequencies

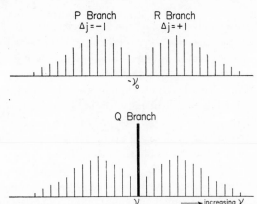

FIG. 11. Appearance of fine structure in the vibration-rotation bands of a linear molecule. The upper figure is for parallel vibrations and the lower half for perpendicular vibrations.

that $\Delta j = \pm 1$. In calculating the frequencies associated with the transitions we have then the two cases:

$$\nu_{1,j+1}^{0,j} = \nu_0 + \frac{h}{4\pi^2 I}\,(j+1) \quad \text{for} \quad \Delta j = +1 \quad \text{and} \quad j = 0, 1, 2 \cdots$$

$$\nu_{1,j-1}^{0,j} = \nu_0 - \frac{hj}{4\pi^2 I} \quad \text{for} \quad \Delta j = -1, \quad \text{and} \quad j = 1, 2, 3 \cdots$$

These then supply two branches of the fine structure. The $\Delta j = +1$ branch is known as the positive or R branch and $\Delta j = -1$ gives what is known as the negative or P branch. The general appearance of such branches is shown in the upper half of Fig. 11. For the perpendicular frequencies the selection rules are the same except that the transition $\Delta j = 0$ is allowed. This gives an intense line known as the Q branch. The increase and decrease of intensity of the lines with increasing j for the P and R branches is the result of the thermal distribution of the rotational states in accordance with Boltzmann statistics (14).

In the case of symmetrical top molecules such as NH_3, PH_3, and the methyl halides there is an added degree of complexity due to the fact that there are two axes of inertia. We now let j represent the total angular momentum quantum number and specify by k the angular momentum about the symmetry axis. The energy levels associated with a particular vibrational frequency are now given by:

$$E_{n,j,k} = (n + \tfrac{1}{2})h\nu_0 + \frac{h^2 j(j + 1)}{8\pi^2 A} + \left(\frac{1}{C} - \frac{1}{A}\right)\frac{h^2 k^2}{8\pi^2} \qquad (25)$$

For the parallel frequencies the selection rules are $\Delta j = 0, \pm 1$ and $\Delta k = 0$. We thus have for this case the relatively simple situation of a P, Q, and R branch such as demonstrated in the lower portion of Fig. 11. However, perpendicular frequencies are complicated by the selection rules $\Delta j = 0$, ± 1 and $\Delta k = \pm 1$. Now for each change in k there will be complete set of P, Q, and R branches constituting what is known as a subsidiary band. The complete band is then a superposition of these subsidiary bands and is very complicated in that it is made up of many closely spaced lines. In fact for most cases it is only possible to obtain the contour for the complete band.

It is clear that for spherical molecules only those vibrations will be infra-red active which produce dipole moment changes antisymmetrical with respect to the center of symmetry. We may think of these as corresponding to the perpendicular type of bands of above. Because of the center of symmetry there will be no active vibrations corresponding to the parallel bands. The energy levels of a spherical molecule for a particular vibrational frequency are given by

$$E_{n,j} = (n + \tfrac{1}{2})h\nu_0 + \frac{h^2}{8\pi^2 A}\, j(j + 1)$$

and the selection rule is $\Delta j = 0, \pm 1$. Thus, we have a P, Q, and R branch in every observable band. Note the actual branches in the spectrum for CH_4 seen in Fig. 10. For the asymmetrical top molecules it is not possible to present simple general rules as above for the types of fine structure to be encountered (4).

A discussion of the correlation of infrared and Raman data and the assignment of observed frequencies to definite vibrational modes will be given in Section II, 7.

II. RAMAN SPECTROSCOPY

The Raman effect, so named in honor of Sir C. V. Raman who discovered it, is a phenomenon in the scattering of light. If a sample of material is irradiated by a light source possessing a discrete line spectrum the scattered light will possess, in addition to these lines, additional lines that are relatively weak. These additional lines, known as Raman lines, do not originate in the light source but depend upon the interaction of the light and the sample. Each exciting line is accompanied by one or more of the weak Raman lines and the displacements are independent of the frequencies of the former. Furthermore, as we shall see later, these displacements are directly related to the vibrational and rotational energy levels of the molecules in the sample and thus there is a close relationsihp between Raman and infrared spectra. It is important to point out the difference between this effect and Rayleigh scattering and fluorescence. In Rayleigh scattering the exciting light is scattered without change of wavelength. In fluorescence the light quanta are completely absorbed to activate ex-

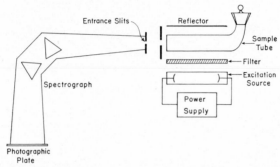

FIG. 12. Schematic lay-out of equipment used in Raman spectroscopy.

cited electronic states which then decay with a finite life time and with the emission of radiation of considerably lower frequency than that of the exciting light. Also, the amount of re-emitted light in fluorescence may be comparable to the amount of exciting light; whereas, the Raman lines are always feeble compared to the exciting lines.

The Raman effect has been comprehensively discussed in a number of publications which may be consulted if the reader desires a more complete treatment than is possible here (4, 14, 19, 20, 21, 22).

I. EXPERIMENTAL METHODS AND EQUIPMENT

In Fig. 12 may be seen in a schematic way the essential items of equipment needed for obtaining Raman spectra. An excitation source irradiates the sample in such a way that the spectrograph catches some of the light scattered at right angles. This is dispersed by the spectrograph and is recorded by the photographic plate. The spectrograph should have a high speed, good resolution, and reasonable dispersion. The appearance of the

Raman spectra as it is recorded by this method may be seen in Fig. 13, which is for cyclopropane.

For excitation the most common source is probably the mercury arc. In it mercury vapor is excited by an electrical discharge with the consequent emission of the atomic lines of Hg. Among these are four main ones 2537, 4049, 4358, and 5461 A. which are useful for Raman work. As the effect is weak, a reflector is almost always used as indicated in Fig. 12.

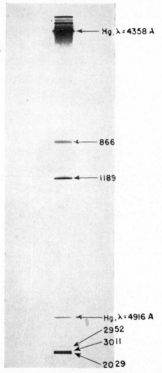

FIG. 13. Raman spectrum of cyclopropane (courtesy of Dr. D. K. Coles).

A filter between the source and the sample is necessary for two reasons. One is to cut out the source lines for which the Raman displacements are not desired and the other is to diminish the continuous spectrum emitted by the Hg discharge. A number of inorganic materials in aqueous solutions are suitable for filters (23). For example, a saturated solution of sodium nitrite will remove the violet and ultraviolet light when it is desired to use the 4358 A. for excitation. If it is desired to keep this line out of the spectrograph a solution of potassium ferricyanide is useful.

In determining the intensity in the various Raman lines the usual method has been to measure the degree of blackening of the photographic plates by means of a microphotometer. In recent years progress has been made in measuring the intensities directly, using photomultiplier tubes (24, 25). These are essentially photocells with an internal amplifier. By multiplication through secondary emission within the photomultiplier tube, the original photoelectron current is amplified many times. This method of determining line intensities offers considerable promise for future uses as it eliminates the difficulties inherent in the photographic method. In Fig. 14 may be seen the Raman spectra of C_6H_6 obtained in this manner.

Fluorescent impurities are very undesirable in such studies as the consequent continuous background may seriously mask the Raman lines. In

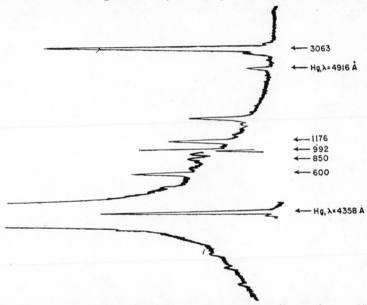

FIG. 14. Photoelectrically recorded spectrum of benzene (from reference 25).

cases where the various physical-chemical treatments such as repeated distillation and selective adsorption are not successful in removing these, some improvement has at times been achieved by adding small amounts of nitrobenzene, which has the property of quenching the fluorescence by collisions of the second kind, i.e., where the excitation energy of the fluorescent molecule is transferred to kinetic energy of the molecule rather than emitted as radiation.

2. GENERAL NATURE OF THE RAMAN EFFECT

As stated above, the Raman effect involves the scattering of light with discrete changes in frequency. Both changes to the high and low frequency side of the excitation line are observed. For changes such that the Raman lines are of lower frequency than the excitation line it means that a portion of the energy of the photon has been imparted to the molecule. Conversely, for displacements to higher frequency, the photon has extracted energy from the molecule. The energies imparted to or extracted from the molecule are, of course, discrete and are those involved in transitions between vibrational and rotational levels. Hence, the close relationship with infrared spectra. Let us designate by $\Delta\nu$ the displacement in wave numbers for a particular line. Then we have $\Delta\nu = (\Delta E/h) = (E_n - E_m)/h$, where E_n and E_m are different molecular energy levels. The $\Delta\nu$'s are independent of the frequency of the excitation line. For gases there are observed two sets of Raman lines, one with very small values of $\Delta\nu$ which are those due to transitions between rotational levels and one with larger values of $\Delta\nu$ which are due to transitions between vibrational levels.

In the interaction processes between photons and molecules wherein the Raman shifts occur the polarization of the molecule by the electric field of the electromagnetic waves is fundamental. When a molecule is subjected to an external electric field an electric dipole moment M is induced. It is related to the external field F by the equation

$$M = \alpha F \tag{26}$$

wherein M and F are vector quantities and α is the polarizability. The polarizability is not a constant but depends upon the orientation of the molecule relative to the applied field. When it is plotted for a fixed set of conditions, as a function of orientation angles in three dimensional polar coordinates it yields what is known as the polarization ellipsoid. Since it depends on the interatomic distances and bond angles it is obvious that it will vary with molecular vibrations and, relative to a fixed axis, with molecular rotations. In order to see the connections between molecular motions, polarizability, and Raman shifts we may first consider the system classically. We may express the variation of the polarizability during vibration as:

$$\alpha = \alpha(0, v) + \alpha(1, v) \sin 2\pi\nu_0 t \tag{27}$$

where t is the time, $\alpha(0, v)$ and $\alpha(1, v)$ are the equilibrium position polarizability and amplitude of polarization change, respectively, and ν_0 is the frequency of the molecular vibration. The electric vector F of the incident radiation may be expressed as:

$$F = F_0 \sin 2\pi\nu t \tag{28}$$

Combining equations 27 and 28 in equation 26 and using the rules of trigonometry we obtain:

$$M(v) = \alpha(0, v) \, F_0 \sin 2\pi v t + \tfrac{1}{2}\alpha(1, v) \, F_0 \{\cos 2\pi(v - v_0)t \\ - \cos 2\pi(v + v_0)t\} \tag{29}$$

We thus see from equation 29 that the induced dipole moment changes with the two frequencies $(v - v_0)$ and $(v + v_0)$ in addition to the exciting frequency v. Classically, an oscillating dipole radiates light of the same frequency as its own oscillations. Thus our model would radiate with the three frequencies (above) and this in agreement with experiment in that the exciting frequency and displacements on both sides of it are obtained.

A similar consideration of the molecular rotations may also be made. For this, we may write the polarization during rotation as:

$$\alpha = \alpha(0, r) + \alpha(1, r) \sin 2\pi \, 2v_r t \tag{30}$$

where v_r is the rotational frequency and it is multiplied by a factor of 2 in the equation because the polarization must necessarily be the same in opposite directions. Operations as above yield the equation for the induced dipole as:

$$M(r) = \alpha(0, r) \, F_0 \sin 2\pi v t + \tfrac{1}{2}\alpha(1, r) \, F_0 \{\cos 2\pi(v - 2v_r)t \\ - \cos 2\pi(v + 2v_r)t\} \tag{31}$$

Here again we have an oscillating dipole moment which now has the three frequencies $v, (v - 2v_r)$, and $(v + 2v_r)$. If in accordance with quantum notions, we assume only discrete rotational frequencies are allowable, the rotational Raman displacement value $2v_r$ is twice the rotational line separation observed by infrared. This is in agreement with experiment for linear molecules.

Since the polarizability of a molecule depends upon its orientation the induced dipole will not in general point in the same direction as the electric field. Rather it will be inclined in the direction of the greatest polarization. The components of the induced dipole are given by:

$$\begin{aligned} M_x &= \alpha_{xx}F_x + \alpha_{xy}F_y + \alpha_{xz}F_z \\ M_y &= \alpha_{yx}F_x + \alpha_{yy}F_y + \alpha_{yz}F_z \\ M_z &= \alpha_{zx}F_x + \alpha_{zy}F_y + \alpha_{zz}F_z \end{aligned} \tag{32}$$

where v_x, F_y, and F_z are the components of the electric vector. The probability of transition between two states is proportional to the square of the quantity P^{nm} which is a vector with components given by equations of the type

$$P_x^{nm} = F_x \int \alpha_{xx}\Psi_n\Psi_m{}^* \, d\tau + F_y \int \alpha_{xy}\Psi_n\Psi_m{}^* \, d\tau + F_z \int \alpha_{xz}\Psi_n\Psi_m{}^* \, d\tau \tag{33}$$

where Ψ_n and Ψ_m are eigenfunctions as discussed in the preceding section. Similar equations hold for the y and z components of P^{nm}, and for a transition to be forbidden we must therefore have all such integrals as above equal to zero.

3. SELECTION RULES FOR VIBRATIONAL TRANSITIONS

Rather than evaluate the integrals of the type shown in equation 33, it is possible to deduce which vibrations will be Raman inactive from symmetry considerations. We know that for the emission or absorption of radiation, a vibration must entail the oscillation of an electric dipole moment. Infrared active frequencies are those such that the molecular motion produces an oscillating dipole. For the Raman case the oscillating dipole comes from the interaction of the incident radiation and the molecule and the change in polarizability throughout the molecular vibrations. Since the polarizability depends on the interatomic distances it is evident that it will vary during a vibration that is symmetrical relative to a point of symmetry. We thus have modes of motion observable in the Raman effect which were not observable in infrared. For example, the totally symmetric molecules such as H_2, O_2, and N_2 possess Raman spectra but no infrared spectra. Furthermore, the symmetrical vibration ν_1 of the linear YX_2 molecule seen in Fig. 7 will be Raman active as well as the symmetrical and infrared inactive vibrations ν_1, ν_2, and ν_5 of the linear Y_2X_2 molecule shown in Fig. 9.

It is clear that for the fundamental of a frequency to be Raman inactive the polarizability remain unchanged during vibration. This means that $\left(\dfrac{\delta\alpha}{\delta x_i}\right)_0 = 0$ where x_i is the normal coordinate for the frequency under consideration and the derivative is evaluated for the equilibrium configuration. The polarizability is not a directed quantity, and so for a vibration that is antisymmetrical with respect to a center of symmetry it will have the same value for displacements from equilibrium in opposite directions. Thus the polarizability will have a maximum or minimum value for the equilibrium configuration and the criterion for the frequency to be Raman inactive will be satisfied. Examples of Raman inactive frequencies are ν_2 and ν_3 in Fig. 7 and ν_3 and ν_4 of Fig. 9. These same frequencies are the only ones that are infrared active for their respective molecules. Thus we see that for molecules possessing a center of symmetry infrared and Raman spectra are complementary. For these molecules the vibrations that are symmetrical to the center of symmetry will be infrared inactive and Raman active while those which are antisymmetrical to the center of symmetry will be infrared active and Raman inactive.

4. PURE ROTATIONAL RAMAN SPECTRA

Whereas pure rotational spectra in the infrared are difficult to obtain because they generally lie in the long wavelength region where the equipment is inadequate, the pure rotational Raman spectra is difficult to obtain because the lines are so close to that of the exciting frequency. This is of course because the energy differences between rotational levels are small and the consequent Raman displacents are small. An ingenious method of alleviating this difficulty was used by Rassetti (26) who used the 2537 A. line of Hg for the excitation of Raman displacements in gases. This is a resonance line and is strongly absorbed by mercury vapor. Rassetti, therefore, used a filter of cold mercury vapor in the spectrograph, thus reducing the intensity of the scattered excitation line.

As was shown by the above classical treatment, the rotational Raman effect is due to the variation in polarizability, relative to a fixed direction, of a molecule as it rotates. Thus a molecule which is spherically symmetric will have no pure rotational Raman spectra. This is borne out by methane, for example, for which no such displacements have been observed even with very long exposure times. However, all other types of molecules will necessarily show pure rotational lines if examined in the gaseous state. For linear molecules the energy levels will of course be given by equation 17. The selection rule now is $\Delta j = 0, \pm 2$. Thus there will be a P and an R branch, the P branch on the low frequency side and the R branch on the high frequency side of the excitation line. Because j changes by two, the spacings of the lines in wave numbers will be twice those of the pure infrared rotational spectra. The appearance of the rotational spectra will be similar to the lower figure in Fig. 11 with the excitation line in the center instead of a Q branch.

For symmetrical top molecules it is clear that there will be no rotational Raman spectra for rotations about the symmetry axis. However, for rotations about an axis perpendicular to it there is a rich array of lines. The rotational energy levels of a symmetrical top molecule are given by

$$E_{j,k} = \frac{h^2}{8\pi^2 A} \, j(j + 1) + \frac{h^2 k^2}{8\pi^2} \left(\frac{1}{C} - \frac{1}{A} \right) \tag{34}$$

where A and C have the same meanings as defined in Section 7, I. Note that equation 34 is the same as equation 25 except that it includes no term for vibrational energy. The selection rules for this case are $\Delta j = 0, \pm 1, \pm 2; \Delta k = 0$. This then gives a total of five branches with the $\Delta j = 0$ branch coinciding with the excitation frequency. For $\Delta j = -1, +1$ the branches are designated as the P and R branches, respectively, and for $\Delta j = -2, +2$ they are designated as the O and S branches, respectively. It is clear that for every second line the O and S branches will give the same frequencies as the P and R branches. The appearance of such a spectrum may be seen in Fig. 15. For asymmetrical top molecules the theory is much more difficult and there are very few experimental data available.

5. DEPOLARIZATION OF RAMAN LINES

It is well known that radiation due to Rayleigh scattering is partially polarized when viewed from a direction at right angles to the direction of incident radiation. This is due to the fact that electromagnetic waves are transverse and to the fact that radiation from an oscillating dipole is greatest on the meridian plane perpendicular to the line of oscillation. As the Raman effect is also a scattering phenomenon we have polarization and depolarization effects in the Raman lines. These are related to the types of vibrations in which they originate. Let us denote by i the intensity of the radiation scattered in a direction perpendicular to the direction of exciting light and with its electric vector vibrating in a direction parallel to the

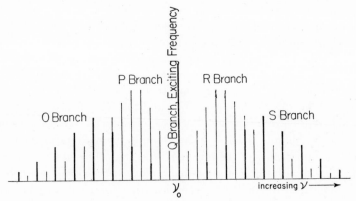

FIG. 15. Rotational Raman band for a symmetrical top molecule. The thin lines correspond to $\Delta j = \pm 1$ and the thick lines $\Delta j = \pm 2$.

direction of the exciting light. Let us denote by I the intensity of light scattered in the same direction with its electric vector vibrating at 90°, i.e., perpendicular to the direction of incident light. The ratio of these, $\rho = i/I$ is called the depolarization factor. Its value is a measure of the depolarization as for $\rho = 0$ we would clearly have complete polarization of the scattered light.

Let us first consider a molecule of spherical polarizability. When light polarized in the y direction is incident on it the induced dipole oscillations will be in the y direction. Scattered radiation will therefore be polarized, having the direction of the oscillating electric vector also in the y direction. Let us suppose now that the polarizability of the molecule is ellipsoidal and that the direction of greatest polarizability is not in the same direction as the vibrations of the electric vector of the incident radiation. The induced polarization will then not be parallel to the direction of polarization of the incident light and it will have a component perpendicular to it. This component will then be responsible for a depolarization intensity in the scattered radiation. A detailed theory of polarizability (27) yields several rules correlating the depolarization with type of vibration. It is found that those vibrations that are antisymmetrical with respect to one or more elements of symmetry and which are not forbidden are depolarized. If the incident radiation is linearly polarized $\rho = 3/4$, and if it is not polarized $\rho = 6/7$. For symmetrical vibrations the Raman lines are polarized or nearly so, i.e., ρ has a value close to zero. These relations are of great aid in analyzing Raman spectra as they allow an immediate assignment to classes of vibrations.

The experimental determination of the depolarization is quite difficult since all parasitic light should be eliminated. In the measurement of the intensity of the two perpendicular components a combination of a mica half-wave plate and a Nichol prism may be used (28). These are placed between the tube holding the sample being examined and the spectrograph. By suitable orientation, relative to each other, of the Nichol prism and the half-wave plate first one component and then the other may be admitted to the spectrograph. A determination of the densities of the resulting lines on the photographic plate may then be used to evaluate ρ. In cases where the depolarization is being observed for a sample irradiated with polarized light some sort of polarizing arrangement must be used between the radiation source and the sample tube. In one example this was achieved by wrapping the tube with Polaroid (29).

6. VIBRATION-ROTATION RAMAN SPECTRA

In Section 6, I, was given a discussion of the normal modes of motion of a polyatomic molecule and of the mathematical approach to the theoretical determination of these modes. Also in the same section was given a discussion of Dennison's method of extreme fields, which can readily yield a qualitative picture of the normal vibrations in the simpler molecules. Since Raman displacements are due to transitions between vibrational and rotational states these earlier considerations apply here also. There is no difference between the type of basic information supplied by infrared and Raman spectra.

The rotational lines in the vibration-rotation bands are considerably more difficult to obtain in Raman than in infrared spectra. This is a consequence of the experimental difficulties as they require a very high dispersion spectrograph and the examination of the material in the gaseous state. Since the concentration of material in the gaseous state is low, long exposures are necessary. An increase of pressure will in general not improve matters due to the effect known as pressure-broadening. In this the widths of the individual lines are broadened with increase of pressure due to the shortening of the time intervals between collisions (30, 31, 32). Experimental results on vibration-rotation Raman spectra are meager and some of the theoretical predictions concerning band structure have not as yet been fully confirmed. For a linear molecule the selection rule for the change of angular momentum quantum number is $\Delta j = 0, \pm 2$ for rotational transitions accompanying transitions in the vibration frequency parallel to the molecular axis (see Section 6, I). This gives P, Q, and R branches with the line separation just twice that for the infrared spectra. For vibrations of the same molecule perpendicular to the axis the selection rule is $\Delta j = \pm 1, \pm 2$ which yields O, P, R, and S branches. For a symmetrical top molecule the two rotational quantum numbers j and k must be considered. In the case of vibrations parallel to the symmetry axis we have $\Delta k = 0$ and $\Delta j = 0, \pm 1, \pm 2$, which predicts the five branches O, P, Q, R, and S. The situation is even more complicated for those vibrations perpendicular to the symmetry axis as now the selection rule is $\Delta j = 0, \pm 1, \pm 2$ and $\Delta k = \pm 1$ or ± 2. This predicts a maximum of nine separate branches (including the Q branch) and it is clear that to identify them extremely high dispersion and clarity of results would be necessary. In Section 4, II, we saw that no pure rotation spectra are observable for spherically symmetric molecules due to the spherical polarizability. In the case of totally symmetric vibrations for the same molecule there will also be no rotational fine structure. For antisymmetric vibrations there will be, however, a rotational fine structure, and for these the selection rule $\Delta j = 0, \pm 1, \pm 2$, which gives five branches.

7. CORRELATION AND ASSIGNMENT OF INFRARED AND RAMAN FREQUENCIES

In Section 4, I, we saw that to a first approximation the vibrations of a specific diatomic group may be considered as independent of the remainder of the molecule. Thus different molecules possessing a common type of diatomic group will, in general, all have a fundamental vibrational frequency of about the same value which may be assigned to this group. This is a very convenient situation as it makes the immediate recognition of some of the fundamental frequencies possible. The typical absorption frequencies observable by infrared for a number of diatomic groups were seen in Table I. These data are augmented by those in Table III, which gives a number of frequencies assignable to diatomic groups that have been determined by Raman spectroscopy. They further illustrate the degree of invariance of such frequencies in progressing through a series of halo-methanes.

In the preceding sections we have seen how in some cases infrared and Raman spectra give essentially the same information about a molecule and in others how they are complementary. We have also seen how the rotational fine structure depends on the nature of the molecule and the type of vibration, i.e., parallel or perpendicular, with which it is associated. With these data it is possible in many cases to determine at least qualitatively the modes of vibration of a molecule, and to obtain information concerning force constants and details of structure. As expressed by Sutherland (4) there are three problems in analyzing vibration spectra. They are (a) to determine from the observed infrared and Raman bands those which represent fundamental frequencies and those which represent combinations and overtones, (b) to assign correctly the fundamental frequencies to definite vibrational modes of a particular molecular model, and (c) to deduce the values of such fundamental frequencies as are not directly observable. In

TABLE III

CHARACTERISTIC C-X FREQUENCIES FOR A SERIES OF HALO-METHANES (20)

Substance	Bond	Frequency (cm.⁻¹)	Av. (cm.⁻¹)
$CHCl_3$	C—H	3020	
$CHCl_2F$		3014	
$CHBr_2F$		3017	3018
$CHBrCl_2$		3020	
CH_3F	C—F	1048	
CH_2ClF		1046	
$CHCl_2F$		1065	1050
CCl_3F		1067	
CH_3Cl	C—Cl	732	
CH_2ClBr		726	730
$CHBr_2Cl$		750	
CBr_3Cl		734	
CH_3Br	C—Br	610	
CH_2IBr		616	618
CH_2Br_2		637	
$CHCl_2Br$		610	
CH_3I	C—I	532	532

answering these problems there is no definite set of rules that can be followed to analyze the data for any particular molecule. Because of the complexity each molecule constitutes a separate problem wherein deductions unique to it alone are necessary. However, there are a number of generalizations and observations that are very useful.

In the inspection of data the intensity of a band is a good guide in establishing whether or not it is a fundamental as, in general, such transitions are much more probable than overtones or combination frequencies. The position of the band in the spectrum is also useful. From such data as those in Tables I and III we know where the fundamental vibrations assignable to diatomic groups lie and we know where to expect overtones of such frequencies. In the choice of a molecular model the investigator can be guided by very reliable information from other approaches such as the chemistry of the compound, electron and X-ray diffraction data, dipole moment measurements, ultraviolet absorption data, and the use of actual atom models (33). In the assignment of frequencies to vibrational modes use may be made of the selection rules given earlier wherein the number and types of fine structure bands determine whether the frequency is of the symmetrical or antisymmetrical type. The absence of certain bands in either the infrared or Raman spectra will also help to indicate the types of frequencies since it is known what types are forbidden in the two cases. The position is a further guide since vibrations involving the stretching of valence bonds will have higher frequencies than those involving bending. The examination of a sequence of molecules in which successive members differ only in the substitution of a single atom often may yield useful information towards the

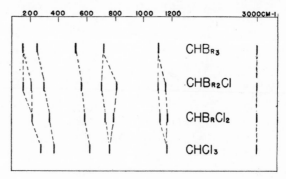

Fig. 16. Vibrational frequencies observed by Raman spectroscopy for a series of halo-methanes (from reference 34).

assignment of frequencies. In this way the different modes of motion may be traced through the sequence and problems of degeneracy and symmetry settled. Glockler and Leader (34) have obtained such data for a number of halo-methanes and some of their results may be seen in Fig. 16. Note here how a single substitution may remove or restore degeneracy, and also the invariancy of the C—H group frequency near 3000 cm.$^{-1}$ In such cases where a fundamental frequency is forbidden in both the infrared and Raman spectra it may be necessary to use an indirect method to find it. One such approach is to assume a definite frequency and compare specific heat values calculated on this assumption with experimentally observed values.

In Section 6, I, were described the vibrational modes of the collinear Y_2X_2 molecule, Fig. 9, of which acetylene, C_2H_2, is an example that has been satisfactorily studied. In Table IV are given the observed infrared bands for acetylene and the vibrational modes to which they are due. It is to be noted that most of the bands are due to combination frequencies involving two modes. With the exception of the 1326 cm.$^{-1}$ band these are weak compared to those due to single modes. The frequency designation here is the same as that used in Fig. 9. In addition to these data there are two vibrational frequencies observed in the Raman spectra, at 1974 and 3372 cm.$^{-1}$ The first of these is due to the ν_1 vibrational mode and the latter to the ν_3 mode. The discussion of Raman frequency assignment to a number of other molecules and applications of the data to other topics such as thermodynamic properties, force constants, equilibrium constants, molecular structure, and hindered rotation has been given by Glockler (20).

TABLE IV
OBSERVED FREQUENCIES AND THEIR ASSIGNMENTS FOR C_2H_2 MOLECULE

Observed frequency (cm.$^{-1}$)	Vibrational modes involved
730	ν_4
1326	ν_4, ν_5
2643	ν_2, ν_4
2670	ν_3, ν_5
2702	ν_1, ν_4
3288	ν_3
3882	ν_3, ν_5
3910	ν_4, ν_5
4092	ν_2, ν_4

III. ULTRAVIOLET ABSORPTION SPECTROSCOPY

When gaseous material is excited by an electrical discharge it will emit light that may extend in wavelength from the far ultraviolet into the visible region. In such a process several phenomena may be acting to produce the radiations and the complete analysis is very difficult. We shall, first of all, not be concerned here with emission spectra nor shall we be particularly concerned with the visible region. We shall consider primarily the absorption spectra, and transitions they represent, lying in the ultraviolet region between about 2000 and 4000 A. In general, hydrocarbons have no absorption in the visible region and so far as is known only those possessing unsaturation will absorb in this region of the ultraviolet. When light is absorbed in the ultraviolet the energy is used to produce transitions between electronic energy levels. In these the changes involve the distribution and energy of the valence bonding electrons. Although such transitions may be accompanied by changes in vibrational and rotational states the energy absorbed is of an order of magnitude greater than that absorbed in exciting pure vibrational and rotational transitions. The absorption of a photon of wavelength 3000 A. involves an energy of 65.5×10^{-13} ergs, while the absorption of a photon of wavelength 6 μ involves an energy of 3.28×10^{-13} ergs.

1. EXPERIMENTAL METHODS

In the study of ultraviolet absorption spectroscopy a spectrograph or spectrometer is needed with optics which will pass wavelengths in this region. Fused quartz is suitable and the most commonly used material. When a study is being made of the fine details of band structure it is necessary to have high resolution. However, it is possible to do a great deal of work on materials in solution and since most hydrocarbons exhibiting ultraviolet absorption are studied as liquids instruments of somewhat lower resolution are commonly used.

For that reason the reader is referred to other sources (35, 36) for details of the higher resolution instruments and we shall describe here a photoelectric spectrometer of very wide usage (37). A schematic diagram of the optics of this instrument may be seen in Fig. 17. Here S represents the source, which may be a hydrogen discharge lamp. Light is reflected to the collimating mirror W through the entrance slit R by means of the two mirrors M

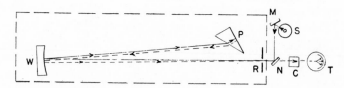

FIG. 17. Optical diagram of quartz prism spectrophotometer for ultraviolet absorption measurements (from reference 37).

and N. From there it goes to the quartz prism P where it is doubly refracted due to a reflecting coating on the back face of the prism. Some of it will return to W and pass out through the exit slit which is just above R in a direction perpendicular to the plane of the figure. It passes through the sample cell C and on to the photoelectric detector T.

The photoelectric detector yields a current which is proportional to the radiation intensity and, by means of electronic amplifiers, a very conveniently handled electrical signal is obtained. The wavelength of the radiation passing through the absorption cell is controlled by rotating the prism. For work wherein the highest resolution is not desired the photoelectric measurement of the radiation intensity has advantages over the use of a photographic plate. In the former a value porportional to the light intensity is immediately available whereas in the latter method the plate must be developed and the intensity of blackening determined.

For the examination of solutions and pure liquids the absorption cell windows must, of course, be of a material such as quartz which is transparent for this spectral region. As shall be discussed in detail later, many compounds are transparent in this region. Of great convenience is the fact that paraffins, alcohol, distilled water, and others are among these. This makes it possible to study many substances in solution without interference from absorption by the solvent. Of those compounds which do have ultraviolet absorption many absorb very strongly and in a cell 1 cm. in thickness they must often be examined in very dilute solution, of the order of one part in many thousands. Because of this, care must be taken that contamination of other samples or of the solvent does not occur.

2. GENERAL NATURE OF ELECTRONIC TRANSITIONS

Ultraviolet spectra are the result of transitions between electronic states of the molecules when quanta are absorbed. These electronic states are quantum states obeying the same general rules of quantum mechanics given in the earlier sections. The energies involved are much higher than in rotational and vibrational states and for any particular level the total electronic energy that must be considered is the sum of the kinetic and potential energy of the binding electrons plus the electrostatic interaction energy of the nuclei. The observed spectra may be quite complicated since transitions between electronic levels are generally accompanied by transitions between vibrational and rotational states. Thus an ultraviolet absorption spectrum due to a single transition between two electronic states may show a wealth of fine structure due to concurrent changes in vibrational and rotational modes of motion. For the complete spectra one must then consider a series of energy level diagrams such as seen in Fig. 18 for a diatomic molecule. Here may be seen the vibrational energy levels for one mode of vibration for the ground and excited electronic state. Since this represents but one mode of vibration it is clear that for a polyatomic molecule a complete consideration would involve similar diagrams for the other modes. In Fig. 19 may be seen the absorption spectrum for benzene between 220 and 280 mμ. Here is plotted the per cent transmission as a function of wavelength for the sample in a paraffin solvent which does not absorb radiation in this range itself. Structure due to different vibrational transitions accompanying the change in electronic state is clearly visible. Ordinarily, for diatomic molecules, no strict general rule is applicable relative to changes in the vibrational quantum number and thus many transitions are possible. In Fig. 18 the allowable transitions are shown originating with the lowest vibrational level since at the lower temperatures the probabilities of finding the higher levels excited are small.

In Section I, 2, it was stated that the vibrational and rotational motion of a molecule may be considered independently of the electronic states. We may then, to a good approximation, express the total energy of the molecule as the sum of three parts

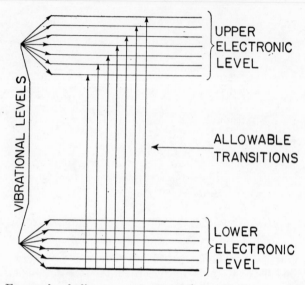

FIG. 18. Energy level diagram and allowable transitions between vibrational energy levels associated with two electronic states.

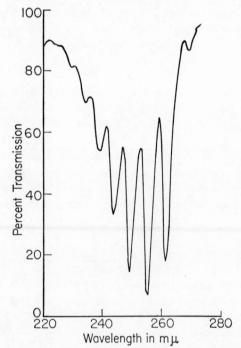

FIG. 19. Ultraviolet absorption spectrum for benzene in a paraffin solvent.

$$E = E_e + E_v + E_r \qquad (35)$$

where E_e is the electronic energy, E_v is the vibrational energy, and E_r is the rotational energy. In a transition all three terms on the right hand side may change. Let us consider the potential energy as a function of internuclear distance for a diatomic molecule. This we see in Fig. 20 where A and B represent the potential energy curves for the ground and first excited electronic states respectively. The minima of these two curves will, in general, not occur at the same value of internuclear separation. Only the ground vibrational state is shown for A since the transitions observed by absorption will orig-

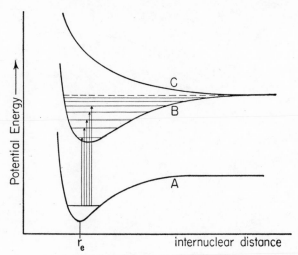

FIG. 20. Potential energy curves for the ground state, the first excited state and a repulsive state of a diatomic molecule.

inate there. In the series of transitions from this state to the vibrational states of B the successive separations will decrease until a point is reached beyone which there is a continuum of absorption corresponding to transitions to points on the diagram above the dashed line which is the asymptote for B. As the intensity of such a series decreases with the higher vibrational levels a continuum is not often observed. In this figure C represents the potential energy for an unstable or repulsive electronic state. Excitation to such a state results in immediate dissociation.

In considering the intensities of the various vibrational transitions attendant to change of electronic state it is necessary to utilize the Franck-Condon principle (38). This states that an electronic transition in a molecule takes place in such a short time that the positions and velocities of the nuclei are not appreciably altered. In other words, in a diagram such as Fig. 20 the transition is always vertically up, so that the internuclear distance after excitation is the same as before. The manner in which this will affect the transition probabilities may be seen from Fig. 21. Here are shown two potential energy curves in a case where the minima occur at different values of internuclear separation. In this figure the curves for the probability density distribution or Ψ functions (see Section I, 2) for the various vibrational states are shown with their corresponding energy levels. The vibrational quantum number for the ground state is designated as v^{11}, and for the excited state as v^1. For the ground state, v^{11}, $= 0$, the most probable value of the

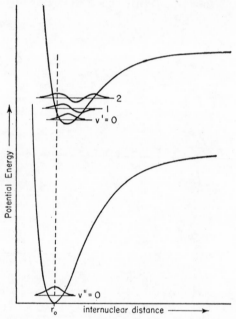

FIG. 21. Potential energy curves and probability distribution functions illustrating the Franck-Condon principle.

internuclear separation at the time of excitation will be that for which Ψ is at a maximum. Hence, the most likely transition will be along the dashed line. The probability of transition to one of the upper excited states depends upon the value of $\Psi(v^1)$ for that state in the immediate vicinity of the dashed line. For $v^1 = 0$ we note that $\Psi(v^1)$ is small so that the intensity of that transition is small. The transition to $v^1 = 1$ will be greater, and to $v^{11} = 2$ it will be greater yet. In this presentation we have indicated that the probability depends upon the value of $\Psi(v^1)$ on the dashed line. Actually, in the mathematical formulation of this principle it will depend upon the value of the integral $\int \Psi(v^{11}) \, \Psi(v^1) \, d\tau$. The value of this integral is a measure of the overlap of the Ψ functions for the two electronic states.

In the consideration of polyatomic molecules these general considerations hold true. A quantum description of the electronic states is possible in terms of the orbital angular momentum and spin quantum numbers of the binding electrons (38, 39). This approach is very complicated and entirely outside the scope of the present chapter. For that reason we shall in the remaining material present an account of a semiempirical theory which has had considerable success in correlating results for different compounds. This theory has recently been reviewed by Lewis and Calvin (40).

3. ABSORPTION DUE TO SPECIFIC GROUPS; CHROMOPHORES

In an empirical examination of a large number of compounds in the spectral range under discussion it is found that some classes will absorb whereas others will not. As examples of the absorbing compounds, it is found that benzene and its derivatives will absorb in the region between 250 and 290 mμ and that the ketones will absorb between 200 and 300 mμ. The paraffins and the alcohols are examples of classes that do not absorb in this region. The absorption of any one class is found to be due to a specific group common to all members; these are called chromophores and generally involve unsaturation. A number of them with the approximate centers of the absorption bands for which they are responsible may be seen in Table V.

The wavelength values of Table V cannot be regarded as exact. For one thing the absorption band due to the chromophore will generally be broad and possessed of structure as may be seen in Fig. 19. Furthermore, the center of the band will move about as one progresses through a homologous series of compounds. The wavelengths shown for the naphthalene and anthracene skeletons refer to the longest wavelength bands observable as these groups will also show absorption in the benzene ring region. When two of these chromophores occur conjugated or adjacent in the same molecule it effectively creates a new chromophore with different absorption bands. This will be discussed in more detail later.

Some chromophores not shown in Table V give rise to absorption further out in the ultraviolet. The absorption may not be of a band nature but rather as a continuum beyond a certain onset region. Thus for compounds containing the hydroxyl group absorption starts in the neighborhood of 190 mμ. Materials possessing the olefin group have been studied by E. P. Carr and her associates (41, 42, 43, 44) and they show heavy absorption below about 200 mμ, this value for the onset of absorption varying considerably between compounds. In Fig. 22 this is illustrated by the spectra for several olefins. Here, in contrast to the previous figures, the intensity of absorption rather than per cent transmission is plotted as a function of frequency. This arises from the nature of light absorption, which obeys Beer's law given by

$$I = I_0 e^{-acl} \tag{36}$$

where I is the intensity of the transmitted light, I_0 the intensity of the incident light, a is a constant called the extinction coefficient, c is the concentration of the material in the absorption cell, and l is the thickness of the absorption cell. The term optical density is often used. This is represented by D where $D = \log (I_0/I) = acl$. The extinction coefficient will depend on

TABLE V

CHROMOPHORIC GROUPS AND WAVELENGTHS

Group	Wavelength in mμ
	265
	311
	475
C=O	280
-N=N-	350
	366
-S-H	228
	302

the material under examination and the wavelength of the observation, and it is a measure of the intensity of absorption. It is seen from the figure that for the simpler olefins the onset of absorption occurs at about 52000 cm.$^{-1}$ (192 mμ) whereas for the heavier ones it occurs at about 46000 cm.$^{-1}$ (218 mμ). This low wavelength range is known as the Schumann region and here the optics must be of fluorite because of the transmission limits of quartz. Since cyclohexane and ethane do not show absorption below about 57000 cm.$^{-1}$ (175 mμ) (45) we may assume that, insofar as the saturated carbon-

carbon linkage may be regarded as a chromophore, it produces no absorption in the region of interest to us.

4. ELECTRONIC OSCILLATIONS, CONJUGATION

In the empirical theory due to Will, Stieglitz, Lewis, Calvin, and others the absorption of light by chromophores is ascribed to electronic oscillations within these groups. These oscillations are not defined in a detailed sense but they are believed to be closely associated with the electronic resonance forms wherein there is a charge transfer. Thus, in benzene it is

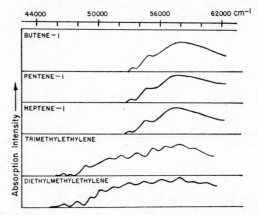

FIG. 22. Ultraviolet absorption spectra for a series of olefins (from reference 43).

believed that the absorption is due to oscillation between resonance forms of the type

rather than the Kekule forms. The frequency of the absorption bands and hence of electronic oscillations is related to the effective restraints to displacement and vibration in the same manner that the frequency of a classical oscillator is related to its force constant. In this respect Lewis and Calvin (40) have considered the series of chromophores $C=C$, $C=N$, $C=O$, $N=N$, and $C=S$. With the known data for these and reasonable assumptions concerning the absorption for those not observed they have formulated the potential energy curves seen in Fig. 23. Here the potential energy for the resonance electrons is plotted as a function of displacement from equilibrium. These curves are not meant to convey the same exact physical meaning as previously presented ones but to illustrate the increase of strain in the double bond in passing through the series from $C=C$ to $C=S$.

When a dipole moment is induced in a molecule the net charge displacement may be regarded as due to a single electron moving a distance x from its equilibrium position. This produces a dipole moment P given by $P = ex$ where e is the charge of the electron. The relation between P and the applied field is $P = \alpha E$ where α is the polarizability. The force on the electron will be eE, and this will be related to x by $eE = kx$ where k is the force constant. From these relations the equation

$$k = e^2/\alpha \tag{37}$$

may easily be derived. Since the force constant is a measure of the steepness of the associated potential energy curve it is evident that, insofar as they are correct, the curves of Fig. 23 show increasing polarizability of the bonds in passing through the series from C≡C to C≡S.

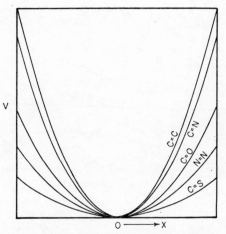

FIG. 23. Potential energy curves for electronic displacements in a series of chromophores (from reference 40).

In general, when two chromophoric groups are conjugated, an oscillation of lower frequency than is characteristic of either one results. For example, 1,3-butadiene containing two conjugated C═C bonds has an onset of absorption at about 230 mμ, which is in contrast to the onset of absorption for ethylene which occurs at about 196 mμ. Such a displacement to longer wavelengths may be predicted by our simple theory. We may now consider the oscillating electrons in the conjugated chromophores to be coupled and oscillating in phase so that the entire oscillation may be regarded as that of a charged element of mass nm where n is the number of conjugated chromophores and m is the mass of one electron. In such a system the electrons will be displaced the same amount in each individual oscillator, and the effective force constant for the entire oscillator is the same as used before. The frequency of an oscillator in terms of mass of oscillating element and force constant was given in equation 6. It is

$$2\pi\nu_0 = \sqrt{\frac{k}{nm}} \quad \text{or} \quad \lambda^2 = (2\pi c)^2 (m/k)n \tag{38}$$

for the case at hand. Thus, a plot of the wavelength of the absorption maximum vs. number of conjugated chromophores for a series wherein this number successively increases should yield a stright line plot. Experimental

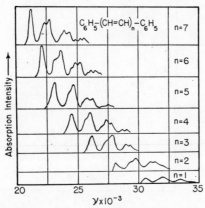

FIG. 24. Absorption spectra of a series of diphenylpolyenes (from reference 40).

verification of this may be seen in Figs. 24 and 25. These data are for a series of diphenylpolyenes of the general form

$$\langle\!\!\!\!\bigcirc\!\!\!\!\rangle(-CH\!=\!CH)_n\!-\!\langle\!\!\!\!\bigcirc\!\!\!\!\rangle$$

The extinction coefficient as a function of wave numbers is plotted in Fig. 24 for a series of these compounds for n between 1 and 7. It is to be observed that the general nature of the bands is maintained throughout the series. In Fig. 25 is plotted $\lambda^2 \times 10^6$ for the first maximum (lowest frequency) vs. n. As may be seen, the fit to a straight line is very good. A similar treatment for data obtained for the cyanine dyes (46, 47) has been carried out (40) and a good fit to a straight line obtained.

When two chromophores are connected through a CH_2 group it may act as a block or insulator to the conjugation. For example, 1,4-pentadiene with the carbon skeleton $C\!=\!C\!-\!C\!-\!C\!=\!C$ does not show the absorption exhibited by the conjugated diolefins but rather that of a monoolefin. A further example of this insulating effect may be seen in Fig. 26, which gives the results for three diazo dyes in which the resonating system comprises the two phenyl rings joined through the two nitrogen atoms (48). The data for the two resonating systems conjugated may be seen in curve 1 whereas data

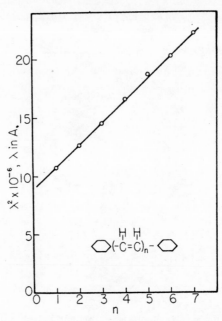

FIG. 25. Plot of λ^2 vs. n for a series of diphenylpolyenes (from reference 40).

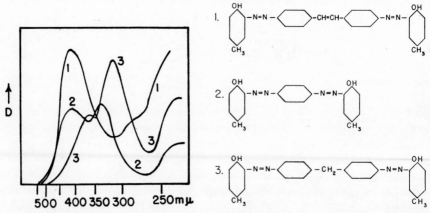

FIG. 26. Absorption spectra for three diazo dyes illustrating effects of conjugation and insulation (from reference 48).

for the case of two resonating systems with CH_2 insulation between them is presented in curve 3. Curve 2 represents the case where the two systems are cumulative, i.e., where they share a central group. It is to be noted that both the cumulative attachment and the case of conjugation result in absorption at longer wavelengths compared to the case of insulation. The data for the latter is very similar to that obtained for a molecule containing but a single resonating system.

5. FURTHER DETAILS

A very interesting application of the relation between frequencies of absorption bands and conjugation of chromophores is in the study of steric

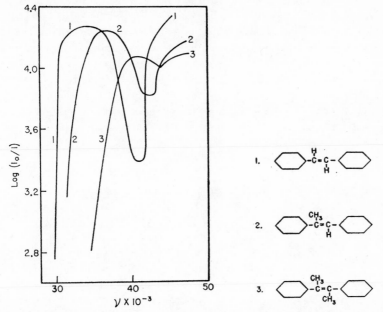

FIG. 27. Absorption spectra for stilbenes showing the effects of steric hindrance (from reference 40).

hindrance. If two chromophores are conjugated and together possess absorption bands at longer wavelengths than each does individually it is expected that the groups essential to the resonance will be coplanar (49). If some of the substituent groups sterically hinder this coplanarity it is observable in the absorption data. This is illustrated in Fig. 27, which gives the absorption spectra for stilbene, monomethylstilbene, and dimethylstilbene. It is to be observed that curve 1 shows absorption at the lowest frequencies (longest wavelengths) indicating uninhibited conjugation or coplanarity of the phenyl rings. Curve 2 shows some effects of steric hindrance to resonance as the absorbing frequencies are shifted to higher values, and curve 3 shows strong hindrance to resonance. This hindrance to coplanarity is the result of the repulsion due to the methyl groups. Such observations as these are very valuable in the determination of substitution in compounds of unknown structure.

Up to this point we have considered the absorption bands appearing at longer wavelengths due to conjugation. These are almost always accompanied by bands in the short wavelength regions. These are ascribed to partial oscillation of the chromophores, i.e., oscillations in which they are independent of each other. Not much is known on this point although it is fairly clear that in progressing to the shorter wavelengths the absorption spectra appear more and more to be characteristic of the individual chromophores. Another point on which it is possible to make only qualitative predictions at best is the expected behavior when two unlike chromophores are conjugated. In general, it is to be expected that the frequency of absorption of the conjugated resonators will be governed by their individual behavior. Thus, in progressing through the series where one of the groups is progressively $C=C$, $C=N$, $C=O$, and $N=N$, it is expected that the frequency will progressively decrease. An example of this behavior may be seen from a comparison of three compounds

$$\underset{H_2C=C-C=CH_2,}{\overset{H \quad H}{\overset{|\quad|}{}}} \qquad \underset{H_2C=C-C=O,}{\overset{H \quad H}{\overset{|\quad|}{}}} \quad \text{and} \quad \underset{O=C-C=O}{\overset{H \quad H}{\overset{|\quad|}{}}}$$

which have absorption maxima at 220, 350, and 460 mμ, respectively.

In the earlier material we saw that the observed bands in the ultraviolet are the result of transitions involving changes in both the electronic state and the vibrational modes. Each broad absorption band is due to a transition between two electronic states whereas the detailed structure within the band is due to the accompanying vibrational transitions. The intensities of the latter will be governed by the Franck-Condon principle, which is difficult to apply for complicated molecules. Rather, we may take the general rule that as the complexity of substitution increases in a homologous series the detailed band structure decreases. This we would expect from a consideration of the effect of further substitution on allowable transitions. It furnishes a greater number of vibrational modes by virtue of a greater number of participating nuclei. The large number of transitions may then produce a blurring of the band structure due to the overlapping of individual transition bands. Figure 28 shows the progressively decreasing structure for the series: p-cresol, p-t-butylphenol, 2,4-di-t-butylphenol, and 2,4,6-tri-t-butylphenol (50).

The spectra of many compounds will depend upon the solvent in which the material is examined. For example, a comparison between the spectra of phenol in a paraffin solution and the spectra in an ethanol solution shows that in the latter case the band structure is greatly blurred, and that there is a shift of the band towards the red (lower frequencies). These effects are not understood in detail but it is assumed that they are the results of displacements of the upper electronic energy levels by the interaction between the polar groups of the polar solvent and the polar forms of the excited state. Some recent work on substituted phenols (50) has shown that to produce large spectral changes it is necessary that the alcohol molecules come in close proximity to the hydroxyl group of the phenol. This was done by using a series of substituted phenols wherein steric hindrance to the approach of the alcohol molecules to the hydroxyl group of the phenol was achieved by using phenols possessing t-butyl groups on both ortho positions.

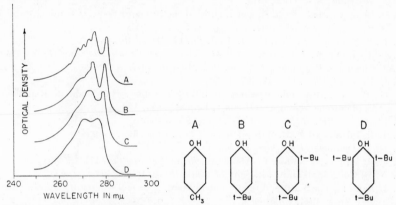

FIG. 28. Ultraviolet absorption spectra for a series of phenols with increasing complexity of substitution.

REFERENCES

1. R. B. Barnes, R. S. McDonald, V. Z. Williams, and R. F. Kinnaird, *J. Applied Phys.* **16**, 77 (1945).
2. J. Strong, Procedures in Experimental Physics. Prentice-Hall, New York, 1939, p. 305.
3. E. E. Bell, R. H. Noble, and H. H. Nielsen, *Rev. Sci. Instruments* **18**, 48 (1947).
4. G. B. B. M. Sutherland, Infra-Red and Raman Spectra. Methuen and Co., London, 1935.
5. R. B. Barnes, *Rev. Sci. Instruments* **5**, 237 (1934).
6. L. Pauling and E. B. Wilson, Jr., Introduction to Quantum Mechanics. McGraw-Hill, New York, 1935.
7. M. Born and J. R. Oppenheimer, *Ann. Physik* **84**, 457 (1927).
8. P. M. Morse, *Phys. Rev.* **34**, 57 (1929).
9. R. B. Barnes, R. C. Gore, U. Liddel, and V. Z. Williams, Infra-Red Spectroscopy. Reinhold, New York, 1944.
10. J. J. Fox and A. E. Martin, *Proc. Roy. Soc. London* **175**, 208 (1940).
11. L. Pauling, The Nature of the Chemical Bond. Cornell University Press, Ithaca, New York, 1944, Chapter IX.

12. J. J. Fox and A. E. Martin, *Proc. Roy. Soc. London* **162**, 419 (1937).
13. M. Czerny, *Z. Physik.* **34**, 227 (1925)
14. G. Herzberg, Molecular Spectra and Molecular Structure, I. Diatomic Molecules. Prentice-Hall, New York, 1939, Chapter III.
15. D. M. Dennison, *Revs. Modern Phys.* **3**, 280 (1931).
16. D. M. Dennison, *Revs. Modern Phys.* **12**, 175 (1940).
17. *See*, for example, E. T. Whittaker, Analytical Dynamics. Cambridge University Press, London, 1927, Chapter VII.
18. A. H. Nielsen and H. H. Nielsen, *Phys. Rev.* **48**, 864 (1935).
19. J. H. Hibben, The Raman Effect and Its Chemical Applications. Rheinhold, New York, 1939.
20. G. Glockler, *Revs. Modern Phys.* **15**, 111 (1943).
21. G. Herzberg, Infra-Red and Raman Spectra of Polyatomic Molecules. D. Van Nostrand, New York, 1945.
22. S. Bhagavantam, Scattering of Light and the Raman Effect. Chemical Publishing Co., New York, 1942.
23. R. F. Stamm, *Ind. Eng. Chem. Anal. Ed.* **17**, 318 (1945).
24. D. H. Rank, R. J. Pfister, and P. O. Coleman, *J. Optical Soc. Am.* **32**, 390 (1942).
25. J. Chien and P. Bender, *J. Chem. Phys.* **15**, 376 (1947).
26. F. Rassetti, *Phys. Rev.* **34**, 367 (1929).
27. G. Placzek, Rayleigh Streuung und Raman Effect, Handbuch d. Radiologie. Akademische Verlagsgesellschaft, Leipzig, 1934, Vol. 6.
28. F. Stitt and D. M. Yost, *J. Chem. Phys.* **5**, 90 (1937).
29. J. T. Edsall and E. B. Wilson, Jr., *J. Chem. Phys.* **6**, 124 (1938).
30. D. M. Dennison, *Phys. Rev.* **31**, 503 (1928).
31. J. H. Van Vleck and V. F. Weisskopf, *Revs. Modern Phys.* **17**, 227 (1945).
32. N. D. Coggeshall and E. L. Saier, *J. Chem. Phys.* **15**, 65 (1947).
33. L. Pauling, The Nature of the Chemical Bond. Cornell University Press, Ithaca, New York, 1944, Chapter V.
34. G. Glockler and G. R. Leader, *J. Chem. Phys.* **8**, 699 (1940).
35. W. R. Brode, Chemical Spectroscopy. Wiley, New York, 1939.
36. T. R. P. Gibb, Optical Methods of Chemical Analysis. McGraw-Hill, New York, 1942.
37. H. H. Cary and A. O. Beckman, *J. Optical Soc. Am.* **31**, 682 (1941).
38. *See*, for example, W. A. Noyes, Jr. and P. A. Leighton, The Photochemistry of Gases. Reinhold, New York, 1941, Chapter III.
39. R. S. Mulliken, *J. Chem. Phys.* **7**, 14, 20, 121, 339, 353, 356, 364, 570 (1939).
40. G. N. Lewis and M. Calvin, *Chem. Revs.* **25**, 273 (1939).
41. E. P. Carr and M. K. Walker, *J. Chem. Phys.* **4**, 751 (1936).
42. E. P. Carr and G. F. Walter, *J. Chem. Phys.* **4**, 756 (1936).
43. E. P. Carr and H. Stucklen, *J. Chem. Phys.* **4**, 760 (1936).
44. E. P. Carr and H. Stucklen, *J. Chem. Phys.* **6**, 55 (1938).
45. G. Scheibe and H. Grieneisen, *Z. physik. Chem.* **B25**, 52 (1933).
46. N. I. Fisher and F. M. Hamer, *Proc. Roy. Soc. London* **A154**, 703 (1936).
47. B. Beilenson, N. I. Fisher, and F. M. Hamer, *Proc. Roy. Soc. London* **A163**, 138 (1937).
48. J. D. Piper and W. R. Brode, *J. Am. Chem. Soc.* **57**, 135 (1935).
49. *See*, for example, A. E. Remick, Electronic Interpretation of Organic Chemistry. Wiley, New York, 1943, Chapter VI.
50. N. D. Coggeshall and E. M. Lang, *J. Am. Chem. Soc.* **70**, 3283 (1948).

CHAPTER 5

OPTICAL METHODS OF HYDROCARBON ANALYSIS

By

NORMAN D. COGGESHALL

Gulf Research and Development Co., Pittsburgh, Pennsylvania

CONTENTS

The applications of the three fields of infrared, Raman, and ultraviolet spectroscopy are discussed in turn in this chapter. Greater space is devoted to infrared than to the others since it has in general provided a greater range of applications and since certain general principles are discussed which also apply to the others. For a discussion of the fundamental nature of these phenomena the reader should consult Chapter 4. As was done in that chapter, the absorption frequencies are specified in terms of wavelengths and wave numbers interchangeably.

I. Analysis by Infrared Absorption

1. introduction

As was discussed in the preceding Chapter, the manner in which a compound absorbs in the infrared region is determined by its internal geometry and the force constants of the valence bonds. Since these possess differences for unlike species the spectra of different compounds will not be the same. It is these differences in spectra that form the basis of infrared analytical techniques. If, in examining a series of compounds, a wavelength for each one can be found such that the absorption there is stronger for it than for any of the others it is highly probable that an analysis by infrared of a multicomponent mixture of these compounds will be successful. If the absorption characteristics of the individual components are known then it is possible to "unravel" the spectra of the mixture in terms of them. By virtue of their uniqueness the spectra of the individual molecules are often referred to as their fingerprints.

Most compounds ordinarily encountered obey Beer's law of absorption which may be written as:

$$I/I_0 = e^{-acl} \text{ or } D = \log I_0/I = acl \tag{1}$$

where I and I_0 are the transmitted and incident radiation intensities respectively, a is the extinction coefficient which depends upon the material and the wavelength, D is known as the optical density, c is the concentration of the material, and l is the thickness of the absorption cell. Since the calibration work and actual analytical data may be taken using the same cell thickness, a and l may be combined into a single constant to give:

$$D_i = A_{ij}C_j$$

where the subscript i refers to data taken at an ith wavelength and the subscript j refers to data for the jth compound. In a mixture the optical density is linearly additive so for a mixture of, say, six compounds we have:

$$D_i = A_{i1}C_1 + A_{i2}C_2 + A_{i3}C_3 + A_{i4}C_4 + A_{i5}C_5 + A_{i6}C_6 \tag{2}$$

where the symbols have the meanings expressed above. If data were taken at six separate wavelengths then we would have six separate equations such as (2). If the A_{ij}'s were available from the examination of the pure compounds these six equations could be solved for the C_j's, the component concentrations, by straightforward algebraic means. This outlines in essence what is actually done to make a quantitative infrared analysis. A number of wavelengths equal to the number of components in the mixture are chosen so that at each the absorption is dominated by one compound only and so that each compound is thus represented. The pure compounds are examined at these wavelengths and the A_{ij}'s evaluated. Then with the D_i's from an actual sample the system of equations are solved for the individual concentrations. Details of these procedures will be given below.

2. MULTICOMPONENT GAS ANALYSIS

In this section we shall discuss the analysis of mixtures of gases which obey Beer's law and shall treat those that do not, due to pressure broadening, in a separate section. In the attempt to analyze a system of gases it is generally inadvisable to work on systems containing too many components. In recent years the analysis of mixtures of the seven common C_4 hydrocarbons has been developed to a high state of perfection (1). However, as the number of components becomes larger the chances of finding suitable wavelengths becomes less due to the overlapping of bands and also the algebra necessary to solve the simultaneous algebraic equations becomes cumbersome. In such cases it is desirable to separate the material into cuts by means of fractional distillation and to analyze these separately.

The spectral region currently of greatest usefulness for hydrocarbon systems lies between about 7 and 15μ. Rock salt optics are suitable here and there are available at present several commercial instruments which are excellently designed for this work. In obtaining the data it is necessary to measure the transmitted energy and the incident energy at each wavelength used. If the spectrometer is equipped with a vacuum thermocouple a galvanometer with a sensitivity of about $.05\mu$ V./mm. may be connected directly to it or be used as a null indicating device in an electrical network wherein the thermocouple voltage is bucked out (2). A diagram of the optics of a spectrometer for such work may be seen in Fig. 1 of Chapter 4. Here the wavelength at which measurements are being taken is controlled by the angle of rotation of the mirror behind the prism. A mechanical coupling is used between this mirror and an external vernier which allows the instrument to be calibrated for the wavelength observed as a function of vernier setting.

The transmitted energy I is measured with the absorption cell in the optical path and filled with the gas being studied. To obtain the incident energy I_0 it is necessary to remove the gas from the cell or to remove the entire cell. In the latter case the absorption cell may be replaced by a comparison cell either evacuated or filled with a nonabsorbing gas such as N_2 or O_2. Also I_0 may be determined with no cell in the optical path if this same region is kept free of absorbing vapors such as CO_2 and H_2O. If either of the latter two methods of determining I_0 are used the correct ratio (I_0/I) for use in equation (1) is not obtained directly due to the absorption and reflection by the absorption cell windows. To obtain the true ratio, the ratio obtained directly as above must be divided by the (I_0/I) ratio determined with the absorption cell evacuated or filled with nonabsorbing gas.

a. Calibration. In preparing for a specific quantitative analysis it is of course necessary to know what compounds are present. This information may be known from the chemistry of the process from whence the sample originated or it may be determined from the spectrum of the sample itself. In the latter instance the spectrum is compared to the spectra of known,

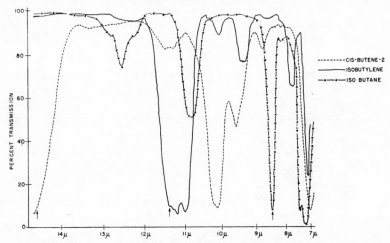

FIG. 1. Absorption spectra for three of the C_4 hydrocarbons in the $7-14\mu$ region.

pure compounds until all the compounds present in appreciable quantity are identified. With this knowledge the spectra of the compounds known to be present are examined to select a set of wavelengths suitable for the analysis. For this it is convenient although not necessary to have the spectra all plotted on the same figure. This then allows an immediate visual selection. An example of this may be seen in Fig. 1 where the data for three of the C_4 hydrocarbons are plotted. The arrows indicate suitable wavelengths to be at those points at which the absorption is dominated by the one compound only.

The values of I and I_0 obtained as above will not in general be exactly true. The measured energy will have a minor component which is due to scattered light within the monochromator. This scattered light will be of other wavelengths than the one for which the instrument is set and hence will not be attenuated by the sample in the same manner. For accurate results it is necessary to determine the intensity of the scattered light at the different wavelengths used and to correct for it. This is done by subtracting its value from both I and I_0 before forming the ratio. The scattered light intensity may be readily determined by the method of total absorbers. In this a compound is chosen which has strong absorption at the wavelength for which the scattered light intensity is desired. A large concentration of it is used to attain total absorption and the resulting weak I is measured in the vicinity of this wavelength. If the measured I is essentially constant through this region it is an indication that it is due entirely to scattered light and hence a direct evaluation is achieved. Special filters and shutters may be used to reduce this correction with considerable success (1).

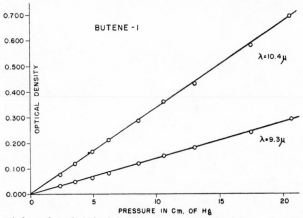

FIG. 2. Beer's law plot of optical density vs. pressure for butene-1 at 10.4 and 9.3μ.

To obtain the A_{ij}'s of equation 2, the calibration coefficients, requires that each of the gases be examined in pure form at each wavelength. To be certain that Beer's law is obeyed for each it is necessary that every gas be examined under a variety of pressures. A plot of optical density at a particular wavelength as a function of pressure not only will indicate this but serve as a means of obtaining A_{ij} through use of the slope. If Beer's law is obeyed the plot will be a straight line, whereas if it is not a curve will generally result which is fairly linear in the low pressure region and concave towards the pressure axis for higher pressures. For precision of analyses it is necessary that the calibration coefficients be carefully determined with optimum accuracy. In Fig. 2 may be seen such calibration curves for butene-1 at wavelengths 10.4 and 9.3μ.

b. *Specific Examples.* One of the most important applications of infrared analysis of gaseous hydrocarbon systems has been in the analysis for the seven C_4 isomers; *n*-butane, isobutane, butene-1, isobutylene, *cis*-butene-2, *trans*-butene-2, and 1,3-butadiene. If the process is one such that only C_4's are involved the gas mixtures may be analyzed directly. For more complicated systems containing material of higher and lower molecular weight the C_4's are removed as a cut from a fractional distillation. At present there is no other method that can compete with the infrared for this particular analysis in regard to accuracy of results and time per sample. A complex mixture containing all seven compounds may be analyzed with

TABLE I

WAVELENGTH VALUES AND CALIBRATION COEFFICIENTS FOR INFRARED ANALYSIS OF MIXTURE OF C_4 GASES

Wavelength (μ)	*cis*-Butene-2	*n*-Butane	Isobutylene	*trans*-Butene-2	Butene-1	Isobutane	Butadiene
14.5	4.64	0.28	0.06	0.23	0.28	0.03	0.18
13.4	0.17	1.08	0.04	0.05	0.20	0.02	0.14
11.4	0.41	0.04	9.31	0.32	2.16	0.03	7.62
10.4	4.74	2.15	0.22	17.0	3.08	0.05	3.41
9.2	0.37	0.09	0.62	1.08	1.40	0.03	0.94
8.5	0.16	0.07	0.08	0.34	0.41	3.21	0.02
6.2	0.46	0.21	0.81	0.39	0.28	0.08	9.72

TABLE II

RESULTS OF A TYPICAL INFRARED ANALYSIS OF A SYNTHETIC BLEND OF C_4 HYDROCARBONS

Compound	Synthetic %	Calculated %	% Difference
n-Butane	19.7	19.1	−0.6
Isobutane	10.4	10.6	+0.2
Butene-1	19.8	20.4	+0.6
Isobutylene	16.8	16.9	+0.1
cis-Butene-2	14.8	14.6	−0.2
trans-Butene-2	18.5	18.3	−0.2
Butadiene	0.0	0.1	+0.1

an average error of only a few tenths per cent of total sample in a total operator-time of about forty minutes or perhaps less in special cases. Above in Table I are given the values of a suitable set of wavelengths for this analysis and the values of the A_{ij}'s of each compound for each wavelength. Due to variations in slit widths used, cell lengths, and in resolving power these data are peculiar to the instrument on which determined and cannot be used with a different one. These data were obtained with a cell length of 9.5 cm. and units of pressure equal to 100 cm. of mercury.

It is observed in the table that each row of the A_{ij}'s is dominated by a particular compound and that each compound dominates but one row. For example the first gas, *cis*-butene-2, has the greatest value of A_{ij} in first row; the second gas, *n*-butane, has the greatest value of A_{ij} in the second row, etc. This satisfies the discrimination necessary for best results. In Table II may be seen the results obtained for a typical synthetic mixture in which the gases were blended together under controlled conditions so that the concentration of each was accurately known. The mixture was then analyzed under the same routine conditions as used in the day-to-day analyses. It may be seen that the average error for each sample is only a few tenths per cent of total sample.

Any mixture containing fewer of the seven C_4 hydrocarbons may of course be analyzed with even greater ease. In general the method may be

TABLE III

RESULTS OF INFRARED ANALYSES OF TWO TYPICAL SYNTHETIC MIXTURES OF C_3, C_4, AND C_5 PARAFFINS

Compound	Synthetic %	Calculated %	% Difference
Propane...................	53.6	52.9	−0.7
n-Butane.................	12.2	12.6	+0.4
Isobutane.................	16.3	16.6	+0.3
Isopentane...............	17.9	17.9	0.0
Propane...................	23.3	23.4	+0.1
n-Butane.................	29.1	29.1	0.0
Isobutane.................	17.2	17.3	+0.1
Isopentane...............	30.4	30.2	−0.2

applied to any system which does not contain too many components and in which the compounds present obey Beer's law. An example of a further application over a greater molecular weight range but with a smaller number of components is the system of propane, *n*-butane, isobutane, and isopentane. Excellent accuracy is attainable as can be appraised from Table II, which gives the results of analyses of two typical mixtures under routine conditions.

A recent application of interest has been the control of plant operations by the analyses of multicomponent C_5 mixtures (3). As many as eight of the C_5 compounds were considered. These were *n*-pentane, isopentane, 1-pentene, *cis*- and *trans*-2-pentene, 3-methyl-1-butene, 2-methyl-1-butene, and 2-methyl-2-pentene. Due to the difficulties of holding such volatile compounds in a liquid cell the analyses were carried out on gaseous mixtures.

c. Preparation of Synthetic Mixtures. Although the gases contained in a mixture may all obey Beer's law at all of the wavelengths used for an analysis the accuracy to be relied on may best be assayed from actual tests on mixtures of known compositions. Since the spectroscopic method often is more accurate than other types of analyses such as fractional distillation, it is necessary to blend such mixtures synthetically. Since the inherent accuracy of the analytical method is high the blends themselves must be prepared with care.

The preparation of gas mixtures of accurately known compositions is more involved than has often been recognized. Corrections for temperature changes and gas law deviations must be made and the components must be thoroughly mixed. Langer (4) has described a blending system wherein the pressure of each component is measured separately in a constant volume and then completely transferred to a storage chamber. Mixing is done in this case by repeated expansions and compressions of the gas through a porous disk. This method eliminates pressure corrections due to gas law deviations as the partial pressures are those read on the gases while in the separate volume.

3. ANALYSIS FOR GASES NOT OBEYING BEER'S LAW

A number of the light gases such as CO, CO_2, CH_4, C_2H_4, and C_2H_2 do not obey Beer's law of absorption. This is due to the phenomenon of pressure broadening wherein the optical density evidenced by a gas is dependent not only on its own partial pressure but also on the partial pressure of the other gases with which it may be mixed (5). As these gases possess low moments of inertia they have rotational fine structure of relatively wide spacing between lines. The type of instrument ordinarily used for analytical work, however, does not have sufficient resolution to show these lines and the measured optical density is necessarily the result of an integration over a number of them. With increasing pressure these individuals lines broaden in a nonlinear manner and the measured optical density is therefore not linear with the partial pressure of the absorbing gas. The broadening is due to the decrease of the time between collisions and hence is dependent on the pressure of the nonabsorbing gases (6, 7, 8).

In Fig. 3 may be seen the optical density plotted against pressure for methane in the absence of any foreign gas. It is to be observed that the curve possesses a considerable curvature in contrast to those seen in Fig. 2 where Beer's law was obeyed. The dependence on foreign gas concentration may be seen in Fig. 4 where the optical density for a constant partial pressure of methane is plotted as a function of the pressure of the nonabsorbing foreign gases. Without the pressure broadening effect the optical density would have been constant whereas we see here a very large increase with increase of foreign gas pressure. These results suggest that, if the factors responsible for the pressure broadening can be either corrected for or maintained under controlled conditions, accurate analyses are possible. One method of doing this has been to construct empirical calibration

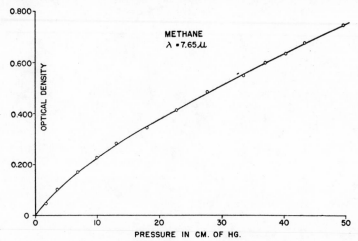

FIG. 3. Optical density vs. pressure plot for methane at 7.65μ. The curvature of the plot indicates that Beer's law of absorption is not obeyed (from reference 2).

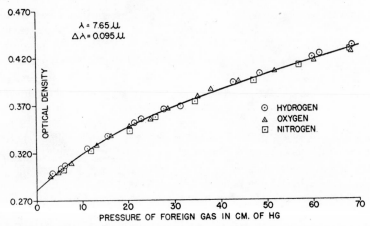

FIG. 4. Optical density vs. foreign gas pressure plot for a constant partial pressure of methane at 7.65μ (from reference 2).

curves for the gases to be analyzed (2). These are constructed from gas blends in which the absorbing gas is mixed in varying concentrations with the foreign gases to be expected in the application of the method. All such blends are examined under the same pressure which is the pressure used in examining the unknown samples. The resulting calibration curves are of the same general shape as the one in Fig. 3. Variations of this procedure wherein the apparent absorption coefficients are corrected for have recently been reported (9, 10). In Table IV may be seen some results of analysis of synthetic samples which gives an idea of the accuracy possible. These results are for the analyses in which the method was applied to the determination for CH_4 in hydrogen rich gases encountered in hydroforming operations, and to the determination of CO, CO_2 and SO_2 in flue gases from catalytic cracking units and burn-off gases from catalyst regeneration.

The successful application of this method depends upon the composition of the nonabsorbing portion of the mixture. In Fig. 4 it was seen that O_2,

TABLE IV

ACCURACY TESTS ON SYNTHETIC SAMPLES CONTAINING GASES NOT OBEYING BEER'S LAW OF ABSORPTION (FROM REFERENCE 2)

Compound	Synthetic %	Calculated %	% Difference
Methane..........................	14.5	14.7	+0.2
Methane..........................	6.00	6.05	+0.05
Methane..........................	0.83	0.85	+0.02
Carbon dioxide...................	6.7	6.9	+0.2
Carbon monoxide................	9.4	9.5	+0.1
Sulfur dioxide....................	1.4	1.4	0.0
Carbon dioxide...................	1.7	1.9	+0.2
Carbon monoxide................	3.4	3.1	−0.3
Sulfur dioxide....................	0.6	0.6	0.0

N_2, and H_2 had the same effect on the methane absorption. This was a fortuitous case and in general the effect due to unlike foreign gases will be different (8). As the complexity of the foreign gas molecules increases due to increased number of component atoms the effect on the optical density of the absorbing gas will become larger. This is only a trend however and it is not possible to accurately predict the influence of various gases without experimental data.

4. ANALYSIS OF LIQUID MIXTURES

The analysis of liquid mixtures follows the same general pattern as given in 2a, i.e. a selection of wavelengths is made from the spectra of pure compounds, the calibration coefficients are obtained, and data are taken at the same wavelengths for the samples of unknown composition. The techniques are, however, quite different and it is ordinarily more difficult to obtain high precision of results in liquid analysis than in gas analysis. Due to the high concentration of absorbing centers liquids are either examined in very thin cells, of the order of 0.006-inch thick or in solution. The fabrication of such cells will be briefly described later. Since any solvent is itself a compound it will possess absorption in certain portions of the spectrum. However, for particular regions it is possible to select solvents which are very transparent. Carbon tetrachloride is a very good solvent for the region 2-6μ, carbon disulfide is quite suitable from about 7 to about 15μ, and cyclohexane is suitable from about 12.3 to about 15μ. Other solvents and their regions of usefulness have been listed elsewhere (11). In some cases the solvents are so transparent that cells up to several cm. in length may be used, allowing the determination of very minute concentrations of solute.

   a. *Correction for Cell Absorption.* When I and I_0 are determined for a liquid in a cell there is, in addition to the absorption due to the liquid, an attenuation of the radiation due to absorption by the windows and to reflection from the cell windows and from the interfaces between the windows and the liquid. This may be reduced but not eliminated by using a blank of the window material in the light path when I_0 is measured. This attenuation term enters into the absorption equation as:

$$I/I_0 = e^{-(acl+k)} \tag{3}$$

where k is the cell attenuation factor. Methods of determining k based on using cells of controllable thickness have been developed (12), but for wide spread semiroutine usage it is doubtful if they are desirable. A true value for I_0 cannot be obtained with an empty cell due to changes in reflection conditions. Fortunately, it is possible for many applications to eliminate k from the equations without explicitly evaluating it. Consider the optical density at λ_1 for a cell filled with the first of the pure compounds used for calibration. Then:

$$\bar{D}_1 = A_{11}C_1 + k \tag{4}$$

where $\bar{D}_1$ is the measured optical density, A_{11} is the true calibration coefficient (with cell length absorbed), and C_1 is the concentration of the first compound. Since in this case $C_1 = 1.00$ we have:

$$A_{11} = \bar{D}_{11} - k \tag{5}$$

   Let us now consider a ternary mixture. Then for λ_1 we have:

$$D_1 = A_{11}C_1 + A_{12}C_2 + A_{13}C_3 + k \tag{6}$$

where D_1 is the observed optical density for the mixture. If now we substitute the results of equation (5) and similar results for the other true calibration coefficients in equation (6) we obtain:

$$D_1 = \bar{D}_{11}C_1 + \bar{D}_{12}C_2 + \bar{D}_{13}C_3 - (C_1 + C_2 + C_3)k + k \qquad (7)$$

However, since $C_1 + C_2 + C_3 = 1.00$ we have:

$$D_1 = \bar{D}_{11}C_1 + \bar{D}_{12}C_2 + \bar{D}_{13}C_3 \qquad (8)$$

It is obvious that we will have similar equations for the other wavelengths wherein the observed optical densities for the cell filled with the pure compounds enter in the equations just as did the true calibration coefficients in equation (2). We thus obtain a set of equations that may be solved by the general algebraic methods used for gas analysis and which will be discussed in more detail later. The above equations and methods apply when the same absorption cell is used for both calibration and analysis. It is clear that the $\bar{D}_{ij}$ and k values will depend upon the individual cells. Since these calibration coefficients are thus partially dependent upon the cell condition it is desirable to calibrate frequently. Due to the difficulty of reproducing absorbing conditions exactly in so thin a sheath of liquid, methods which attempt to obtain "absolute" calibration coefficients must be carefully evaluated. The same general method of using total absorbers to obtain the scattered radiation corrections as described above may be used for liquid analysis work.

b. Examples of Specific Analyses. In the field of hydrocarbon chemistry one of the most important applications of this technique is in the analysis for the individual isomers through the gasoline range. Of course a gross mixture like a gasoline cannot be analyzed directly but must be distilled into cuts. If it is only desired to obtain information about the paraffins present the olefins may be removed before or after the fractionation. For convenience and ease of analysis it is desirable that these cuts be fairly narrow and if possible not contain more than about five components. This latter is not a binding restriction, however, and mixtures with as many as ten components have been analyzed.

Unless the chemical history of the material plus a knowledge of the boiling point ranges make possible a reliable prediction of the compounds to be found in the cuts it is desirable that the spectrum for each be obtained. This allows the absorption bands to be identified in terms of the compounds present and it will show up materials not suspected of being present. When it is known what compounds are present the wavelengths for analysis may be selected and the calibration coefficients determined. In all of this work an automatic recording unit for the spectrometer is a practical necessity if extensive work is to be done. In Fig. 5 may be seen the recorded spectra of three isomeric dimethylhexanes. Here the energy received by the thermocouple is recorded as a function of the wavelength. The arrows indicate suitable points for analysis.

In appraising the accuracy and suitability of an analytical technique there is no method that can compete with that of directly comparing the results of an analysis with the known composition of a sample as blended. Furthermore, any technique is necessarily open to some suspicion and cannot be regarded as foolproof unless it can successfully meet such a test. In comparison to the preparation of gas blends, liquid mixtures are easy to prepare. This may be done by volume, using graduated pipettes. The sample should always be shaken to achieve thorough mixing and care must be used with relatively volatile liquids that excessive evaporation does not

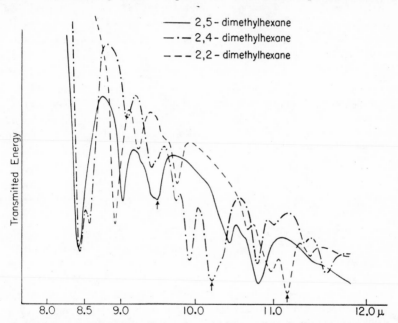

FIG. 5. Automatically recorded spectra for three dimethylhexane isomers.

materially alter the blended composition. In Table V may be seen the comparison between synthetic and analyzed compositions for a variety of paraffin mixtures.

The samples reported in Table V were both blended and analyzed under routine conditions. Further accuracy is obtainable but generally at the expense of greater care. If the calibration data is on hand a four- or five-component analysis may be carried out in less than 1 hour. It is to be remembered that quantitative analyses such as these require that the pure compounds be available for calibration. Without them, qualitative analysis are still possible if published spectra for the compounds present are available. This is done by comparing the absorption bands shown by the sample with published absorption spectra. In Table V the results were all for systems of paraffins. However, the method can be extended to olefins and other unsaturated compounds when they become available for calibration.

TABLE V

COMPARISON BETWEEN BLENDED AND ANALYZED COMPOSITION
OF PARAFFIN MIXTURES

Compound	Synthetic %	Calculated %	% Difference
2,3,3-Trimethylpentane...........	50.0	49.2	−0.8
2,3,4-Trimethylpentane...........	50.0	50.8	+0.8
n-Heptane.......................	22.2	21.8	−0.4
Methylcyclohexane...............	27.8	27.8	0.0
Methylcyclopentane..............	50.0	50.4	+0.4
2,3-Dimethylhexane..............	33.3	33.1	−0.2
2,3,3-Trimethylpentane...........	33.3	33.4	+0.1
2,3,4-Trimethylpentane...........	33.4	33.5	+0.1
2,5-Dimethylhexane..............	22.2	21.5	−0.7
2,4-Dimethylhexane..............	22.2	22.5	+0.3
2,3,4-Trimethylpentane...........	22.2	22.8	+0.6
2,3,3-Trimethylpentane...........	11.2	11.3	+0.1
2,2,3-Trimethylpentane...........	22.2	21.9	−0.3

TABLE VI

RESULTS FOR SEPARATE ANALYSES FOR TEN COMPONENTS OF A PARAFFIN MIXTURE
(FROM REFERENCE 13)

Compound	Synthetic %	Analyzed %	Analyzed %	Analyzed %	Analyzed %	Average error %
2,3,4-Trimethylpentane.......	20.0	20.0	19.6	19.7	20.1	0.2
2,2-Dimethylpentane.........	18.8	19.4	19.2	19.5	19.4	0.6
2,2,3-Trimethylbutane........	20.2	21.0	20.2	20.8	20.4	0.3
2,2-Dimethylpentane.........	0.0	−0.7	−0.4	−0.2	0.0	0.3
3-Ethylpentane..............	1.0	1.0	1.0	1.1	1.0	0.0
2,4-Dimethylpentane.........	20.0	19.6	20.0	19.9	19.7	0.2
3,3-Dimethylpentane........	0.0	0.4	0.1	0.0	−0.3	0.2
3-Methylhexane..............	0.0	0.1	−0.1	−0.3	−0.4	0.2
2-Methylhexane..............	0.0	0.0	0.3	0.0	−0.3	0.2
n-Heptane...................	20.0	20.0	20.1	19.5	20.2	0.2

An idea of the reproducibility of these methods may be obtained from Table VI, which shows a comparison between the known composition and four separate analyses for ten possible components.

c. *Analyses Based on Recorded Spectra.* In the examples described so far the calculations were based on data in which I and I_0 were both measured. In many recording systems the spectra are recorded as total energy transmitted as in Fig. 5. For accurate work it is not particularly convenient to attempt to evaluate I_0/I for these as it means a separate run to determine the variation of I_0 with wavelength. However, it has been found possible to analyze a number of systems from data which are taken from the recorded spectra and in which there is a change of depth of certain bands with change of concentration. In Fig. 6 may be seen the method due to Wright (18) of forming a ratio between measurements between successive maxima and minima in the spectra. This ratio is evaluated for a number of synthetic mixtures and plotted to produce an empirical calibration

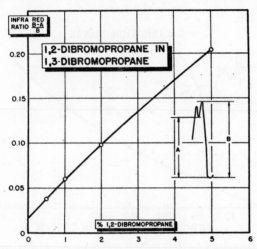

FIG. 6. Infrared analysis method for 1,2-dibromopropane in 1,3-dibromopropane based on change of band depths in recorded spectra (from reference 18).

curve. A similar method has been used to construct an empirical curve for octene-1 in octene-2; it was used in some studies of rubber (19). This is seen in Fig. 10.

A method of computing optical densities to be used in simultaneous equations such as equation (2) wherein effective values of I and I_0 are read from the recorded spectra has recently been described (20). In this, the spectral curve is extrapolated across a band to get an effective I_0. It has proven successful for systems of paraffins containing up to seven components.

5. ANALYSES WITH THE USE OF A SOLVENT

Earlier it was remarked that analyses could be carried out with the sample in solution in solvents which were themselves transparent in the spectral region used. With this method both liquid and solid samples may be handled, provided of course that the latter are soluble. In this case it is possible to actually eliminate the cell attenuation factor from the measurements by measuring I_0 with the cell filled with the solvent. Log I_0/I then gives a true value for AC, where A is the calibration coefficient incorporating the cell thickness and C is the concentration of the absorbing material in the solvent expressed in volume per cent, in weight per cent, or in grams per liter, etc.

In addition to being able to analyze mixtures of solid materials there are other advantages to working with solutions. Many compounds such

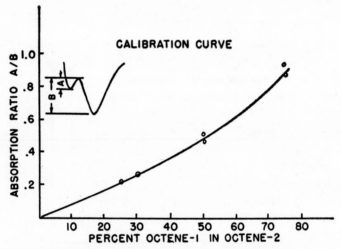

Fig. 7. Infrared analysis method for octene-1 in octene-2 based on change of band depths in recorded spectra (from reference 19).

as the oxygenated ones and some of the unsaturated hydrocarbons absorb very strongly and it is difficult to fabricate absorption cells which are thin enough to give suitable absorption values. For most accurate work the per cent absorption for a band should be between 25 and 50% (14). To obtain absorption values in this range for many materials in pure form would require the use of cells allowing a sample thickness of the order of 0.001 inch or less. These are generally more difficult and expensive to fabricate than those of greater thickness, and there is often a serious problem of getting the sample in and out of the cell.

a. Analysis of Oxygenated Compounds. Although oxygenated compounds do not fall in the same class as hydrocarbons they are of great interest to many engaged in research and production work on petroleum products and by-products. Among these the cresols and phenols are of considerable interest to many and we shall use an analysis of these as an example of the method (15). In Fig. 8 may be seen the spectra of the *o*, *m*, and *p*-cresols and of phenol. Here the per cent absorption is plotted as a function of wavenumbers for several different concentrations in carbon disulfide. It is clear to see that in the right hand portion of the figure three wavelengths, one for each of the cresols, are available for analytical work. In the case of phenol, the lowest spectrum in the figure, a heavy vertical line indicates a wavelength suitable for use. The concentrations here are by weight.

In comparison to the paraffin mixtures discussed in Section 4, I, systems of the oxygenated compounds involve more difficulties to achieve the same

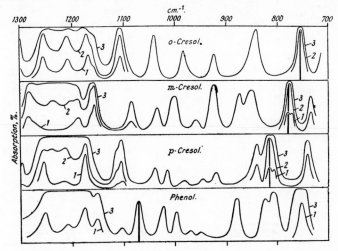

FIG. 8. Absorption spectra for phenol and the various cresols. The bands suitable for analytical work are designated by dark lines drawn vertically through their centers (from reference 15).

degree of accuracy. When the optical density is plotted vs. concentration for various compounds and wavelengths it is often found that there is a deviation from a straight line Beer's law plot. This may necessitate a final determination of the component concentrations by graphical methods. If the compound, such as one of the highly substituted phenols, is solid at room temperature, there may be danger of cross contamination of samples occurring in the absorption cell. This may occur if the absorption cell is cleaned by flushing with solvent, with subsequent vacuum removal. When the solvent evaporates, what remains of the solute may crystallize out, remaining in the cell. At present a number of unknown factors, among which is molecular association, apparently are effective in limiting the accuracy.

With a technique that may yield average errors for paraffin mixtures of only a few tenths per cent of the total sample, the errors for mixtures of oxygenated compounds may be of the order of 1%. This accuracy is, however, very good for many cases, and in view of its speed and the number of components that may be determined simultaneously there are hardly any other competing methods. In addition to the four component system of Fig. 8 the method will satisfactorily analyze mixtures of the heavier phenols such as the mono and di-*t*-butylcresols, meta and para. It may also be used on mixtures of alcohols and ketones. In working with the light alcohols, care must be taken to avoid change of the samples' composition through excessive evaporation. As is well known, the relatively high boiling points of the alcohols, as compared to other classes of compounds, are due to hydrogen bonding forces between the molecules. As these are short range forces due to the dipoles of the hydroxyl groups, they are not operative in dilute solutions where the average distance between solute molecules is many times that for the pure form. Therefore, the tendency of the alcohol molecules to escape is relatively greater. To achieve reproducible results a definite time sequence between time of dilution and of analysis must be followed for both calibration and unknown samples.

b. Analysis Using the C-H Band Structure. In an instrument of ordinary resolution equipped with a NaCl prism the vibrational stretching frequencies of the C-H valence bonds are not fully resolved. Generally a single band is observed and in some cases a slight amount of structure. Using an instrument of considerably higher resolution Fox and Martin (16) showed a large amount of structure in these bands and also obtained a correlation between them and the type of groups present in hydrocarbons. They correlated certain frequencies with the various types of C-H groups:

$$=CH_2, \quad =\overset{|}{C}-H, \quad \overset{\diagdown}{\underset{\diagup}{C}}-H, \quad \overset{\diagdown}{\underset{\diagup}{C}}H_2, \quad \text{and} \quad -CH_3$$

The availability of prisms of synthetic LiF of high quality now makes it possible to obtain this structure on instruments used for analytical work. In Fig. 9 may be seen the overall C-H band with its structure obtained for *n*-octane with such an instrument. A further example may be seen in Fig. 10 which shows the spectra of the three compounds: benzyl alcohol, *n*-octanol, and methyl ethyl ketone. It is obvious that these C-H structures offer further absorption bands for analytical uses. In fact use has been made of them for special analyses (17) and in Fig. 10 the arrows indicate the wavelengths used for analyses of mixtures of the three compounds shown. As the maximum number of discrete bands obtainable in this region is limited, the method cannot be used for mixtures containing a large number of components. However, for a number of special analyses it is very convenient and offers better accuracy than the longer wavelength region. From

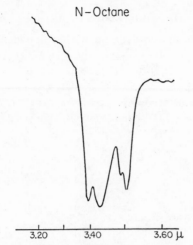

FIG. 9. Band structure for C-H groups found in *n*-octane. Spectrum obtained with a LiF prism.

FIG. 10. C-H Band structure in 3.4µ region as observed for benzyl alcohol, *n*-octanol, and methyl ethyl ketone (from reference 17).

Table VII may be obtained an idea of the variety of systems handled as well as the accuracy.

6. COMPUTATIONAL METHODS

From the preceding material we know that in general the analysis of an
n-component system involves solving the n simultaneous linear equations:

TABLE VII

RESULTS FOR ANALYSIS OF MIXTURES USING STRUCTURE OF C—H BAND RESOLVED
BY A LiF PRISM (FROM REFERENCE 17)

Compound	Synthetic %	Calculated %	% Difference
2,4,4-Trimethyl-1-pentene.........	50.0	50.4	+0.4
2,4,4-Trimethyl-2-pentene........	50.0	49.6	−0.4
n-Octane........................	20.0	18.9	−1.1
Octene-2........................	30.0	31.0	+1.0
Octene-1........................	50.0	50.1	+0.1
n-Heptane......................	75.0	75.1	+0.1
Benzene........................	25.0	24.9	−0.1
n-Octanol......................	30.0	30.3	+0.3
Methyl ethyl ketone.............	30.0	29.4	−0.6
Benzyl alcohol...:..............	40.0	40.3	+0.3
Carbitol........................	47.4	47.1	−0.3
n-Octane......................	18.0	17.6	−0.4
Octene-2........................	34.6	35.3	+0.7
Methylcyclohexane...............	25.0	24.6	−0.4
Methyl ethyl ketone.............	35.0	34.7	−0.3
Toluene........................	40.0	40.7	+0.7
Methyl alcohol..................	51.6	52.0	+0.4
Ethyl alcohol..................	48.4	48.0	−0.4

$$D_1 = A_{11}C_1 + A_{12}C_2 + A_{13}C_3 + \ldots A_{1n}C_n$$
$$D_2 = A_{21}C_1 + A_{22}C_2 + A_{23}C_3 + \ldots A_{2n}C_n \qquad (7)$$
$$\text{---}$$
$$D_n = A_{n1}C_1 + A_{n2}C_2 + A_{n3}C_3 + \ldots A_{nn}C_n$$

Anyone who has attempted to solve such a set, where n is greater than 3, by
the process of elimination or the use of determinants knows that the work
is tedious and lengthy. Methods of obtaining the solutions in short times
are now available and without them the current wide-spread usage of infrared would be limited. Electrical network methods of solving such sets of
equations have been developed and are now in fairly extensive use (21,

22). In these the analogies between the terms of equations 7 and resistance, current, and voltage are used.

We shall now present a method of obtaining the solutions based on a development by Crout (23). This method is one which allows all the operations to be carried out on a modern calculating machine. Let us return to equations 7. We note that here the D_i's are expressed as linear functions of the C_j's. If the determinant of the A_{ij}'s is not equal to zero, which is the case when wavelengths are chosen as of above, we may in general solve these equations to obtain the C_j's as linear functions of the D_i's. The coefficients will now be linear functions of the A_{ij}'s and we shall have the set of equations:

$$
\begin{aligned}
C_1 &= B_{11}D_1 + B_{12}D_2 + B_{13}D_3 + \ldots B_{1n}D_n \\
C_2 &= B_{21}D_1 + B_{22}D_2 + B_{23}D_3 + \ldots B_{2n}D_n \\
&\text{---} \\
C_n &= B_{n1}D_1 + B_{n2}D_2 + B_{n3}D_3 + \ldots B_{nn}D_n
\end{aligned}
\tag{8}
$$

The problem therefore is to obtain the B_{ij}'s as functions of the A_{ij}'s. With these and the experimental values of the D_i's for a particular sample the concentrations of the individual components may be rapidly evaluated using equations 8.

To illustrate the method we shall consider a set of five simultaneous equations, i.e., $n = 5$. With the A_{ij}'s we formulate an initial matrix which is:

$$
\begin{aligned}
&\underline{A_{11}}\ A_{12}\ A_{13}\ A_{14}\ A_{15}\ 1\ 0\ 0\ 0\ 0\ A_{111} \\
&A_{21}\ \underline{A_{22}}\ A_{23}\ A_{24}\ A_{25}\ 0\ 1\ 0\ 0\ 0\ A_{211} \\
&A_{31}\ A_{32}\ \underline{A_{33}}\ A_{34}\ A_{35}\ 0\ 0\ 1\ 0\ 0\ A_{311} \qquad = (A) \\
&\text{---} \\
&A_{51}\ A_{52}\ A_{53}\ A_{54}\ \underline{A_{55}}\ 0\ 0\ 0\ 0\ 1\ A_{511}
\end{aligned}
$$

Each term in the last column is the sum of all the terms to the left of it in the same row. From this initial matrix an intermediate matrix is constructed. It is:

$$
\begin{aligned}
&\underline{H_{11}}\ H_{12}\ H_{13}\ H_{14}\ H_{15}\ H_{16}\ 0\ \ \ 0\ \ \ \ 0\ 0\ H_{111} \\
&H_{21}\ \underline{H_{22}}\ H_{23}\ H_{24}\ H_{25}\ H_{26}\ H_{27}\ 0\ \ \ \ 0\ 0\ H_{211} \\
&H_{31}\ H_{32}\ \underline{H_{33}}\ H_{34}\ H_{35}\ H_{36}\ H_{37}\ H_{38}\ \ 0\ 0\ H_{311} \qquad = (H) \\
&\text{---} \\
&H_{51}\ H_{52}\ H_{53}\ H_{54}\ \underline{H_{55}}\ H_{56}\ H_{57}\ H_{58}\ H_{59}\ H_{510}\ H_{511}
\end{aligned}
$$

The rules for deriving (H) from (A) are as follows:

(a) The first column of (H) is the same as the first column of (A). For example, $H_{31} = A_{31}$.

has some advantages of economy and allows the building of cells for special purposes. Although it is sometimes desirable to use cells with windows of quartz, AgCl, or CaF_2, the material of greatest general utility and economy is NaCl. This is now available in blanks procured from synthetically grown crystals.* It may be procured with the cleavage planes at random angles to the faces of the blank or with the cleavage planes parallel to the faces. It is clear and of excellent quality. With the procurement of these latter blanks they may be easily cleaved to produce several thinner blanks from the same starting piece. For example, a blank 15-mm. thick and 50-mm. square may readily be cleaved to give two pieces each half as thick. With care each of these can be further cleaved to give a total of four plates from a single starting blank.

To cleave a blank one simple way is to set it on edge and to draw a line on the opposite edge, parallel to the sides and along the center of the thickness. A well-sharpened pocket knife can then be used. The blade is laid on the line and given several brisk taps with some suitable object. This will start the cleavage which may be observed by viewing the blank at an angle so as to make the resulting interference fringes visible. The blank may then be set on another edge and the cleavage "followed around" by tapping the knife with its edge laid on the top edge and coincident with the cleavage line. Some practice for this is required but it is easily mastered.

In preparation for polishing it is sufficient to work the faces of the blanks down on about three or four successively finer grades of grinding and polishing paper or cloth. The last one should be very fine grade such as type 0000 as used for metallurgical polishing. The blank may then be given a polish to a high degree of transparency on a cloth or pitch lap (24). A suitable cloth lap may be made by stretching a piece of material of intermediate softness such as linen or rayon over a flat metal surface. This may be lightly covered with a thin layer of polishing compound.† Lubrication is provided by wetting the lap with ethyl alcohol. The plates are rubbed with random motions on this lap until a good polish is achieved and then given a final polishing with a dry cloth. This method will not give surfaces which are optically flat but this is unnecessary in many cells, particularly if they are in the optical system prior to the entrance slit of the monochromator.

In Fig. 11 may be seen the construction of a simple absorption cell for gases. The butt surfaces here on the glass are achieved on a grinding wheel. In Fig. 12 may be seen the construction of a simple absorption cell for liquids (25). In general construction it consists of two salt plates separated by an amalgamated lead shim and equipped with needle valves for filling and flushing. The two salt plates are denoted by 1 and 2, the separating

---

* Available from the Harshaw Chemical Co., Cleveland, Ohio.

† Such as Buffing Powder A ⚹1 Fine, from Carborundum Co., Niagara Falls, N. Y.

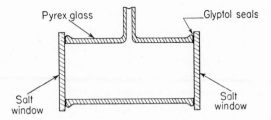

FIG. 11. Schematic diagram of infrared absorption cell for gases.

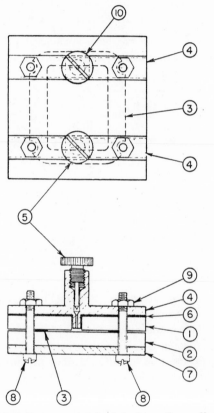

FIG. 12. Construction diagram of infrared absorption cell for liquids utilizing needle valves for filling (from reference 25).

shim by 3 and the cell filling unit by 4. This latter consists of a stainless steel piece so machined as to constitute the seat of a needle valve and to provide a filling tube for the cell. This enters a hole drilled in one plate as shown and connects with the space between the plates. The two needles are not the same, 5 is machined so that there is a tolerance of only about

0.0002 inch between the shank of the needle and the wall of the hole in 4 leading directly to the valve seat. This allows 5 to act as a plunger when inserted, thus providing pressure to force viscous fluids into the absorption region. Needle 10 has its corresponding tolerance much larger so that it will not build up a back pressure when screwed down. Units 4 and 7 together with machine screws 8 provide pressure on the salt plates. The pressure is transmitted to shim 3 to provide a vapor-tight seal. Holes for the machines screws and also for units 4 are drilled through the salt plates using an ordinary drill press with kerosene to lubricate the drill.

8. FILTER TYPE INFRARED ANALYZERS

In the past few years there has been considerable development of filter type infrared analyzers for the continuous recording of the concentration of

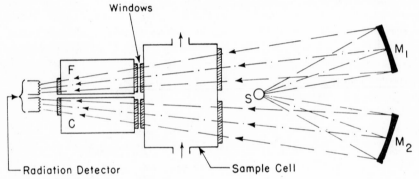

FIG. 13. Optical diagram of filter type, continuous flow, infrared gas analyzer. (Courtesy of Baird Associates, Inc.)

one component in a gas stream (26, 27, 28). In Fig. 13 may be seen the optical diagram for one such type of instrument. It consists of five principal components: a radiation source, S; three absorption cells, F, C, and the sample cell; and radiation detectors in a bridge network. Light from the source is focussed by the two mirrors, M_1 and M_2, into two beams, one of which goes through the sample cell and the filter cell F and the other goes through the sample cell and the comparison cell C. They then fall on separate bolometer elements which are radiation detectors and which are arms of the Wheatstone bridge arrangement.

The filter cell is filled with the absorbing gas it is desired to detect and measure in the flow stream. Therefore at those wavelengths at which this gas absorbs the energy will be essentially all removed from the beam and thus the corresponding bolometer arm will be unaffected by variations of that gas in the sample cell. If the comparison cell is filled with a nonabsorbing gas such as N_2, the energy received by the corresponding bolometer arm at the same wavelengths will vary inversely with the concentration of the absorbing gas in the sample cell. Therefore, a variation of the absorbing gas in the sample cell will produce a differential variation in the energy received by the two bolometers. This differential is suitably amplified and recorded.

Let us suppose that a second absorbing gas is present in the sample cell which has no overlapping of absorption bands with the gas in the filter cell. Such a gas will reduce the energy received by both bolometers equally and hence will not affect the bridge balance and will not affect the determination of the gas in the filter cells. Similar considerations apply to other absorbing gases which might be present and whose absorption bands do not overlap those of the gas in the filter cell.

The system is therefore suitable for selecting only one of several gases with nonoverlapping absorption bands and supplying a continuous record which may be quantitatively interpreted to give the concentration of that gas in the stream flowing through the sample cell. Although the nonoverlapping of bands places a limitation on the various compositions which the instrument may analyze the fact that it gives a continuous record of a single component, unaffected by composition changes in the remainder of the stream gas, makes it very valuable for many particular cases. Some of the gases for which such an instrument may successfully perform continuous analysis are CH_4, CO, CO_2, SO_2, C_2H_6, etc.

II. Analysis by Raman Spectroscopy

1. introduction

In Chapter 4 was given a discussion of the fundamentals of Raman spectroscopy. When a molecular substance is irradiated with monochromatic light the scattered radiation will be observed to possess a number of different frequencies. In addition to the light scattered without change of frequency (Rayleigh scattering) there will be a number of lines of lesser intensity which are displaced in frequency from the exciting line. These are the Raman lines and the frequency displacements are correlated with the vibrational and rotational transitions allowable in the molecules of the sample under study. In analogy to the infrared spectra each species of molecule gives rise to its own unique pattern of Raman lines. It is this uniqueness that forms the basis for the analytical applications of Raman spectroscopy.

Except in the case of molecular interactions such as hydrogen bonding which are of no interest here, the Raman spectrum of a mixture is the superposition of the Raman spectra of all the components. The intensity of each line is proportional to the concentration of the component to which it is due. The method of application to analytical work is therefore similar in general outline to that used in infrared analysis. Using pure compounds,

Raman lines are chosen for a multicomponent analysis and suitable calibration data acquired. With these it is then possible to operate on the lines and intensities observed for a mixture and to compute the component concentrations. Although use is made of the same fundamental processes, i.e., vibrational transitions, the technique is quite different from infrared work. Up to the present time it has not received the same amount of attention and has not reached the same state of development with regard to simplicity and ease of operations.

In absorption spectroscopy the light is absorbed in an exponential process so that the small concentrations of absorbing material may often be determined with great accuracy. On the other hand, these methods are not particularly accurate in determining large concentrations where heavy absorption is encountered. In contrast to this behavior Raman spectroscopy generally is good for determining heavy concentrations accurately and poor for detecting small concentrations, i.e., of the order of 1% and less. This is a result of the fact that the intensity of the scattered light is essentially linearly dependent on the concentration of the scattering molecules.

Infrared, ultraviolet, and Raman spectra are complementary in a number of ways, and with future developments it will become more evident as to where each is used with greatest advantage. As commercial equipment for Raman work is not so readily available at present as for infrared and ultraviolet we shall discuss the experimental technique in somewhat greater detail.

2. EXPERIMENTAL METHODS

For Raman work it is usually desired to have a spectrograph which is a reasonable compromise between the two contradictory requirements of high light-gathering power and high dispersion. The instrument must have a fairly high light-gathering power as the intensities of the Raman lines are weak in comparison to the intensity of the scattered excitation light. It must also have a fairly high resolution so as to suitably resolve and separate the individual Raman lines.

The optical system of an instrument built by Stamm (29) for industrial research and analytical applications of Raman spectra may be seen in Fig. 14. This utilizes an off-axis paraboloid mirror for collimating the light and achieves its wavelength separation by means of an echelette diffraction grating of 15,000 lines per inch. From the grating the light passes through an objective to be focused onto a photographic plate. The light entering the entrance slit is that collected from the sample tube, not shown here.

The sample tube is always one from which light scattered at right angles to the exciting radiation is collected and focused onto the entrance slit.

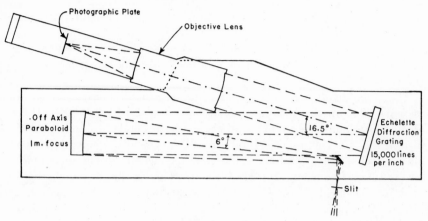

FIG. 14. Optical diagram of a spectrograph designed for Raman spectroscopy (from reference 29).

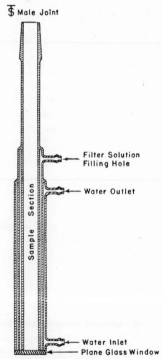

FIG. 15. Diagram of glass sample tube with concentric filter and water jackets used for Raman studies (from reference 30).

In Fig. 15 may be seen the construction details of one such sample tube (30). The central section is filled with the sample under study and it is irradiated by lamps placed parallel to it. The excitation light thus passes through the constant temperature water jacket and the filter solution jacket. The light scattered in a direction parallel with the axis of the tube is then reflected by a plane mirror to a lens which focuses it onto the entrance slit of the spectrograph.

The usual light source for irradiating the sample consists of several mercury vapor discharge lamps (for example, General Electric Type H-1 or H-2). These lamps are tubular and are arranged parallel to such a tube as seen in Fig. 15. The use of several serves to augment the amount of available scattered light. The 4358 A. line from the mercury discharge is a popular excitation frequency. To reduce the overlapping due to the nearby Hg lines of 4078 and 4047 A. they are filtered out by using a solution of sodium nitrite. When alternative lines are used and it is desired to remove interference in other frequency ranges there are a variety of filter solutions available (29). Praseodymium ammonium nitrate may be used to remove some of the continuous background radiation from the Hg arc between about 4400 and 4700 A. It should be pointed out that the frequency of the exciting light must be less than the absorption bands of the material being studied. Otherwise the Raman effect may not be obtained, but rather excitation of the molecules to higher electronic states, possibly followed by fluorescence and photodecomposition.

Often times samples submitted for Raman study contain small amounts of fluorescent materials. This is very objectionable as such compounds give rise, through fluorescence, to an increase in the continuous background radiation. Also objectionable in the sample is dust or suspended particles as they increase the background through Tyndall scattering. To reduce or eliminate these effects, the sample often has to be given some purification. For this a simple bulb-to-bulb distillation wherein the receiver is the actual sample tube is often used. Sometimes it is necessary to use silica gel absorption to remove the objectionable material (30). Due to danger of contamination by fluorescent or suspended material, it is advisable to avoid stopcock greases, rubber stoppers, corks, and plastic bottle caps while handling the samples.

In Fig. 14 the spectrograph is shown equipped with a photographic plate onto which the Raman lines are focused and photographically recorded. In such a case the density of blackening depends upon intensity of the lines and to measure this it is necessary to determine the density of blackening with such a device as a Leeds & Northrup recordng microphotometer. In the next section dealing with calibration the manner of correlating concentrations of materials in the sample with intensity of lines will be discussed.

It was pointed out in Chapter 4 that photoelectric detection and measurement of the individual Raman lines held great promise for simplifying the radiation detection problem. Although this method is not at present in wide-spread routine use it has been extensively developed by Rank and his associates (30–33), and it is hoped that in the next few years commercial units will be available. In this system the light to be detected is focused onto the cathode of a photomultiplier tube. This type of tube achieves an internal stage of amplification through the secondary emission of electrons from successive electrodes. In scanning the spectrum the monochromator element, such as the echelette diffraction grating in Fig. 14 is slowly rotated, thus bringing the successive lines onto the cathode. A narrow slit in front of the tube ensures that only a small spectral band width reaches it any time. The angular position of the grating may be correlated with a vernier on a mechanical drive mechanism to provide a simple and usable

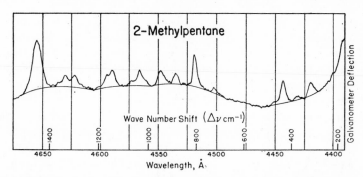

FIG. 16. Raman spectrum for 2-methylpentane as recorded with automatic recording equipment utilizing photoelectric detection of radiation (from reference 30).

wavelength calibration. In Fig. 16 may be seen the Raman spectra for 2-methylpentane obtained by these means and reproduced from reference 30. In this the recorded galvanometer deflection, the signal for which comes from an amplifier to which the phototube is connected, is recorded as a function of wavelength. Below the baseline scale may be seen the actual wavelengths in A. of the Raman lines and just above the baseline may be seen the values of the displacements from the exciting frequency in wave numbers.   The solid line drawn through the base of the curve furnishes a convenient and reliable means of evaluating the continuous background radiation at any point.

3. CALIBRATION PROCEDURES

In preparing for a specific analysis of a multicomponent mixture it is first necessary to select the wavelengths at which intensity values are to be taken. The principle here is the same as for infrared absorption, a line must be chosen for each compound such that the intensity of the scattered light is dominated by that compound alone. In general, it is not necessary to use simultaneous equations as it is often possible to find a sufficient number of characteristic lines which are not seriously overlapped by other lines. However, when appreciable overlapping does occur, suitable corrections must be made. These will be discussed in the next section. In choosing a group of lines, it is convenient if a set of the spectra such as seen in Fig. 16 or as obtained from microphotometer traces can be superimposed. This allows an immediate choice of lines with the least amount of overlapping.

If a photographic plate is used to register the spectra, a quantitative relation between the intensity of blackening and the intensity of light received (for constant exposure time) must be obtained. To achieve this plate calibration a series of exposures of known relative intensity are run and the resulting plates are microphotometered. This gives the necessary data to construct a plate optical density vs. radiation intensity curve. Rosenbaum and his coworkers (34) have reported a simplified version of this procedure that has worked quite successfully. They used the equation $E =$ antilog D, where E is the exposure and is proportional to the intensity of light in the Raman line, and D is the optical density ($D = \log I_0/I$) of the Raman line as measured with a microphotometer. This relation is based on the fact that the characteristic curve of D vs. $\log E$ has a linear portion, $D = k \log E$, where the constant k is often nearly unity. Of course, if the phototube method of measuring intensities is used, the output of the last amplification stage may be made proportional to the intensity of Raman line.

One of the major problems in the calibration of a Raman spectrograph for analytical work is the proper correlation of observed intensities with the concentrations of the materials in the sample. Ordinarily it is assumed that the intensities are proportional to the amounts of material in the sample. However, this may not be true due to overlapping of bands and intermolecular interaction effects. Furthermore, since the scattered light is also proportional to the intensity of exciting light, any variation of the latter will make the measurements unreliable on an absolute basis.

One method of correlating line intensities to concentrations is to use an internal standard. In this a known amount of a standard material is always added to the sample and the intensities of the Raman lines for compounds of interest are compared to the intensity of a particular line of the standard material. It is obvious that this method eliminates difficulties due to variations in intensity of the exciting radiation. In the work of Fenske et al. (30) carbon tetrachloride was used as the standard material and all intensities were related to the intensity of its $\Delta\nu = 459$ cm.$^{-1}$ line. A unit of intensity called the scattering coefficient was defined as ratio of the intensity of the Raman line for the compound to that of the $\Delta\nu = 459$ cm.$^{-1}$ line of carbon tetrachloride. One objection to the internal standard method is the necessary contamination of sizable quantities of pure materials often needed for the calibration of other types of instruments. This is a problem when working with pure compounds that may cost several dollars per milliliter.

Rosenbaum *et al.*, who used the photographic technique, have used an empirical averaging process wherein essentially direct correlations between photographic blackening and sample concentrations were obtained under conditions which allowed for the overlapping and interaction effects that may occur in mixtures. In this method it is important that the exposure conditions and photographic processing be very reproducible. Data were obtained for the compounds in pure form and in known mixtures. For each Raman line chosen for analytical work a ratio between the intensity I_e observed for the mixture and the intensity I_e^0 observed for the corresponding pure compound was formed to give an apparent percentage of the compound in the mixture. If several lines were used for the same compounds the apparent percentages were averaged to give P_{av}. These values of P_{av} were then normalized to 100% for the sample to give corrected percentage values, P_c. Next a ratio, R, was formed between the corrected percentage and the known percentage in the sample for each compound. As several mixtures were used, the values of R were averaged for each compound to yield an R_{av}. The observed intensity of each analysis line for the pure compound was then multiplied by the proper R_{av} to yield a quantity I_c, which is the intensity of the line as corrected for deviations from average conditions encountered during operating procedures. In applying these data to an unknown mixture, the observed effective intensity, I_e, observed for each line is divided by the proper I_c to give the percentage of each compound present. If several lines are used for the same compound, it allows an average to be evaluated. This method, although a bit lengthy, has been quite successful, as reported in reference (34).

In working with binary mixtures it is possible to calibrate in terms of ratios of intensities in such a manner as to eliminate the need of actually evaluating the individual scattering coefficients (29). Consider a mixture of compound A and compound B. From a series of known samples, it is possible to plot (Int.A/Int.B) vs. relative concentration where Int. A and Int. B are the observed intensities for the analysis lines for compounds A and B. Such a plot may then be used to determine the relative concentrations in unknown samples.

4. APPLICATION TO SPECIFIC ANALYSES

Perhaps the most important application of Raman spectroscopy to analytical work to date has been to systems of C_8, C_9, and C_{10} aromatics. The Raman technique is more suited to the analysis of systems of aromatics than of paraffins as the former possess larger scattering coefficients. Although the latter may be successfully analyzed the accuracy in general is

TABLE VIII

COMPARISON BETWEEN SYNTHETIC AND CALCULATED CONCENTRATIONS FOR SYNTHETIC SAMPLES OF HYDROCARBONS (FROM REFERENCE 30)

Compound	Synthetic %	Calculated %	% Difference
1,2,3-Trimethylbenzene...........	50.0	50.1	+0.1
1,3,5-Trimethylbenzene...........	50.0	50.2	+0.2
Ethylbenzene....................	50.0	50.1	+0.1
2,2,5-Trimethylhexane...........	50.0	50.4	+0.4
1-Methyl-3-ethylbenzene..........	13.9	16.1	+2.2
1-Methyl-4-ethylbenzene..........	13.4	15.6	+2.2
n-Propylbenzene.................	72.7	72.2	−0.5
1,3,5-Trimethylbenzene...........	35.2	34.0	−1.2
n-Propylbenzene.................	15.6	15.6	0.0
1-Methyl-2-ethylbenzene..........	17.2	16.2	−1.0
1,2,4-Trimethylbenzene...........	13.7	12.7	−1.0
tert-Butylbenzene................	18.3	19.3	+1.0
1,2-Dimethylbenzene.............	13.3	13.8	+0.5
Isopropylbenzene................	16.7	16.1	−0.6
n-Propylbenzene.................	16.7	15.3	−1.4
1-Methyl-3-ethylbenzene..........	13.3	14.6	+1.3
1-Methyl-4-ethylbenzene..........	3.3	4.2	+0.9
2-Cyclopentylbutane.............	36.7	36.7	0.0
n-Propylbenzene.................	6.1	5.2	−0.9
1-Methyl-3-ethylbenzene..........	8.9	9.5	+0.6
1-Methyl-4-ethylbenzene..........	1.6	2.3	+0.7
1,3,5-Trimethylbenzene...........	2.4	2.3	−0.1
Paraffin-naphene mixture.........	81.0	82.0	+1.0
2-Methylpentane.................	30.8	32.6	+1.8
3-Methylpentane.................	30.8	29.5	−1.3
n-Hexane.......................	38.4	37.9	−0.5
3-Methylpentane.................	30.8	31.6	+0.8
n-Hexane.......................	38.4	38.5	+0.1
Methylcyclopentane.............	30.8	30.7	−0.1

poorer. In Table VIII may be seen the results for a series of synthetic mixtures analyzed by this method. These data were taken from reference (30).

It should be observed that the calculated percentages in Table VIII have not been normalized to 100% as is often done. In some cases this would improve the accuracy. The general scale of accuracy attainable for the aromatics should of course be possible for mixtures of aromatic derivatives. A further application which may become quite important in some cases is the detection and determination of inorganic compounds in aqueous solutions. Stamm (29) has demonstrated the feasibility of the method. A discussion of the Raman spectra of a large number of inorganic compounds has been given by Hibben (35).

III. Analysis by Ultraviolet Absorption Spectroscopy

In Chapter 4 there was given a discussion of the different types of molecules which possess absorption in the spectral region between about 200 and 400 mμ. It has been found that there are certain types of atomic groupings generally unsaturated, called chromophores (36), which will give rise to absorption in a molecule, and that with no disturbing influences different molecules possessing the same chromophore will absorb similarly. For example, the alkyl benzenes all have a broad absorption band centering near 260 mμ which is due to the benzene ring. Ketones possess a band centering near 280 mμ due to the carbonyl group. For further examples and a discussion of the electronic oscillations responsible for the absorptions the reader should consult Section III, Chapter 4.

In a way, the fact that in general only compounds possessing unsaturation absorb in the ultraviolet is a very fortunate circumstance for those working with hydrocarbons. As we shall see later, it allows analyses for specific compounds or classes of compounds in the presence of paraffins and monoolefins whose composition is immaterial to the determination. Although the fact that the technique is in general only sensitive to those compounds possessing chromophores is a limitation to its uses, it is at the same time a factor of great importance since it does allow the detection of specific compounds in gross mixtures. It is of particular importance in the petroleum industry for the analysis of aromatics in the presence of paraffins, naphthenes, monoolefins, and nonconjugated diolefins; for the determination of conjugated diolefins in similar mixtures, the analysis for higher aromatics, and the detection of other special compounds possessing unsaturation.

The absorption of radiation in the ultraviolet obeys the same general laws as does radiation absorption in the infrared. Beer's law as given by equation 1 (Section I) is ordinarily obeyed and the same definitions for the symbols also apply here. The rule of additivity of optical densities also is followed so that an equation such as equation 2 (Section I) applies when a mixture of absorbing compounds is examined. The analysis of multicomponent mixtures is therefore carried out by procedures that parallel those used in infrared. For multicomponent analyses it is necessary to inspect the spectra of the pure compounds, to choose wavelengths suitable for analytical determinations, and to obtain the calibration coefficients. An unknown sample is then examined at these wavelengths and the data used in a set of simultaneous linear equations to calculate the individual components.

Ultraviolet absorption spectroscopy admits a limited use for qualitative analysis in multicomponent mixtures of absorbing compounds. In this respect, it is at a disadvantage compared to infrared. There each molecule possesses a unique absorption spectrum and often large and usable differences exist between homologues. In the ultraviolet however the absorption of a group of homologues is due to a common chromophoric group and differences in substitutions may alter the absorption spectra but slightly. It may however be used to great advantage at times to detect and furnish estimated total concentrations of a class of compounds in the presence of nonabsorbing material. An example of the latter may be the concentration of naphthalenes in the presence of paraffins and olefins.

1. EXPERIMENTAL METHODS

In the earlier work in this field a photographic technique was generally used. In this a photographic plate was used to receive and register the intensity of the light. The sample under investigation was usually placed in the light beam at a position before the entrance slit of the monochromator (37). The degree of blackening on the plate therefore was a measure of transmitted energy and a quantitative correlation could be obtained by measuring the density of blackening with a microphotometer and the use of a calibration curve relating blackening to light intensity. In recent years the newer phototubes and electronic components available have made it possible to use an all electronic system for measuring the transmitted radiation.

A diagram of such an instrument may be seen in Fig. 17 of Chapter 4. This instrument (38), manufactured by the National Technical Laboratories, South Pasadena, California, has been quite successful for analytical applications in the petroleum industry and is in wide use today. The radiation is received by a phototube placed behind the exit slit of the monochromator. This radiation results in a photoelectric current which is suitably amplified for convenient utilization. The instrument is used with two cells, one containing the pure solvent and one the solution of the sample. The scheme of registering the amplified photocurrents allows a direct determination of either the per cent transmission or of the optical density.

Since optical glass will not transmit radiation throughout the entire range of 200–400 mμ, the optical parts are of quartz. It is customary to use absorption cells with parallel quartz plate windows and which have matched transmission properties. This eliminates the necessity of making corrections for differences in cell absorption and makes possible the direct determinations of optical density. Most compounds which do possess absorption in the ultraviolet absorb strongly and generally it is necessary to work with very dilute solutions.

Isooctane (2,4,4-trimethylpentane) is a popular solvent and if it is free of aromatic impurities may be conveniently used. When such impurities are present, they may be removed by absorption on silica gel. Other pure paraffins are suitable as are the alcohols. In the latter case it is sometimes necessary to remove traces of organic acids. Distilled water is an excellent solvent for many compounds which are soluble in it. With an absorption cell of 1 cm. thickness dilutions of one part in several thousand are generally required, and in some cases they may be as low as one part in several hundred thousand. The use of such low concentrations requires exacting procedures in order to avoid contamination and to insure that the concentrations are accurate.

To avoid contaminations it is advisable always to use chemically clean bottles for each solution. Also, it is wise to avoid the use of rubber, cork, and plastic stoppers. Ground-glass-stoppered bottles may be satisfactorily used and these may be washed with a detergent solution, followed by an oven drying, to insure clean containers. To attain accuracy of concentrations when preparing dilutions as great as one part in several thousand it is desirable to make a series of successive dilutions, each of which can be done accurately. For example, if a dilution of one part in 8000 is desired it can be done in three steps of one-in-twenty. Such a procedure allows the use of pipettes and burettes wherein the smallest amount measured out at any time is of the order of 1 ml. This avoids errors, such as improper delivery, attendant to the use of the very small volume pipettes and also trouble due to appreciable evaporation when dealing with fairly volatile components.

2. QUANTITATIVE ANALYSIS FOR THE LIGHT AROMATICS

An application of ultraviolet absorption methods that is now used routinely in many laboratories is the analysis of gasoline fractions for the C_6, C_7, and C_8 aromatics which are benzene, toluene, ethylbenzene, o-xylene, m-xylene, and p-xylene. An illustration of how the wavelengths may be selected from the various spectra may be seen in Fig. 17, which is for the three xylene isomers. Note here that throughout its range p-xylene absorbs so strongly that for visual comparison it was plotted for a dilution factor four times those for the other isomers. This is unfavorable as it makes it impossible to select a unique wavelength for each compound such that it is the dominant absorber. Despite this, sufficient accuracy is obtainable that the method has become very valuable. More discussion of this will be given below.

It is possible to choose six wavelengths for analysis such that a multi-component analysis may be carried out for all six compounds. However,

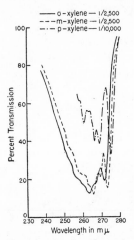

FIG. 17. Ultraviolet absorption spectra for the xylene isomers in the 240–280 mμ region.

TABLE IX

WAVELENGTH VALUES FOR THE DETERMINATION OF AROMATICS

Compound	Wavelength in mμ
Benzene	255
Ethylbenzene	261.5
Toluene	268.5
o-Xylene	271
m-Xylene	272.5
p-Xylene	274.5

since it is not possible to select dominant wavelengths for each constituent the accuracy will in general not be sufficient. It is preferable to fractionally distill the sample with a precision column and to obtain cuts which may be called the benzene cut, the toluene cut, and the xylene cut. Satisfactory temperature ranges for these are: 60°–95° C. for the benzene cut, 95°–120° C. for the toluene cut, and 120°–150° C. for the xylene cut. With the benzene cut a simultaneous analysis may be made for benzene and toluene, with the toluene cut a simultaneous analysis may be made for benzene, toluene, and ethylbezene, and with the xylene cut a simultaneous analysis may be made for the o-, m-, and p-xylene and ethylbenzene with a check for toluene content.

In choosing the wavelengths it is advisable to plot the spectra of all the compounds on the same graph so as to demonstrate the dominant bands. When this is done a set of wavelengths such as given in Table IX is chosen. Here the wavelengths are given in values that are approximately at the centers of individual bands and are expressed to the nearest half mμ.

TABLE X

COMPARISON BETWEEN BLENDED COMPOSITIONS AND CALCULATED CONCENTRATIONS
FOR AROMATIC ANALYSES

Compound	Synthetic %	Calculated %	% Difference
Benzene	7.7	7.4	−0.3
Toluene	15.4	15.1	−0.3
Total aromatics	23.1	22.5	−0.6
Benzene	3.0	3.1	+0.1
Toluene	7.0	7.0	0.0
Total aromatics	10.0	10.1	+0.1
Benzene	0.5	0.6	+0.1
Toluene	2.0	2.1	+0.1
Ethylbenzene	0.5	0.3	−0.2
Total aromatics	3.0	3.0	0.0
Toluene	9.0	9.3	+0.3
Ethylbenzene	1.0	0.2	−0.8
Total aromatics	10.0	9.5	−0.5
Ethylbenzene	0.5	0.6	+0.1
o-Xylene	1.5	1.3	−0.2
m-Xylene	4.0	4.5	+0.5
p-Xylene	4.0	4.2	+0.2
Total aromatics	10.0	10.6	+0.6
o-Xylene	6.0	5.6	−0.4
m-Xylene	3.0	3.0	0.0
p-Xylene	1.0	1.0	0.0
Total aromatics	10.0	9.6	−0.4

The calibration coefficients are obtained from a series of accurately made dilutions of the pure compounds. In many samples, especially those originating from catalytically cracked material, there may be some styrene, conjugated diolefins, and sometimes sulfur compounds which interfere with the analysis and may produce serious errors. These may be removed by scrubbing the diluted sample with a strong alkaline permanganate solution. In Table X may be seen typical results of the analysis of synthetic samples under routine conditions. In general the accuracy for ethylbenzene will not be as high as for the other components. This is a consequence of the fact that it possesses no unique wavelength at which it is the dominant absorber.

With a thorough training in careful procedure nontechnical personnel may do such analyses. The average time per sample will vary but should be less than one hour.

3. ANALYSIS FOR 1,3-BUTADIENE

The application of ultraviolet absorption to the analysis for butadiene content is actually only a single example of the many instances where it is possible to analyze for conjugated diolefin content. However, due to its im-

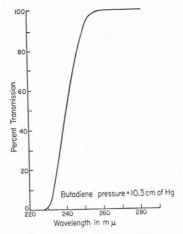

FIG. 18. Ultraviolet absorption spectra of 1,3-butadiene in the 220–280 mμ range.

portance it is herewith treated separately. Due to the conjugation of the two C=C groups, 1,3-butadiene has an onset of absorption that occurs at about 240 mμ. Since paraffins and monoolefins do not absorb in this region it is possible to make a very accurate and convenient determination for butadiene in the presence of C_4's and other compounds. In Fig. 18 may be seen the behavior of the absorption in the 220–280 mμ region. It is seen that below about 228 mμ there is essentially complete absorption. Starting at about 250 mμ the intensity of absorption increases in progressing to the shorter wavelengths. This variation of intensity with wavelength makes it possible to accurately determine the butadiene content throughout a large range of concentrations.

The procedure for the analysis is quite simple. A calibration may be attained by making a series of blends of butadiene and the gases expected in the samples. The butadiene content in the blend should vary over the range of concentration expected in the unknowns. If the optical densities are recorded at one or more wavelengths between 225–250 mμ and are plotted against partial pressure of butadiene they will produce straight line plots. These may then be used for the data from unknown samples to give a rapid evaluation of the butadiene concentration.

Olefinic and acetylenic materials may cause some interference if the measurements are taken in the lower wavelength region and if the concentration of butadiene is very small. On an equal concentration basis, however, their contribution to the absorption is very small. The accuracy attainable in this analysis is very high. For samples containing of the order of 50% butadiene the analyses should be accurate to within a few hundredths per cent of total sample.

The measurements may be taken with the hydrocarbon mixture in the liquid phase by using an absorption cell capable of withstanding the necessary pressure. However, it is, in general, more convenient to examine the material in the gas phase. Beckman (39) has described an automatically operated ultraviolet spectrophotometer which is set to operate at 230 mμ. This is used either for continuously sampling the stream to record the butadiene concentration or for automatic control of the reflux ratio for optimum performance.

4. ANALYSIS FOR NAPHTHALENES

Another example of quantitative analysis for unsaturated materials is in the analysis for naphthalene and the methylnaphthalene isomers (40). This is often of importance in distillation cuts lying in the kerosene range. Such mixtures may comprise paraffins, naphthenes, olefins, alkyl-substituted benzenes, mononuclear aromatics with unsaturated side chains, and naphthalenes. As may be seen in Table V of Chapter 4, the naphthalenes possess absorption around 311 mμ. Very fortunately none of the other constituents possess characteristic absorption maxima in this region. Since there is a large difference in boiling point between naphthalene and the methylnaphthalenes it is possible to make cuts which do not contain the latter. If the boiling point ranges are close to the naphthalene boiling point a direct evaluation of the concentration by the methods discussed earlier is feasible. It often happens, however, that it is desired to analyze a sample for naphthalene which has a low initial boiling point and thus may contain appreciable amounts of mononuclear aromatics with unsaturated side chains wherein an olefin group is conjugated with the benzene ring. Although such materials may not possess characteristic absorption maxima in the 311 mμ region, they may contribute to the "background" absorption due to a slow decrease of absorption with increasing wavelength.

For samples exhibiting background absorption it is necessary to determine a suitable correction. This may be done by utilizing the shape of the absorption spectra of pure napththalene. The spectra for naphthalene in a sample exhibiting appreciable background may be seen in Fig. 19. The wavelengths designated as A, C, and B lie at 308.5, 311, and 318 mμ, respectively. The method of correction will now be described. The following ratios are determined for pure naphthalene:

$$R_1 = D_c/D_a \text{ and } R_2 = D_c/D_b$$

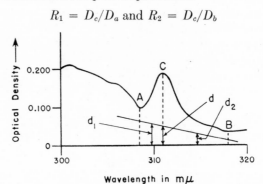

FIG. 19. Ultraviolet absorption spectrum of naphthalene in a sample exhibiting appreciable background absorption in the 300–320 mμ region (from reference 40).

TABLE XI

COMPARISON BETWEEN BLENDED AND CALCULATED NAPHTHALENE CONCENTRATIONS (FROM REFERENCE 40)

Sample No.	Known % of naphthalene	Calculated % of naphthalene	% Error
1	8.28	8.07	−0.21
2	6.16	6.05	−0.11
3	3.22	3.33	+0.11
4	2.40	2.33	−0.07
5	3.27	3.30	+0.03
6	1.02	1.03	+0.01

where D_a, D_c, and D_b are the optical densities at the wavelengths A, C, and B. The corresponding optical densities for the samples, termed $D_{a,s}$, $D_{c,s}$, and $D_{b,s}$ may now be determined. An average background correction d_1 may be assumed to apply between points A and C and a similar correction d_2 between C and B. These may then be evaluated using the equations:

$$R_1 = (D_{c,s} - d_1)/(D_{a,s} - d_1)$$
$$R_2 = (D_{c,s} - d_2)/(D_{b,s} - d_2)$$

An average background correction may then be calculated from d_1 and d_2 to apply at wavelength C for a direct determination of the naphthalene content. This method is fairly rapid and easy to apply and will yield a reliable naphthalene content in the presence of large concentrations of unsaturated materials. In Table XI may be seen comparisons between the blended and calculated compositions of a series of synthetic samples. In these there were large concentrations of materials contributing to the background at 311 mμ.

The same general method as described earlier for the analysis for the C_6, C_7, and C_8 aromatics may be applied for an analysis for naphthalene, alpha-methylnapthalene, and beta-methylnaphthalene. The spectra of the pure compounds may be seen in Fig. 20 and here the wavelengths used for the analysis are indicated by arrows. Such a method is not satisfactory if the samples contain interfereing compounds which contribute to a back-

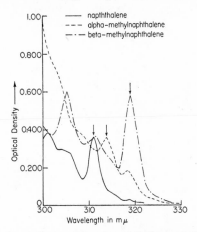

FIG. 20. Ultraviolet absorption spectra of naphthalene, alpha-methylnaphthalene, and beta-methylnaphthalene in the 300–330 mμ (from reference 40).

ground of absorption in the 300–330 mμ region. However, many of such interfering compounds may be removed by distillation and others may be removed by treatment of the sample with alkaline permanganate. In Table XII may be seen the analyses of a number of distillation cuts from an aromatic-rich hydrocarbon sample. Tests made using synthetic blends indicate the average errors to be of the order of a few tenths per cent of total sample.

5. OTHER MISCELLANEOUS ANALYSES

At this point it is clear that the ultraviolet absorption technique is the ideal method of analysis in many cases where it is desired to determine the concentration of an absorbing compound in the presence of nonabsorbing materials. Many examples of such applications could be cited. In this section we shall consider a few cases which illustrate the range of applications.

a. Ketone Analyses. In Section 3, III, of Chapter 4 the C=O group was tabulated as possessing an absorption band with maximum near 280 mμ. This is demonstrated by the behavior of the ketones which possess a broad band in this region. This absorption allows the detection and quantitative analysis for ketones in alcohols, hydrocarbons, and other nonabsorbing compounds. As the simple ketones are not strong absorbers, the absorption tends to be masked out by appreciable concentrations of aromatics in the samples.

b. Styrene and Other Aromatics. The benzene ring constitutes a chromophore with a characteristic absorption band in the 240–280 mμ region. If the substituents on this ring are saturated there will be only minor differences in the spectra in passing from compound to compound. This therefore limits the usefulness for simultaneous analysis of mixtures containing

TABLE XII

ULTRAVIOLET ANALYSES OF DISTILLATION CUTS OF AROMATIC RICH HYDROCARBON SAMPLE FOR NAPHTHALENES (FROM REFERENCE 40)

Boiling pt. range, °C.	Naphthalene	α-Methylnaphthalene	β-Methylnaphthalene
210–215	9.4	0.0	0.0
215–220	17.1	0.0	0.0
220–225	18.2	0.0	0.0
225–230	8.2	0.3	2.1
230–235	0.3	0.9	8.9
235–240	0.0	4.2	27.3
240–245	0.0	13.5	45.0

several homologous species. An example of this was seen in Section 2, III, where it was stated that a simultaneous analysis for all six of the compounds considered there was not advisable. If the substituent possesses a C=C band conjugated with the benzene ring it will result in a new chromophore with absorption bands at longer wavelengths. An example of this is styrene, the spectra for which is shown in Fig. 21. The two ratios in the figure indicate the dilution factors used in the solutions. This material absorbs much more strongly than the alkyl benzenes, and by virtue of this styrene may be detected in an alkyl-benzene mixture at very low concentrations. The same considerations also apply to the chlorostyrenes. A further example of the type of system occasionally encountered which does not fall into the previously considered classes is that of *p*-cymene, benzene, and toluene. Such a system may often be analyzed by the straight forward methods of Section 2, III, if the number of components is not greater than four. I Table XIII may be seen the results of an analysis of a synthetic mixture containing the materials named. Another example is in the simultaneous analysis for naphthalene and tetralin. Since the former absorbs more strongly than the latter at every point it is not possible to detect and accurately analyze for small concentrations of tetralin. However, if it is present in appreciable quantities it may be measured by an indirect procedure. This entails the evaluation of naphthalene by using a wavelength for which tetralin does not absorb. The optical density at a characteristic tetralin point may be corrected for the naphthalene content and the residual used to determine the amount of tetralin present. From the previous

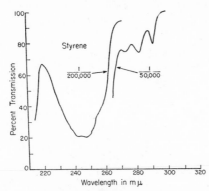

Fig. 21. Absorption spectrum of styrene in the 220–300 mµ region.

TABLE XIII

Comparison between Blended and Calculated Composition for a Mixture of Benzene, p-Cymene, and Toluene

Compound	Synthetic %	Calculated %	% Difference
Benzene.........................	11.7	11.6	−0.1
p-Cymene.......................	10.4	9.5	−0.9
Toluene.........................	13.0	12.3	−0.7

discussion of the analysis of oils for naphthalene it is clear that interfering compounds cannot be tolerated in the present case.

c. *Furfural and Diphenylfulvene.* It is often desired to follow a single compound which may be a solvent or solute through different stages of an extraction or other type of process. If this compound has ultraviolet absorption either at wavelengths for which the other materials do not absorb or of much greater intensity than the other materials it is conveniently followed by the present techniques. Furfural is an example of such a compound. It has an absorption band of very great intensity centering near 267 mµ. This high intensity allows catalytic cracked gas oils which may contain considerable quantities of aromatics and other unsaturates to be analyzed for furfural content with a sufficient accuracy for many purposes. Another example of a material of high absorption which may be detected in gross mixtures containing other absorbing compounds is diphenylfulvene. In Fig. 22, curve A is the spectrum of diphenylfulvene, curve B is the spectrum of an oil with no diphenylfulvene added, and curve C is the spectrum of an oil to which it has been added. It is clear that if the absorbing properties of an oil are determined before adding the diphenylfulvene its concentration can be determined at a subsequent time from the optical density at 323 mμ. In all cases wherein such compounds are added to oils or other mixtures, it is desirable to obtain the absorption properties of the latter prior

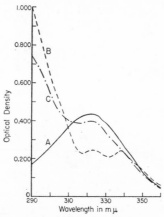

Fig. 22. Absorption spectra of; (A) diphenylfulvene, (B) an oil containing no added diphenylfulvene, and (C) an oil containing added diphenylfulvene.

to the addition. This then allows the optical densities measured for the mixtures to be suitably corrected.

6. QUALITATIVE APPLICATIONS

From the foregoing material and from the discussion of chromophores in Chapter 4 it is evident that ultraviolet absorption may at times be valuable as a qualitative tool when working with complicated mixtures such as oils. The polynuclear aromatics possess absorption bands at relatively long wavelengths due to the condensation of the benzene rings. Although pure samples of many of the possible compounds are not available it is possible to predict their general absorption characteristics. Thus an oil may show absorption bands in the region of 375 mμ which may be interpreted to indicate the presence of anthracenic type materials. An example of such an application may be seen in Fig. 23. The sample under study here was an oil boiling in the 300–350°C. range. The peaks showing at about 355 and 376 mμ indicate the presence of anthracenic compounds. In such an investigation it is often impossible to do more than classify the types of polynuclear aromatics. With the use of closer boiling cuts and the availability of more pure compounds in these ranges, it is quite likely that more quantitative information will become possible in the future.

It is frequently of value to make a direct comparison between the concentrations of polynuclear aromatic content even though the absolute quan-

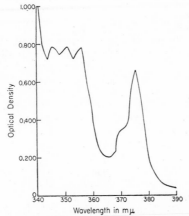

Fig. 23. Absorption spectrum of an oil sample interpreted to contain anthracenic type compounds.

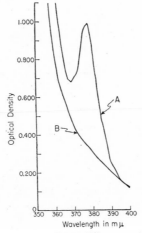

Fig. 24. Absorption spectra of two oils of different origins. In this case a comparison was being made, based on the intensity of the band with center near 380 mμ.

tities are not known. This is particularly useful in the case wherein a process is being used to remove these materials. In that case a comparison of the spectra of the oil obtained before and after the process may yield a reliable quantitative figure for its effectiveness. In Fig. 24 may be seen the spectra of two oils for which a comparison was being made for the material absorbing at 378 mμ. In this case, the two oils were of different origins.

REFERENCES

1. R. R. Brattain, R. S. Rassmussen, and A. M. Cravath, *J. Applied Phys.* **14,** 418 (1943).
2. N. D. Coggeshall and E. L. Saier, *J. Applied Phys.* **17,** 450 (1946).
3. V. Thornton and A. E. Herald, *Anal. Chem.* **20,** 9 (1948).
4. A. Langer, *Rev. Sci. Instruments* **18,** 101 (1947).
5. J. R. Nielsen, V. Thornton, and E. B. Dale, *Rev., Modern Phys.* **16,** 307 (1944).
6. D. M. Dennison, *Phys. Rev.* **31,** 503 (1928).
7. J. H. Van Vleck and V. F. Weisskopf, *Rev. Modern Phys.* **17,** 227 (1945).
8. N. D. Coggeshall and E. L. Saier, *J. Chem. Phys.* **15,** 65 (1947).
9. J. H. Lee, *Ind. Eng. Chem. Anal. Ed.* **18,** 659 (1946).
10. W. O. Seyfried and S. H. Hastings, *Anal. Chem.* **19,** 298 (1947).
11. P. Torkington and H. W. Thompson, *Trans. Faraday Soc.* **41,** 184 (1945).
12. R. R. Gordon and H. Powell, *J. Inst. Petroleum* **31,** 191 (1945).
13. J. W. Kent and J. Y. Beach, *Anal. Chem.* **19,** 290 (1947).
14. R. B. Barnes, R. C. Gore, U. Liddel, and V. Z. Williams, Infra-red Spectroscopy. Reinhold, New York, 1944, p. 29.
15. D. H. Whiffen and H. W. Thompson, *J. Chem. Soc.* 1945, 268.
16. J. J. Fox and A. E. Martin, *Proc. Roy. Soc. London* **A75,** 208 (1940).
17. E. L. Saier and N. D. Coggeshall, *Anal. Chem.* **20,** 812 (1948).
18. N. Wright, *Ind. Eng. Chem., Anal. Ed.* **13,** 1 (1941).
19. J. E. Field, D. E. Woodford, and S. D. Gehman, *J. Applied Phys.* **17,** 386 (1946).
20. J. J. Heigl, M. F. Bell, and J. U. White, *Anal. Chem.* **19,** 293 (1947).
21. T. D. Morgan and F. W. Crawford, *Oil Gas J.* **43,** 100 (August 26, 1944).
22. C. E. Berry, D. E. Wilcox, S. M. Rock, and H. W. Washburn, *J. Applied Phys.* **17,** 262 (1946).
23. P. D. Crout, *Trans. Am. Inst. Elec. Engrs.* **60,** 1235 (1941).
24. J. Strong, Procedures in Experimental Physics. Prentice-Hall, New York, 1939, Chap. II.
25. N. D. Coggeshall, *Rev. Sci. Instruments* **17,** 343 (1946).
26. N. Wright and L. W. Herscher, *J. Optical Soc. Am.* **36,** 195 (1946).
27. W. G. Fastie and A. H. Pfund, *J. Optical Soc. Am.* **37,** 762 (1947).
28. K. H. Luft, *Z. tech. Physik* **24,** 97 (1943).
29. R. F. Stamm, *Ind. Eng. Chem., Anal. Ed.* **17,** 318 (1945).
30. M. R. Fenske, W. G. Braun, R. V. Wiegand, D. Quiggle, R. H. McCormick, and D. H. Rank, *Anal. Chem.* **19,** 700 (1947).
31. D. H. Rank, R. J. Pfister, and P. O. Coleman, *J. Optical Soc. Am.* **32,** 390 (1942).
32. D. H. Rank, R. J. Pfister, and H. H. Grim, *J. Optical Soc. Am.* **33,** 31 (1943).
33. D. H. Rank and R. V. Wiegand, *J. Optical Soc. Am.* **36,** 325 (1946).
34. E. J. Rosenbaum, C. C. Martin, and J. L. Lauer, *Ind. Eng. Chem., Anal. Ed.* **18,** 731 (1946).
35. J. H. Hibben, The Raman Effect and its Chemical Applications. Reinhold, New York, 1939.
36. See, for example: G. N. Lewis and M. Calvin, *Chem. Revs.* **25,** 273 (1939).
37. See, for example: W. R. Brode, Chemical Spectroscopy. Wiley, New York, 1943, Chap. VII.
38. H. H. Cary and A. O. Beckman, *J. Optical Soc. Am.* **31,** 682 (1941).
39. A. O. Beckman, *Petroleum Eng.* **16,** No. 4, 173 (1945).
40. N. D. Coggeshall and A. S. Glessner, *Anal. Chem.* **21,** 550 (1949).

CHAPTER 6

ELECTRICAL PROPERTIES OF HYDROCARBONS

By

ANDREW GEMANT

The Detroit Edison Company,

Detroit, Michigan

CONTENTS

I. Introduction

There are three electrical properties that chiefly characterize a hydrocarbon: The electrical conductivity, the dielectric constant, including the dipole moment, and the dielectric strength. Of these three, only the first will be treated in detail, since it has been developed extensively and from various angles in recent years and has considerable fundamental as well as practical interest. The second property shows little variation for hydrocarbons, and moreover, it will be dealt with in connection with the refractive index. For these reasons its treatment in this chapter will be brief. The third—dielectric strength—has undergone relatively little development during the past fifteen years; a detailed article on this subject would be mere repetition of what can be found in existing monographs (1).

Only the fundamental facts will be stressed in this chapter, omitting details. Experimental results will be dealt with rather than theoretical and mathematical discussions.

II. Electrical Conductivity

Whereas the dielectric constant of hydrocarbons, as will be seen later, is a well-defined quantity which depends on their chemical constitution, the conductivity is by no means a constant. For a given liquid hydrocarbon it may vary from 10^{-19} mho/cm. for an extremely purified sample to 10^{-13} for commercial samples, the variation being one to a million. But even the first of these figures is not a constant because the conductivity appears to decrease indefinitely with continued purification; there is no definite value which it approaches asymptotically. Solid polymer hydrocarbons show the same behavior. The D.-C. conductivity of polystyrene (2) is 10^{-17} to 10^{-19}. As von Hippel (3) has shown, the A.-C. loss factor (ratio of ohmic to charging current) is 10^{-4} if molded *in vacuo*, but about 10^{-3} if molded in air.

This behavior is in striking contrast to that of other substances, water for instance. Ordinary distilled water has a conductivity of about 10^{-6} mho/cm. With repeated distillations this value decreases about 25 times and approaches a well-defined value (4), namely 0.038×10^{-6} at 18°C.

The reason for the difference between water and hydrocarbons is this. The conductivity of pure water is due to the H_3O^+ and OH^- ions into which the water molecule dissociates electrolytically. Other agents that might contribute to the conductivity can be reduced to a concentration sufficiently low that the effect of the dissociation is not masked. In hydrocarbons these contributing agents cannot be eliminated completely, so that, with the degrees of purity attainable today, we do not know what would be the conductivity of an ideally pure sample. Not only the value of this ideal conductivity is unknown, but also the mechanism by which it is produced.

The electrical conductivity of a hydrocarbon, as we understand it today, is that of a sample of medium purity. Its value is not determined by the chemical constitution of the hydrocarbon. The conductivity is determined, instead, by three extraneous and ubiquitous agents, namely: electromagnetic radiation, corpuscular radiation, and chemical admixtures. What the conductivity would be without these three agents is, as has been stated, unknown.

In the following paragraphs we shall give a picture of the mechanism of electrical conduction in a hydrocarbon. (This is a somewhat tentative picture, but it will be useful as a guide.) This mechanism is thought to be valid for all conditions under which a hydrocarbon conducts the current. Next, we will review briefly the pertinent experimental facts on the natural conductivity of hydrocarbons and show how they may be explained on the basis of the mechanism presented. Finally, it will be shown to what extent and in what manner the three external agents cited influence the conductance of hydrocarbons; the usefulness of the tentative mechanism given will be evident from the interpretation of these experimental findings.

Concerning the mechanism of conduction, it is in all probability ionic in nature. If the further question is asked, What kind of ions are present in a hydrocarbon?, we can only give the answer by inference and certain assumptions. It is probable that there are two fundamentally different kinds of ions present in a hydrocarbon.

The one kind is in principle the same as those present in water or alcoholic solvents of medium dielectric constant. They are the result of electrolytic dissociation, hence, according to standard concepts, they probably do not originate from the hydrocarbon molecule. The chief characteristic of these ions is that their concentration is determined thermodynamically by the concentration of the undissociated "mother" molecules from which they originate and the mass action law. The chief agents that cause this type of ion to be generated are chemical admixtures of dipolar and dissociable nature. For the sake of brevity, ions of this type will be called electrolytic ions.

The second kind of ions are similar to those that are formed in gases under the influence of electric discharges (5). Molecules either split into small fragments, radicals, or form large addition compounds. This structural change often enables the molecules either to add or to lose, say, one or two electrons, in this manner transforming into charged molecules, i.e., ions. The essential feature of such ions is that their concentration is not determined thermodynamically by the concentration of the "mother" molecules and the mass action law. They are generated by external agents, namely electromagnetic or corpuscular radiation, and they undergo a process of recombination which may be very fast as in gases, or rather slow as in liquid or solid hydrocarbons. Chemical kinetics of organic reactions (5) offers many proofs that unstable, intermediate compounds are often ionic in nature. Lacking a more precise denomination for this type of ions, they will be called, for the sake of brevity, electromorphic ions. The name implies that the hydrocarbon molecules undergo a certain structural change associated with an electric charge.

1. NATURAL CONDUCTIVITY

This section presents a brief review of some essential experimental results on the natural conductivity of average purity hydrocarbons. The first subject to be dealt with is the variation of the conductivity with *time*. The conductivity decreases with the time elapsed from the moment of closing the circuit, first rapidly, then slower, and finally approaching a more or less constant value. The relatively high currents present shortly after the circuit is closed—the so-called absorption currents—have various causes. Orientation of dipolar molecules is one, but this component disappears mostly after a microsecond or less. The charging of interal surfaces within the dielectric is another, but this component occurs essentially in inhomogeneous dielectrics, and hence is of little significance in the realm of pure hydrocarbons. The third component, sometimes called polarization, is the one that interests us here. It is due to the presence of electromorphic ions, the ones that do not owe their origin to a dissociation. Because of their limited number, they are removed by the field from the space between the electrodes and thus cause a current that is initially high and approaches zero after a few minutes.

The constant component of the current is due to electrolytic ions which, although limited in number, are instantaneously replaced through dissociation, hence, this current is independent of time. When the first component disappears all that is left of the total current is the second component. This situation is shown clearly in the case of paraffin wax, a typical solid hydro-

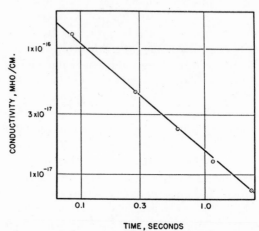

Fig. 1. Electrical conductivity of paraffin wax vs. time (up to 2 seconds). After Scislowski.

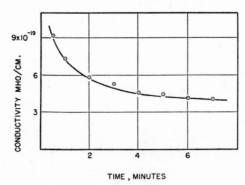

Fig. 2. Electrical conductivity of paraffin wax vs. time (from 30 seconds up). After Scislowski.

carbon. Figures 1 and 2, after Scislowski (6), give an example. These data were obtained at a stress of 20 to 40 kv./cm.; Fig. 1 bilogarithmically shows the drop of the conductivity up to 2 seconds; Fig. 2, from 30 seconds up. As can be seen, the transient conductivity drops from 10^{-16} mho/cm. to zero. The final conductivity, reached after about 5 minutes, is 4×10^{-19} mho/cm.

The conductivity of hydrocarbon oils shows a similar behavior. It is possible to interpret such curves in the light of the theory of removal of ions, and obtain values for the ionic mobility. If σ is the variable conductivity, σ_f the final value, $\sigma_0 + \sigma_f$ the initial value, m_c and m_a the mobilities of cation and anion, V the voltage across a cell of electrode separation a, and t the time, then, according to Gemant (7),

$$\frac{\sigma - \sigma_f}{\sigma_0} = \frac{m_c}{m_c + m_a} e^{-m_c Vt/a^2} + \frac{m_a}{m_c + m_a} e^{-m_a Vt/a^2} \tag{1}$$

The two mobilities are selected to fit an individual curve. Experimental data of J. B. Whitehead (8) were analyzed by the writer, as shown in Fig. 3. The circles are experimental data, referring to a heavy hydrocarbon oil at

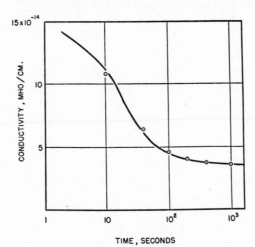

FIG. 3. Electrical conductivity of a hydrocarbon oil vs. time. ○ measured data, after J. B. Whitehead. Curve: calculated after equation (1) of Gemant.

60°C. (viscosity at 60°C., 1.1 poise); the curve is drawn according to equation (1) with $m_c = 3.1 \times 10^{-7}$ and $m_a = 0.37 \times 10^{-7}$ cm./sec. per volt/cm. According to Stokes' equation:

$$r = ze/6\pi \, \eta \, m \tag{2}$$

(r = ionic radius, z = valency, e = electronic charge, η = viscosity of hydrocarbon). Taking z as unity, $r_c = 2.5 \times 10^{-7}$ cm. and $r_a = 2.1 \times 10^{-6}$ cm. From these figures the ions appear to be composed of several molecules. The concentration c_n (number of ions per cm.[3]) of each kind of ion is given by

$$c_n = \sigma_0/ze(m_c + m_a) \tag{3}$$

With $z = 1$, c_n becomes 2×10^{12} per cm.[3] All these calculated data refer to the electromorphic ions present; the corresponding data for the electrolytic ions, as represented by the term σ_f, cannot be computed from the σ vs. t curve.

Next we consider the *temperature* variation of σ in hydrocarbons. The conductivity generally increases with the absolute temperature T according to the relation

$$\sigma = Ae^{-B/T} \qquad (4)$$

where A and B = constants. Plotting the logarithm of σ vs. the reciprocal of the absolute temperature gives a straight line. The slope of this line is, however, constant only in a certain range of temperature. If the range investigated is wide, it is usually found that the slope changes at certain temperatures.

Equation (2) shows that the mobility of ions varies inversely with the viscosity of the solvent. It is known, on the other hand, that the viscosity η decreases with increasing temperature according to an equation analogous to (4); the exponent in this case is positive. Stokes' equation in this manner accounts qualitatively for the $\sigma - T$ relation. This temperature effect is present with both kinds of ions considered, since Stokes' equation is applicable to both.

For electrolytic ions, however, a further temperature effect exists, since the electrolytic dissociation constant K, increases, as a rule, with increasing temperature. While this K vs. T relation is complicated, in a first approximation it obeys an exponential function, analogous to equation (4). Since both K and m increase, the slope for electrolytic ions must be larger than for electromorphic ions for which only m increases. This circumstance might explain, at least qualitatively, those instances in which the σ vs. T slope increases with increasing temperature. Whereas below a certain temperature limit conduction is maintained mainly by electromorphic ions, above that limit dissociation becomes so pronounced that electrolytic ions become prevalent.

An example of this kind is shown in Fig. 4, where log σ is plotted against $10^3/T$. The curve refers to isooctane at a field stress of 4000 volts/cm., as obtained by Pao (9). Between -78 and $-18°$ C. the conductivity increases in the ratio $1:3$, the variation (10) of η for a differential of 60°C. being $1:2$. Between 0 and 60°C., however, the variation of σ is $1:16$, far exceeding that of η. This shows that in this range another effect must be operative.

At low temperatures, hydrocarbon mixtures, which gradually solidify, show a peculiar σ vs. T relation, first observed by Gemant (11) for hydrocarbon oils, and later by Jackson (12) for paraffin wax. The writer's curve for a heavy hydrocarbon oil ($\eta = 100$ poise at 35°C.), as used in the cable industry, is shown in Fig. 5. Down to $-30°$C. the behavior is regular; the

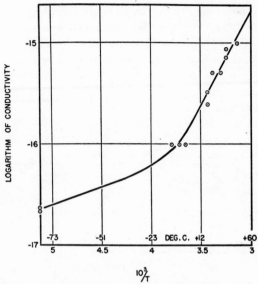

FIG. 4. Electrical conductivity of isooctane vs. temperature. After Pao.

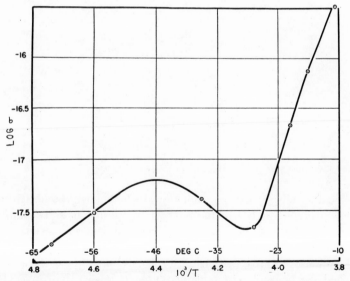

FIG. 5. Electrical conductivity of a heavy hydrocarbon oil vs. temperature. After Gemant.

slope is very steep, corresponding to the considerable increase in viscosity. Below $-30°C.$ σ increases, going through a maximum at $-45°C.$, and still further, down to $-65°C.$, there is again the regular decrease of σ.

There can be little doubt that this peculiar behavior is related to the inhomogeneity of the oil in this range: one component after the other gradually crystallizes out of the mixture. Such a mixture of a liquid and a crystalline phase should theoretically and does, indeed, show large absorption currents. The arrangement used in these experiments was such as to exclude these absorption currents from the data shown in Fig. 5. The writer explained the maximum in the curve by a conductivity of the crystalline phase slightly higher than that of the liquid phase. The correctness of this assumption has not yet been checked on an experimental basis.

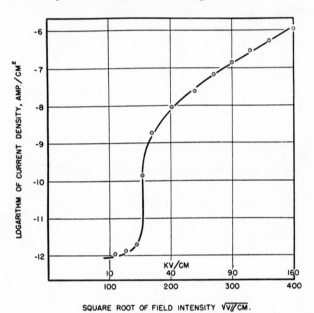

FIG. 6. Current density in toluene vs. field intensity. Ni electrodes, in the presence of O_2. Temperature 45°C. After Baker and Boltz.

The conductivity is further a function of the field *intensity*. Up to fields of about 10 kv./cm. the conductivity of hydrocarbons is constant; from there on, a rather rapid increase with increase of field intensity takes place. As an illustration of this behavior, a typical curve for toluene, as obtained by Baker and Boltz (13), is shown in Fig. 6. The abscissa is the square root of the field, for reasons to be explained later. It is seen that up to about 20 kv./cm., the conductivity is 10^{-16} mho/cm. At about 20 kv./cm. the conductivity suddenly rises to 5×10^{-14} and at 160 kv./cm. it reaches 6×10^{-12}.

Electrolytic ions exhibit a field effect because the dissociation increases with increase of applied field. This effect was discovered by Wien and Schiele (14), and dealt with theoretically by Onsager (15). According to some authors, Plumley (16) for instance, the pronounced effect noticeable in hydrocarbons is due to the same cause. Although this question is not definitely settled, it is probable that only the initial increase, below 150 on Fig. 6, may be due to such a cause. Experiments carried out with well-defined solutions of weak electrolytes indicate that the magnitude of the effect is moderate. With acetic acid in water at 250 kv./cm. Schiele found an increase of conductivity only 16% above that obtained with low fields. With solutions of picric acid in benzene at 42 kv./cm. the writer (17) observed an increase of 50 to 100%. Against these data Baker observed a sudden increase at a ratio 500:1, and a final increase at a ratio $6 \times 10^4:1$ as shown in Fig. 6. It is safe perhaps to say that this appreciable rise in conductivity is due to another effect and is not caused by an increased ionic dissociation.

The major portion of the field effect is probably due to electronic emission from the cathode; these electrons subsequently impinge upon the molecules of the liquid and form ions of the type we have called electromorphic. It is also possible that part of the electrons contribute, as such, to the conductivity before they become attached to organic molecules. In favor of this explanation is the fact that the material and surface condition of the cathode strongly influence the conductivity; the gas adsorbed by the cathode also affects the conductivity values. All these factors determine the value of the electronic work function, and hence the electronic yield for any given field.

The specific mechanism by which electrons are liberated from the cathode is not definitely established. Baker and Boltz assume thermionic emission with the Schottky correction; one then has for the current vs. field characteristic

$$\log_{10} (i/i_0) = 1.91 \sqrt{ED}/T \tag{5}$$

i = current density at field E, i_0 = initial current density, D = dielectric constant of liquid, T = absolute temperature. With $D = 2.39$, the slope in Fig. 6 where the ordinates are log i and the abscissa $\sqrt{E}$ should be 9.3×10^{-3}, and the upper straight portion has, indeed, this required value. Other authors, Dornte (18), for instance, prefer other explanations. According to the latter author, who obtained current-field characteristics for benzene and heptane, cold cathode emission due to the high field at the interface metal-liquid is responsible for the liberation of electrons and the secondary generation of ions.

As a last factor the influence of *dilution* upon the natural conductivity of a hydrocarbon is discussed briefly. Under "dilution" in this connection we understand the dilution of a hydrocarbon with another hydrocarbon, the conductivity of which is negligibly small as compared with that of the first. This implies that the hydrocarbon to be diluted must be one of medium or low purity; as a diluent, a hydrocarbon of high purity must be selected.

The two main types of ions, previously discussed, will behave differently with regard to dilution. The concentration of electromorphic ions and the conductivity due to such ions decrease linearly with increasing dilution. This is generally not the case with electrolytic ions. If the mass action law holds, then the ion concentration decreases with the square root of dilution; the same relation holds true for the conductivity. As a rule, however, the simple mass action law is complicated by complex formations between undissociated molecules, between ions, or between ions and molecules. The relation between conductivity and dilution in these cases might assume a

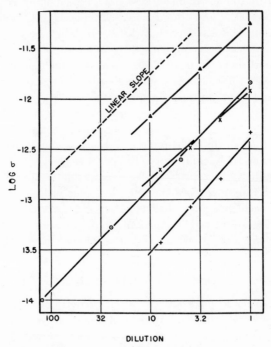

FIG. 7. Conductivity of four deteriorated transformer oils vs. dilution. Data of Gemant.

large variety of mathematical functions including a linear function. If, then, in a given instance a nonlinear relation between σ and dilution is found, one may conclude that electrolytic ions dominate the picture. If, on the other hand, the relation is linear, there is quite a probability, although no certainty, that mainly electromorphic ions are present.

As an illustration, Fig. 7 is given; it presents data of the writer (19). The curves refer to four transformer oils that had deteriorated in service and were subsequently diluted with a new, high-grade transformer oil. The plot, conductivity vs. dilution, is bilogarithmic; in such a plot a linear relation is characterized by a slope of 45 degrees, as shown by the dotted line.

The slopes of the curves for the four different oils are very close, indeed, to the linear slope, indicating the possible presence in the oils investigated of the electromorphic type of ions. Instances of solutions containing electrolytic type of ions will be given in a later section (see Fig. 15).

2. ARTIFICIAL CONDUCTIVITY

Up to this point we have discussed the influence on the conductivity of hydrocarbons of such factors as time, temperature, field intensity, and dilution. The main question, the chemical nature of the ions, has not yet been ascertained. A possible way of obtaining information on this point is to investigate the three main external agents that increase the conductivity artificially. By this means it is hoped that more light will be thrown upon the natural electrical conductivity as well, including the chemical nature of its carriers.

The first external agent to be considered is electromagnetic *radiation* of highest known frequencies, namely X, γ, and secondary cosmic rays.

The mechanism of production of ions by radiation is not definitely established. The primary process is certainly ionization of the molecules, but it is probable that the breaking up of molecules into smaller fragments also takes place; these fragments might assume electric charges secondarily. The ions produced are of the electromorphic type since their number is not determined by the concentration of compounds originally present. They recombine rapidly to a certain extent, but have, partly at least, a remarkably long life. The final result of these structural changes is stable compounds, as is known from photochemistry; it appears that the intermediate molecules are those that lead to the formation of electromorphic ions.

This qualitative picture is borne out by experiments. Figure 8 shows the conductivity of paraffin wax (6) after it had been irradiated for 72 hours by 12 mg. of radium. The curve may be compared with the corresponding Fig. 2 which refers to the natural conductivity of paraffin wax. The ratio of the 1 minute values is 14:1 in favor of the irradiated sample; the ratio of the 7 minute values is only 6:1. Thus, there is a considerable initial increase, due to irradiation, of the number of ions; they recombine partly rather rapidly, but part of the ions formed apparently persist for a longer time.

Figure 9 pictures, after Scislowski, the effect of x-rays. The x-ray tube was operated at 39 kv. and carried a current of 3 ma.; the distance between the anticathode and the paraffin wax sample was 12 cm. Curve A was taken at a field intensity of 4.1 kv./cm. without irradiation. The high values of the conductivity are due to previous irradiations of the particular sample, from which the long life of electromorphic ions in solid hydrocarbons may be seen. Curve B was taken at a field of 3.4 kv./cm. under x-ray irradiation. The clearing action of the field is pronounced, yet the final value is about 7

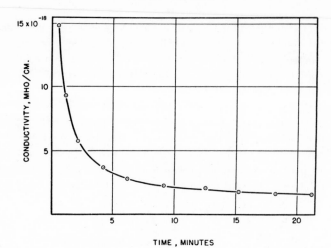

Fig. 8. Conductivity vs. time. Paraffin wax, after irradiation by 12 mg. Ra at 3 cm. distance from sample for 72 hours. After Scislowski.

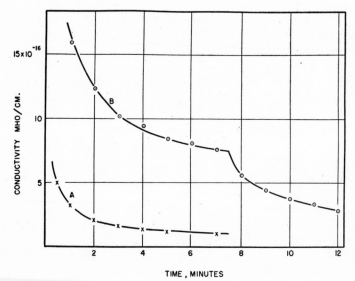

Fig. 9. Conductivity of paraffin wax vs. time.
(A) Without irradiation.
(B) Irradiated by X-rays during the first $7\frac{1}{2}$ minutes.
After Scislowski.

times higher than in the previous case, since ions are permanently generated. After $7\frac{1}{2}$ minutes, irradiation was stopped, and more ions were swept out from the space between the electrodes, as may be seen. These data could be used for a quantitative evaluation of the effect, and a determination of the efficiency of ion generation in terms of number of photons passing through unit volume for each ion generated.

Figure 10 shows data of Pao on isooctane; the curves give current density vs. field intensity. Curves A (electrode gap 0.26 cm.) and B (gap 0.053 cm.) refer to samples irradiated by 2 mg. radium; curve C refers to a sample without irradiation. The ratio between currents with and without irradiation is of the order of magnitude 50 : 1. The different character of the curves is very instructive. Without irradiation there is a sharp upward trend above 12 kv./ cm., as explained in the previous section. With irradiation this effect, although present, is completely masked by a downward trend, typical of saturation. In spite of an increase of the field intensity, the current does not

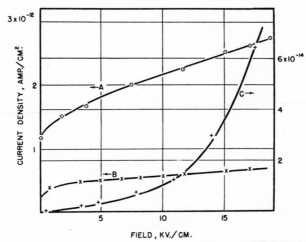

FIG. 10. Current density in isooctane vs. field intensity. A and B irradiated by 2 mg. Ra. Separation of electrodes 0.26 cm. in A, 0.053 cm. in B. C without irradiation. After Pao.

increase beyond a value corresponding to the number of ions generated by the radiation per unit of time. It also may be seen that the currents with irradiation increase about four times when the width of the gap is increased five times. This shows that the radiation is essentially a volume effect: the ions generated are proportional to the volume between the electrodes, that is, to the electrode distance.

In this connection, a fundamental question deserves mention. If radiation increases the conductivity to the extent shown, is it not likely that all residual conductivity is due merely to cosmic radiation? While the nature of cosmic radiation has not been definitely established, it consists, in all probability, of mesons, which are charged particles having a weight about 200 times that of an electron, and of secondary very hard radiation. While the wave length of x-rays extends from 100 to 0.1 A., and that of γ-rays ranges from 1 to 10^{-2} A., these secondary cosmic rays range from 10^{-2} to 10^{-4} A. The results taken from existing literature indicate that a large fraction of the conductivity of highly purified hydrocarbons is due to cosmic rays, but that a certain finite fraction is independent of any radiation.

Moulinier (20) observed that the conductivity of purified hexane, when surrounded by 6 cm. of lead, dropped to 9×10^{-20} mho/cm. Rogozinski (21) carried out a quantitative study of hexane along these lines. He obtained currents i in the laboratory and also (i') in a space shielded by 1 m. of water. In a preliminary test his ionization chamber was filled with argon at 90 atmospheres; the ratio i'/i in this case was identified with the ratio of the cosmic radiation intensities in the two rooms. The ratio was $k = 0.44$. He then replaced the argon by hexane and measured the two currents i and i'. If the natural current is denoted by i_0, and that induced by radiation by i_r, we have in the unshielded space

$$i_0 + i_r = i$$

and in the shielded space

$$i_0 + ki_r = i'$$

from which

$$i_0/i = [(i'/i) - k]/(1 - k) \tag{6}$$

With $i'/i = 0.53$, i_0/i was 0.16; i.e., 16% of the current was due to ions present in the hexane, and 84% was due to radiation.

As a second external agent, *bombardment by particles* is considered. There is an extensive literature (5) with reference to gaseous hydrocarbons subjected to electric discharge in the course of which the molecules are bombarded by electrons and ions. As a result of such bombardment, ionic components are found among the discharge products which have partly lower and partly higher molecular weights than the starting material. Analysis of these products is carried out successfully by means of the mass spectrograph.

The increase of conductivity resulting from electronic bombardment of liquid hydrocarbons has been studied chiefly in connection with high voltage cables in which the oil is often subjected to a corona discharge in the minute voids present in the insulation. Figure 11 illustrates the effect, as obtained by Sticher and Thomas (22), on *n*-hexadecane $C_{16}H_{34}$ and decalin (decahydronaphthalene) $C_{10}H_{18}$. The graph shows the electric conductivity σ as computed from the 60-cycle loss factor tan δ according to the equation

$$\sigma = fD(\tan \delta)/2 \tag{7}$$

where f = frequency of A. C. and D = dielectric constant. The abscissa is the temperature. The conductivity increases about 100 times as a result of bombardment in a discharge tube at 15 kv., 60 cycles, for 4 hours.

The nature of the ions formed is not known with certainty. A large part is of the electromorphic type since application of D.C. causes an appreciable drop in conductivity, as may be seen from Fig. 12, which refers to bombarded decalin tested at 50°C. with A.C. After D.C. has been applied for 30 minutes, the conductivity drops from 9×10^{-12} to 3×10^{-12}. It is interesting to note that the ions swept toward the electrodes are not removed from

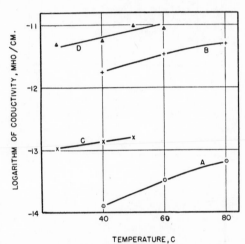

FIG. 11. Electrical conductivity vs. temperature.
(A) n-Hexadecane before electronic bombardment.
(B) n-Hexadecane after electronic bombardment.
(C) Decalin before electronic bombardment.
(D) Decalin after electronic bombardment.
After Sticher and Thomas.

the liquid; after A.C. has been established the conductivity is restored, probably by a rediffusion process, within about 150 minutes.

Sticher and Piper (23) analyzed the bombarded decalin samples and found by means of cryoscopic tests that polymerization had taken place as a result of the action of electrons. The average order of polymerization was less than 3. This is a typical case in which ion generation caused by an external electric agent is connected with an aggregation of the originally present hydrocarbon molecules.

A quantitative experimental study on the primary ionization of solid paraffin wax by beta-radiation was carried out by the writer (23a) using electrons emitted by uranium and carbon 14. Fig. 12a shows the rise of conductivity during irradiation by a C 14 source, and its decrease after removal of the source. By means of a simple theory the solid lines on Fig. 12a were calculated; interpretation of all experimental data then permitted evaluation of the ionic mobility in paraffin and the efficiency of ion pair production. The mobility is of the order of 5×10^{-8} cm./sec. per volt/cm.,

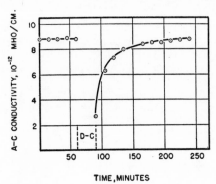

FIG. 12. A. C. conductivity vs. time for decalin that had been bombarded by electrons. After 60 minutes, D.C. (7.2 kv./cm.) was applied for 30 minutes. Temperature 50°C. After Sticher and Thomas.

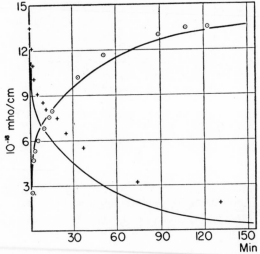

FIG. 12a. Conductivity vs time of paraffin wax during irradiation by C14 (upper curve) and after removal of source (lower curve); solid curves were calculated. After Gemant.

a relatively high figure. The efficiency is a few hundred ion pairs per Mev absorbed; this figure refers only to small primary ions of relatively long mean life, detectable by the conductivity method. No ionization was found in polystyrene and tetrafluoroethylene.

The third external agent causing high conductivity is the presence of *chemical admixtures*. Oxidation products are the most frequent and most typical compounds causing increased conductivity. As an example, Fig. 13 is presented; it shows, after Balsbaugh *et al.* (24), the conductivity of cetane, $C_{16}H_{34}$, as a function of oxygen absorbed at 85° C. in the presence of copper. The initial conductivity, 10^{-13} mho/cm., is relatively high because of the elevated temperature. The initial sharp rise, followed by a drop, and a subsequent gradual rise was observed in many other instances as well. The explanation is not obvious; it is significant, however, that the dielectric constant D remains unchanged (about 2.0) during the first period, and rises gradually up to about 2.15 during the second. As will be shown in the next

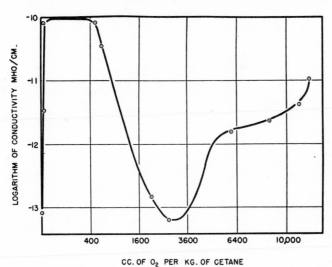

FIG. 13. A. C. conductivity vs. oxygen absorbed by cetane in the presence of Cu at 85°C. After Balsbaugh *et al.*

section, higher values of D are due to polar compounds, and it appears that only in the second stages are polar molecules formed. Since electrolytic ions are produced by polar compounds only, it would seem that such ions characterize the second stage of oxidation. It has been suggested that the first stage of oxidation corresponds to a dehydrogenation of the paraffins to form olefins; the ions formed as a result of this structural change are possibly of the electromorphic type as formed by radiation or electronic collision.

Increased conductivity in hydrocarbons is observed also under conditions in which the liquid becomes heterogeneous, containing colloidal particles. Bormann and Gemant (17) observed conductivities up to 4×10^{-12} mho/cm. in a hydrocarbon oil to which 1% of ethyl alcohol and 0.1% picric acid had been added, the maximum loss factor occurring in the neighborhood of

−20° C., at which temperature the solution formed a two-phase mixture. This subject was explored in a series of extensive researches by J. D. Piper and coworkers (25).

A typical example, taken from Piper's data, is shown in Fig. 14. The conductivity of a 0.042% formic acid solution in liquid paraffin is plotted vs. the temperature. Both A. C. (60 cycle) and D. C. conductivities are given, and it may be seen that they both rise sharply when the clear solution is cooled below 60° C., at which point the liquid becomes cloudy. The excess of the A. C. over the D. C. curve (a very frequent observation) indicates the presence of specific A. C. losses caused partly by rotation of dipoles and partly by charging currents across internal surfaces (Maxwell-Wagner

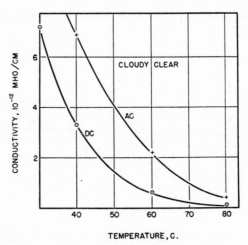

FIG. 14. A. C. and D. C. conductivity vs. temperature of 0.042% formic acid solution in liquid paraffin. After Piper *et al.*

mechanism). Piper's calculations indicate that the latter is significant only if the solute is present at a rather high concentration.

The D. C. conductivity apparent in such systems is probably caused by cataphoresis. The colloidal particles, because of an electrical double layer at their boundary, migrate in an electric field, and hence contribute to the current. Cataphoresis in aqueous solutions usually adds only a small fraction to the large bulk conductivity, but in hydrocarbons this component may be dominating. The ions causing the electric double layer may belong to either of the two main types considered.

Are there well-defined electrolytic solutions in homogeneous hydrocarbons? It might be thought that organic acids, chemically detectable in oxidized hydrocarbons, dissociate into H⁺ ions and an anion, causing conductivities as observed by Balsbaugh, among others. Piper's researches indicated that carboxylic acids generally cause high conductivities only when the system separates into two phases; the electrolytic dissociation in itself is not sufficiently strong to produce an appreciable number of ions. Only strong, yet oil-soluble acids—for example, lauryl sulfonic acid—were found (25) to produce conductivities of 10^{-12} mho/cm. at moderate concentrations and near room temperature.

The writer tried to clarify the question just mentioned by introducing (19) e.m.f. measurements in hydrocarbon investigations. In the electrochemistry of aqueous solutions potentiometric determinations are of great value in that they permit the identification and the measurement of concentration of certain ions for which reversible electrodes exist. The glass electrode, known to be a reversible hydrogen electrode in aqueous solutions, was tried successfully in hydrocarbon solvents, such as xylene, and oils. Solutions of lauryl sulfonic acid, for example, gave potentials ϵ against the glass electrode that agreed with the equation

$$\epsilon = 118(1 - t_H) \log_{10} (c_1/c_2) \tag{8}$$

where ϵ is given in mv., t_H is the transference number of the hydrogen ions, and c_1 and c_2 are the concentrations of H^+ ions in the two halves of a concentration cell.

When the hydrogen electrode was used in oils that were oxidized, an indefinite and low level of H^+ ions was indicated, giving direct proof that the high conductivity in such hydrocarbons is not caused by dissociation of an acid. It was concluded that the cations, like the anions, must be organic. The most common type of organic cations are amines; and amines in combination with aliphatic acids were found to form electrolytic ions in hydrocarbons even at room temperature and concentrations of about 0.03 molar if a third compound, a phenolic, was added. Figure 15 shows some of the writer's data on such solutions in a hydrocarbon. An interpretation of these curves seems to indicate that 1 molecule of amine, 1 molecule of acid, and 3 molecules of phenol combine to form an addition compound which subsequently dissociates electrolytically into a positive and a negative ion. While the order of magnitude of the dissociation constant is 10^{-18}, that of the association constant of the three compounds is 10^4. As a further proof of the electrolytic nature of these solutions the writer has used special electrodes for potentiometric determination of the negative ions in hydrocarbon solutions of the type described.

Such electrodes were made of silver coated with an organic silver salt such as silver propionate or myristate (25a). Such an electrode, an analogue of the familiar Ag-Ag Cl electrode, indicates the concentration of aliphatic acid anions by its potential. Measurements on concentration cells with solutions as just described and with an identical concentration of o-cresol

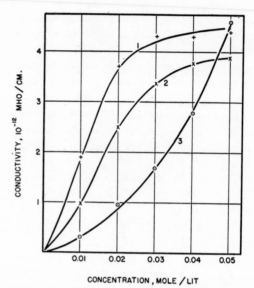

Fig. 15. Conductivity vs. concentration of solutions in hydrocarbon oil. Room temperature. Varying concentration of (1) myristic acid, (2) tributylamine, (3) α-naphthol; the other two compounds in each case being 0.05 mole/liter. After Gemant.

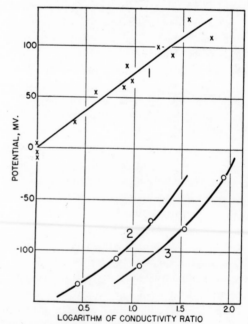

Fig. 16. Potential vs. logarithm of conductivity ratio of concentration cells with propionate solutions in oil; according to Gemant.
Curve 1: Identical cresol concentration, both sides.
Curve 2, 3: Constant difference in cresol content.

throughout are shown in curve 1 of Fig. 16. The agreement of the slope with theory proves the presence of aliphatic acid anions in these solutions in hydrocarbon oil. In the series shown by curves 2 and 3 the solutions having lower conductivity contained also a lower concentration of o-cresol; the shift of the curves toward lower potentials is explainable by theory.

If an oxidized hydrocarbon oil is now measured by means of such electrodes against a reference solution containing acid, amine, and cresol, a negative potential is obtained as indicated by the lowest point on curve 2, Fig. 17. Adding successive amounts of cresol to the oxidized oil, the meas-

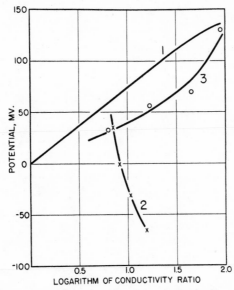

FIG. 17. Potential vs. logarithm of conductivity ratio of cells with a reference solution. After Gemant.
Curve 1: Same as curve 1 of Fig. 16.
Curve 2: Oxidized oil with increasing cresol content.
Curve 3: Oxidized oil at different dilutions and constant cresol content.

ured potential approaches the "normal" level. (Curve 1 of Fig. 17 is identical with curve 1 of Fig. 16.) Diluting this solution with pure oil, but keeping its cresol concentration constant, curve 3 is obtained which has a trend rather close to curve 1. These results indicate that the negative ions in oxidized hydrocarbon oils are very likely anions of aliphatic acids.

If the ions in these solutions are electrolytic, as assumed, their size must be molecular and not colloidal. An indirect support of this statement was supplied by the writer by measuring the diffusion coefficient of C 14 labelled tridecanoic acid in an oil in the presence of an amine and a phenol. A new tracer method developed for this purpose (25b) was used; the molecular radius was computed by means of Stokes' law from the diffusion coefficient. The radius of the labelled compound increased with time from 4 to 8 A., substantiating the view that moderately large molecular addition compounds are formed. Ions originating from such compounds are most likely of comparable size.

III. Dielectric Constant

The dielectric constant D is determined by the polarizability α according to the relation

$$\alpha = \frac{3}{4\pi} \cdot \frac{D-1}{D+2} \tag{9}$$

The polarizability α is the sum of two components:

$$\alpha = \alpha_0 + \alpha_d \tag{10}$$

where α_0 is due to electronic and atomic polarization and α_d to dipolar rotation. In hydrocarbons generally $\alpha_d \ll \alpha_0$. Instead of α the related quantity P, called molar polarization, is often used:

$$P = (4\pi M/3\rho)\alpha \tag{11}$$

(M = molecular weight, ρ = density). Combining 9 and 11, one has:

$$P = \frac{M}{\rho} \cdot \frac{D-1}{D+2} \tag{12}$$

If $\alpha_d = 0$, which is the case for many hydrocarbons, and in the optical frequency range for all substances, Maxwell's relation

$$D = n^2 \tag{13}$$

(n = refractive index) holds. P is then called molar refraction, and is denoted by R:

$$R = \frac{M}{\rho} \cdot \frac{n^2-1}{n^2+2} \tag{14}$$

As to α_d, according to Debye

$$\alpha_d = N\rho\mu^2/3MkT \tag{15}$$

(N = Avogadro's number, 6.06×10^{23}, μ = dipole moment of dipolar molecules, k = Boltzmann's constant = 1.38×10^{-16}, T = temperature in degrees K.)

From these relations it may be seen that the basic quantities R and μ determine the dielectric constant. Concerning the former it is assumed (5) that each bond in the molecule contributes an additive term to R. For hydrocarbons only a few bonds, as shown in Table I, have to be considered. By means of

$$R = (4\pi M/3\rho)\alpha_0 \qquad (11a)$$

α_0 can be computed from R.

TABLE I

BOND REFRACTIONS IN HYDROCARBONS

Bond	R
C—H	1.70
C—C	1.21
C=C	4.15
C≡C	6.02

TABLE II

DIELECTRIC CONSTANTS AND DIPOLE MOMENTS OF HYDROCARBONS

Compound	Dielectric constant (room temp.)	Dipole moment in Debye units	Refractive index (room temp.)
1,3-Pentadiene	2.319	0.50	1.440
Isoprene	2.098	0.15	1.422
Benzene	2.272	0.00	1.501
2,4-Hexadiene	2.224	0.31	1.438
Cyclohexane	2.012	0.00	1.429
Hexane	1.878	0.00	1.375
Toluene	2.31	0.39	1.497
o-Xylene	2.553	0.58	1.507
m-Xylene	2.371	0.37	1.499
p-Xylene	2.269	0.12	1.494
Naphthalene	2.50	0.00	1.582[100]
Tetralin	2.943	1.66	1.546
Decalin	2.154	0.00	1.470
Dibutylacetylene	2.173	0.00	1.431
Diamylacetylene	2.171	0.00	1.437
Polyethylene	2.30	0.00	1.52
Polystyrene	2.55	0.00	1.59

Concerning μ, the dipole moment (measured in 10^{-18} e.s.u., so-called Debye units), there is a similar procedure, with the difference that the addition of the terms resulting from individual groups or bonds is vectorial, not algebraic. For hydrocarbons this procedure has relatively little significance because of the smallness of α_d. Sidgwick (26) assigns the moment 0.2 to each C—H bond; if the structure of the molecule is known μ can be calculated by vector addition.

As an illustration of the above statements, Table II gives the dielectric constant, the dipole moment, and the refractive index for a number of hydrocarbons (2, 27). The dipole moments are generally small, in many instances zero. As an example of the latter case, let us consider benzene. Calculation of R from Table I yields 26.28, which agrees well with the value 26.25 as obtained from equation (14) using $M = 78.11$ and $\rho = 0.879$. Equation (13) yields 2.25 for the dielectric constant as compared with the measured value 2.27.

For the compounds with finite μ it may be seen that with increasing dipole moment D increases and in particular its excess above n^2 becomes larger. As an example of a dipolar hydrocarbon, o-xylene is taken. The value of R from Table I is 35.6, and from equation (14) with $M = 106.2$ and $\rho = 0.874$, the value is 36.2. Equation (13) obviously does not hold true. From equation (15) α_d becomes 0.0138, while from (11a) $\alpha_0 = 0.0707$. The sum α is then 0.0845, of which the dipolar term is about 16%. From equation (9) $D = 2.64$, as compared with the measured value 2.55.

IV. DIELECTRIC STRENGTH

The electric strength of liquid hydrocarbons varies from 300 to 1000 kv./cm. (peak value) according to their degree of purity and the condition of the electrodes. The electric strength of polystyrene and polyethylene is 300 to 400 kv./cm. Spreading of data is so excessive ($\pm 25\%$) that accurate values cannot be assigned to individual hydrocarbons. The values obtained do not appear to approach a well-defined maximum with increasing purification.

There is a great amount of information about the dependence of breakdown strength on various factors (temperature, pressure, frequency of applied voltage, time of application, curvature of electrodes, and many more). All these effects can be explained by consideration of the various possible mechanisms of the breakdown in liquid insulators. This rather extensive experimental and theoretical material cannot be presented here; the reader is referred to various monographs, for instance those by Nikuradse or Gemant (1).

The literature of the past ten years has substantiated one particular fact: that the breakdown of hydrocarbons is very likely electronic. It has been shown in the section on conductivity that at high fields the latter increases exponentially owing to electronic emission from the cathode, the electronic conduction being superimposed upon the ionic conduction present at low fields. When the field intensity becomes sufficiently high for the electrons to acquire energies of a few electron-volts, they will ionize the dielectric, and breakdown will take place. Since the intermolecular distance or the mean free path in liquids is of the order of magnitude 10^{-7} cm., a field of 10^7 volt/cm. would be necessary for an electron to acquire 1 e.v. between two impacts.

Yet the actual strength is 10^5 to 10^6 volt/cm. Von Hippel (28) advanced the theory that the electrons lose their energy by impact only when the energy is below a limit corresponding to the "reststrahl" frequency f_{max} of the lattice. When this limit is reached, they go on accumulating energy in spite of collisions, until the ionization energy is reached. If the field is E, and the intermolecular distance a, then the energy of the electron accumulated between impacts is eEa (e = electronic charge), and if this exceeds hf_{max} (h = Planck's constant), breakdown takes place. Thus the breakdown strength E_{max} is given by

$$e\, E_{max}\, a \;=\; Ch\, f_{max} \tag{16}$$

(C = a constant somewhat greater than 1.0). While this theory is valid for ionic lattices only, for which the "reststrahl" theory of Debye was developed, its basic idea might be applied to liquids as well. Attwood (29) discusses the applicability of this theory to carbon tetrachloride; no attempt has yet been made to apply it to hydrocarbons.

The writer considered (30) current-voltage characteristics of the type obtained by Baker and Boltz, and Dornte (Fig. 6). Experimental results from various fields show that instability with ensuing failure takes place when the current density becomes of the order of 10^{-4} amp./cm.^{2} With these data the impulse strength of hydrocarbon oil was computed as 530 kv./cm. compared with 515 kv./cm. as measured by Sorensen (31).

Experimental investigations by Race (32) complete the proof that hydrocarbon breakdown is electronic. He shows that, even after continued purification, the spread of E_{max} values is considerable; this proves that the condition of the electrodes, which is difficult to control, determines the onset of breakdown. He also shows by means of oscillographic measurements that the duration of breakdown in heptane and a hydrocarbon oil is only part of a microsecond. This short interval is compatible only with an electronic process.

REFERENCES

1. S. Whitehead, Dielectric Phenomena. Benn, London, 1928, Vol. II.
   A. Nikuradse, in Rhenania-Ossag, Isolieröle. Springer, Berlin, 1938.
   Andrew Gemant, Liquid Dielectrics. Wiley, New York, 1933.
2. Modern Plastics Encyclopedia. Plastics Catalogue Corporation, New York, 1948.
3. A. von Hippel and L. G. Wesson, *Ind. Eng. Chem.* **38**, 1121 (1946).
4. S. Glasstone, Introduction to Electrochemistry. Van Nostrand, New York, 1942.
5. G. Glocker and S. C. Lind, Electrochemistry of Gases and Other Dielectrics. Wiley, New York, 1939.
   Henry Gilman, Organic Chemistry. Wiley, New York, 1945, Vol. II.
6. W. Scislowski, *Acta Phys. Polon.* **6**, 403 (1937); **7**, 127 (1938); **7**, 214 (1939).

7. Andrew Gemant, *Phys. Rev.* **58**, 904 (1940).
8. J. B. Whitehead, Impregnated Paper Insulation. Wiley, New York, 1935.
9. Chia-Shan Pao, *Phys. Rev.* **64**, 60 (1943).
10. Landolt-Börnstein, Phyoi Ralisch-chemizche Tabellen. Edward Brothers' Lithoprint, Ann Arbor, 1943, Vol. I.
11. Andrew Gemant, *Z. Physik.* **75**, 613 (1932); *J. Inst. Petroleum Technol.* **22**, 646 (1936).
12. Willis Jackson, *Nature* **133**, 647 (1934); *Trans. Faraday Soc.* **31**, 827 (1935).
13. E. B. Baker and H. A. Boltz, *Phys. Rev.* **51**, 275 (1937).
14. M. Wien and J. Schiele, *Physik. Z.* **32**, 545 (1931).
15. L. Onsager, *J. Chem. Phys.* **2**, 599 (1934).
16. H. J. Plumley, *Phys. Rev.* **59**, 200 (1941).
17. Andrew Gemant, Elektrophysik der Isolierstoffe. Springer, Berlin, 1930.
18. R. W. Dornte, *Ind. Eng. Chem.* **32**, 1529 (1940).
19. A. Gemant, *J. Chem. Phys.* **13**, 146 (1945) **14**, 424 (1946).
20. G. Moulinier. *Compt. rend.* **213**, 802 (1941).
21. A. Rogozinski, *Phys. Rev.* **60**, 148 (1941).
22. Joseph Sticher and D. E. F. Thomas, *Trans. Am. Inst. Elec. Engrs.* **58**, 709 (1939).
23. Joseph Sticher and J. D. Piper, *Ind. Eng. Chem.* **33**, 1567 (1941).
23a. A. Gemant, *J. Applied Phys.* **20**, Oct. 1949.
24. J. C. Balsbaugh, A. G. Assaf, and J. L. Oncley, *Ind. Eng. Chem.* **34**, 92 (1942); *Trans. Am. Inst. Elec. Engrs.* **62**, 311 (1943).
25. J. D. Piper, A. G. Fleiger, C. C. Smith, and N. A. Kerstein, *Ind. Eng. Chem.* **32**, 1510 (1940); **34**, 1505 (1942).
25a. A. Gemant, *J. Electrochem. Soc.* **94**, 160 (1948).
25b. A. Gemant, *J. Applied Phys.* **19**, 1160 (1948).
26. N. V. Sidgwick, The Covalent Link in Chemistry. Cornell University Press, Ithaca, New York, 1933.
27. P. Debye and H. Sack in Tables Annuelles. Hermann, Paris, 1937, Vol. XI, Chapter 22.
28. A. von Hippel, *J. Applied Phys.* **8**, 815 (1937).
29. S. S. Attwood and W. H. Bixby, *J. Franklin Inst.* **235**, 259 (1943).
30. A. Gemant, *J. Franklin Inst.* **234**, 519 (1942).
31. R. W. Sorensen, *Trans. Am. Inst. Elec. Engrs.* **59**, 78 (1940).
32. H. H. Race, *Trans. Am. Inst. Elec. Engrs.* **59**, 730 (1940); **60**, 854 (1941).

CHAPTER 7

SOLVENT EXTRACTION OF HYDROCARBONS

Solubility Relations between Liquid Hydrocarbons and other Liquids*

By

ALFRED W. FRANCIS

Socony-Vacuum Laboratories, Paulsboro, New Jersey

CONTENTS

INTRODUCTION

Selective solubility in a solvent has been used since the early days of organic chemistry to separate two or more substances. The operation is relatively simple when the selectivity is substantially complete, as in the extraction of organic compounds from water and salt solutions by means of ethers, chloroform, carbon tetrachloride, or hydrocarbons. Other examples are the extraction of organic bases from neutral substances by means of acids, and the extraction of phenols and organic acids by means of alkalies. The latter two examples are usually considered chemical, but the method of operation is the same as with physical extraction and the reaction may be incomplete unless equilibria are shifted.

The separation of hydrocarbons from each other is usually much less complete, although olefins may be eliminated from mixtures with saturated hydrocarbons by acid treatment, or by complex formation with salts of mercury, silver, or monovalent copper. The latter three reagents have the limitations of irreversibility, high cost, and low capacity, respectively. With stronger acid a fair separation of aromatics may be accomplished. In most cases these chemical methods give the extract in a form recoverable only by the destruction of the reagent, and are not the subject of this discussion.

* The discussion of triangular diagrams was presented before the Physical Chemistry Division at the Meeting of the South Jersey Section of the American Chemical Society in Woodbury, N. J. on May 18, 1948.

By far the most general method of separation of hydrocarbons is fractional distillation, since the operation normally furnishes its own pumping action. Innumerable forms of columns and other modifications, such as pressure and vacuum distillations, and azeotropic and extractive distillation have added greatly to the efficiency of separation. The last two methods are closely related to solvent extraction because they employ selective solvents to permit a separation otherwise almost impossible because of the small difference in boiling point. A voluminous bibliography on azeotropic distillation is provided by Horsley (91); and extractive distillation is considered by Randall and Longtin (166), by Benedict and Rubin (17), and by many others. These are essentially engineering problems, and will not be treated further in this chapter. A thermodynamic interrelation of these various means of separation was presented recently by Hibshmann (78).

The greater simplicity of distillation makes it logical to use it first, so that it may be assumed that for volatile mixtures the charge stock for solvent extraction has a relatively narrow boiling range. This operation is essential if a solvent is to be employed such as sulfur dioxide, methanol, or acetic acid, whose selectivity depends as much on boiling point as upon type of hydrocarabon. Otherwise selectivity for compounds of different boiling points may obscure selectivity for compounds of different chemical types.

Although selectivity for the desired or undesired type of hydrocarbon is a requirement for a solvent to be considered, many other factors may be equally important in the choice of a selective solvent, e.g., cost or availability, stability, ease of recovery from the hydrocarbons, boiling point, freezing point, density, viscosity, interfacial surface tension, water solubility, toxicity, refractive index, and suitable degree of solubility at a convenient temperature. Adjustment of the solubility by higher or lower temperature increases the cost, and adjustment by adding water or another diluent may complicate the operation greatly.

Since all hydrocarbons are fairly similar in solubility characteristics as compared with nonhydrocarbons, it is hopeless to expect a selectivity approaching the quantitative. Adequate separation of a pair of hydrocarbons is possible only by multiple extraction, preferably by counter-current operations analogous in most respects to fractional distillation in a column. This is an engineering problem discussed comprehensively in many publications (for example 55, 72, 97, 108, 156, 170, 218, 230). One difference between the two processes is that solvent extraction lacks the automatic reciprocal pumping action which is provided by distillation and gravity. Another is the higher viscosities of the liquid phases. Another is the smaller density differential between the two liquid phases as compared with liquid and vapor. These result in a fivefold increase in the H. E. T. P. for solvent extraction (231).

Solvent extraction of hydrocarbon mixtures is most commonly applied to lubricating oils, and there are innumerable patents for that purpose. One reason is that the higher cost of solvent extraction is justified only for products of relatively high value. Another is that for lubricating oils the hydrocarbons of superior quality are always in the raffinate. It is more convenient to extract small fractions repeatedly in order to get high refinement than it would be to recycle the extract, as would be necessary in the case of a gasoline extraction in which the high quality may be in the extract.

The improvement of lubricating oil in solvent refining, largely an increase in viscosity index (V. I.), is due to the removal of cyclic hydrocarbons. Aromatics are commonly blamed for low V. I. although several investigations (21, 38, 137, 177, 178, 179) show little difference in V. I. for hydrocarbons with and without a single benzene ring. The last paper (179) especially, presented a comprehensive study of the effect of structure on properties in the lubricating oil range. Polycyclics, both aromatic and saturated, are poor in V. I., and should be removed as much as possible. It was shown earlier (Fig. 2B of ref. 61) that there is a high degree of correspondence between selectivity of solvents for naphthenes, and that for low V. I. components of oils, both as measured by critical solution temperature (C.S.T.)

A later paper (62) indicated that selectivity for aromatic hydrocarbons is usually about six times as great as that for napthenes. Nonhydrocarbon derivatives of benzene, such as phenol, nitrobenzene, etc., usually show the best selectivity for both types of hydrocarbons, although convenience in operation often takes precedence over selectivity, especially since selectivity for aromatic hydrocarbons does not differ greatly among most of the applicable solvents. Many solvents have been proposed in patents for concentrating aromatic hydrocarbons, but quantitative data are lacking. Smith and Funk (204) made an engineering study of such processes.

Many of the observations are presented in an empirical form in this chapter, partly for economy of space, but mostly because data are largely inadequate to discuss the theoretical considerations such as those developed by Hildebrand (79), and others (78, 134, 176).

I. Ternary Diagrams

Theoretical consideration of a solvent extraction process requires a ternary diagram of the limited mutual miscibilities of the proposed solvent and representative hydrocarbons of the raffinate and extract, respectively. Bancroft (13, 14) and Schreinemakers (181–186) were early exponents of the method of representation by means of equilateral triangular graphs. Any composition is indicated by a point within the triangle which shows by its perpendicular distance to each side the percentage composition of the component represented by the opposite corner.

In the case of hydrocarbons these diagrams are generally of the simple types shown in Figs. 1 and 2. In Fig. 1 two pairs of components are completely miscible, but the third pair shows limited miscibility. The parabolic curve surrounds the region of composition of mixtures separating into two liquid layers. Additions of the most consolute component to a mixture of the other two components make this pair more miscible, until at the plait or

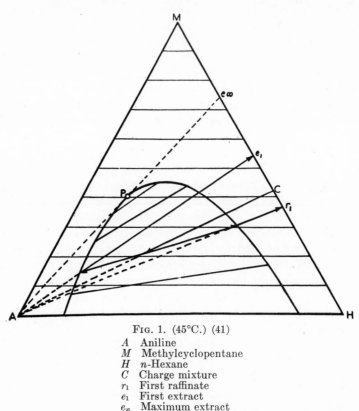

FIG. 1. (45°C.) (41)

A   Aniline
M   Methylcyclopentane
H n-Hexane
C   Charge mixture
r_1 First raffinate
e_1 First extract
e_∞ Maximum extract

consolute point, P, the liquid interface gradually fades out, as at a critical point or a critical solution point.

Attempts have been made to develop algebraic equations for the shapes of these "binodal curves." Bancroft (13) proposed a simple one, $x^n y =$ const., which was discussed by Hand (74). The variables, x and y, are the amounts of the two nonconsolute components relative to that of the consolute component. The exponent, n (not necessarily an integer), takes care of asymmetry. This equation holds well for single curves of the hyperbolic type, which seem to run into both lower corners (though they never do so rigorously). It would fail for systems with double nonconsolute pairs (such as Fig. 2), since x or y becomes zero on the side line. It would fail also for curves which terminate on the base line (Figs. 1, 3, 5, 6, 13, 15, 16) because both x and y become infinite. Bancroft (13) allowed for the latter cases by subtracting the mutual solubilities of the nonconsolute components from the amounts used in the equation. Even this is not adaptable to curves of the parabolic type (Figs. 1, 3, 13) in which moderate amounts of the con-

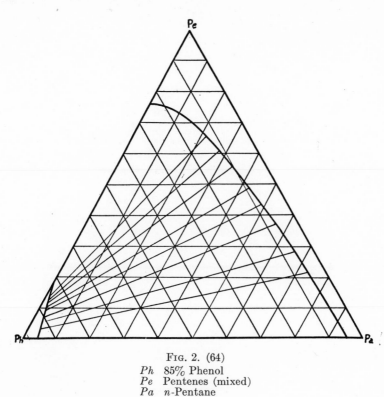

FIG. 2. (64)

Ph 85% Phenol
Pe Pentenes (mixed)
Pa *n*-Pentane

solute component may cause a slight decrease in solubility. Since these curves have oblique axes, the equation for a parabola thus shifted would be too complicated to be useful.

An approximate generalization which is sometimes useful for systems such as Fig. 4, in which the mutual solubility of two components is low, is that the solubility of either of them in the other is proportional to the square of the concentration of the consolute component, over a limited range of the latter. This follows from geometry for tangents to regular curves.

Four sloping chords across the curve of Fig. 1 are tie lines connecting compositions in equilibrium, and these gradually contract to the plait point. For solvent extraction the orientation of the tie lines is even more important than the curve.

Figure 2 shows a system, 85% phenol-mixed pentenes-n-pentane, of which only the hydrocarbons are completely miscible; but these two have

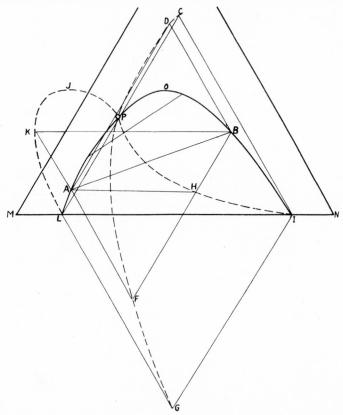

FIG. 3. (18, 28, 41, 64, 100, 198) Conjugate lines for correlating tie lines.

different solubilities in the phenol. Tie lines include part of the base line and part of the sloping border line. There is no plait point.

Unfortunately, the tie lines almost invariably slope down toward the corner representing the liquid used for extraction, thus diminishing the effectiveness of the process. This is shown by the succession of arrows in Fig. 1, in which C is the charge, e_1 and r_1 are the extract and raffinate, respectively, (after removal of solvent) after one stage, and e_∞ is the maximum purity of extract obtainable with the system. The dotted line leading to e_∞ is tangent to the curve, at a point always below the plait point, although usually close to it. With an infinite series of stages the raffinate could be obtained in pure form. With a diagram like Fig. 2 complete separation is theoretically possible, although the sloping of the tie lines is still less favorable. In two systems of that type (8, 228a) the tie lines seem to point exactly toward a corner, indicating no selectivity by that solvent. When the mixture contains an aromatic and a nonaromatic hydrocarbon, the more nearly horizontal lines (Fig. 5) (cf. also 160) indicate a better selectivity. A system

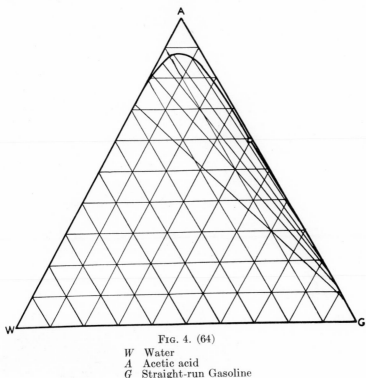

Fig. 4. (64)

W Water
A Acetic acid
G Straight-run Gasoline

probably could not exist in which the tie lines slope so much that their extensions would intersect the base line. Such a graph would mean the concentrating of a less soluble component in the extract. The position of the plait point, mentioned above, is a corollary of this.

Various schemes have been proposed to determine the whole tie line net work or to express it concisely. International Critical Tables (100, cf. also 155) used a conjugate line CDPFG (Fig. 3) slightly curved, running from a point near the top corner (most soluble component) through the plait point, P, across the base line, MN, to a point, G, near the bottom corner of another equal inverted triangle (not shown). (The line stops short of both top and bottom corners; cf. 198). Sherwood (198), Bergelin *et al.* (18), and Briggs and Comings (28) used another conjugate line, *PHI*, through the plait point to the opposite foot of the binodal curve, *LAPOBI*, and Darwent and Winkler (41) used a highly curved line, *PJKL*, from the plait point up and then down to the foot of the binodal curve on the same side (*J* is the same altitude as *O*, the top of the curve). In each case the conjugate curve is determined by the intersection of straight lines drawn from the ends of

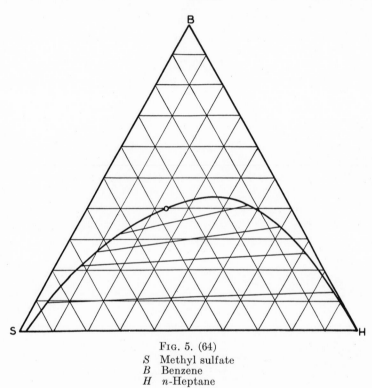

Fig. 5. (64)
S   Methyl sulfate
B   Benzene
H   *n*-Heptane

each tie line, *AB*, parallel to the sides of the triangle, *AD* and *BD* or *AF* and *BF*, *AH* and *BH*, and *AK* and *BK*. Still other conjugate lines could be constructed. By reversing the process the composition of the phase in equilibrium with any phase on the binodal curve can be found.

For systems such as Fig. 4 with very low mutual miscibility of two components, the well known distribution laws hold for low concentrations of the consolute component. For higher concentrations, and for systems such as Fig. 1, Campbell (30) showed that plots of logarithms of concentration of the consolute component in one phase against that in the other phase give straight lines. Other methods of correlating the tie lines were developed by Brancker, *et al.* (26), by Bachman (10), and by Briggs and Comings (28).

A simpler method which holds approximately is to assume that the tie lines converge toward a point near the base line outside the triangle (8, 216, 217). The failure of this was pointed out by Bachman (9). The tie lines have been considered to be tangent to a curve (171). Hand (74) made all of the tie lines of a system horizontal, and put the plait point at the apex of the curve by changing the units of weight of one of the nonconsolute components in calculating compositions. This held well for the systems tested. Two of these schemes would fail for systems of the type shown in Fig. 2, and all three would fail for some of the systems of isopropanol (151, 237, 239), *n*-propanol (238), *tert*-butanol (200a), and pyridine (209), which show a reversal in slope of the tie lines with rising proportions of consolute component. The reason for this reversal is suggested in citations (151, 209), namely, the formation of a solvate.

The tie lines are best determined by analysis of one or both of the liquid phases in equilibrium, usually for a single component, and combination with the knowledge of the total composition of the system. Usually a titration or an observation of refractive index or density will suffice. In cases where such an analysis is impractical, the compositions of the two phases can be estimated from their relative weights (56, 154, 155) or other graphical means (15, 155). Still another method (64) consists in observing the amounts of two of the components required to be added to one or both equilibrium liquid phases separately, in order to bring its composition to that previously determined for the plait point.

It has been common practice in physical chemistry text books and some original articles to use illustrative phase diagrams considerably distorted, with certain relations exaggerated for emphasis. This custom runs the risk of being misleading with regard to other relations in other parts of the diagram, just as a map would be with areas proportional to population instead of to land areas. When these diagrams are copied in other books without adequate consideration, some improbable relations appear to be "established." Attention is called to some of these points in the following discussion.

In most of the real systems with only three components which have been published, the two-phase areas are bounded entirely by convex curves. The only exceptions are either not plotted to scale (182) or only slightly concave (15a, 117, 124a, 228a). Certainly the curves could not be concave at such a point that tie lines must pass outside of the curve (117). Points on such a tie line would have to be both within and outside of a two phase area. An experimental check (64) on that system, water-ethylene glycol-*n*-amyl alcohol, failed to show any concavity. A trace of a fourth component, possibly a hydrocarbon in the amyl alcohol used by Laddha and Smith (117) could have caused the discrepancy (cf. the discussion of Fig. 6 below). On the other hand, most of the other slight concavities in binodal curves (15a, 124a, 228a) have been confirmed (64). These are at portions of the curves which are nearly perpendicular to the tie lines.

Figure 6 represents four systems of alcohols-benzene-lubricating oil. Three of them employ absolute ethanol at 118°C., (※1) and absolute eth-

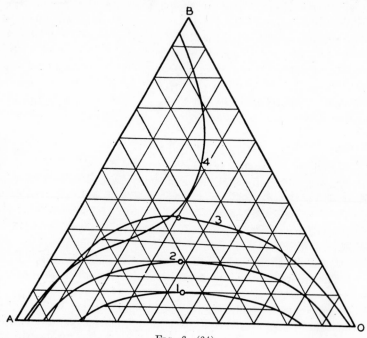

FIG. 6. (64)

B Benzene
O Paraffinic lubricating oil (C.S.T. with ethanol, 128°C.)
A Alcohol (as follows)
1 Ethanol at 118°C.
2 Ethanol at 100°C.
3 Methanol at 100°C.
4 95% Ethanol at 100°C.

anol (※2) and methanol (※3) at 100°C., and have the normal parabolic curves, which are low and flat for systems with high miscibility. Such curves are never deep narrow "bites," illustrated in one text book (68, cf. 100 for an accurate graph of the system). Part of the fourth curve (※4), for 95% ethanol at 100°C., is highly concave because the system is not really ternary. The water is incompatible with hydrocarbons at low alcohol concentrations. Shepherd (197a) presented diagrams with similar reverse curves for systems with two hydrocarbons and alcohols which were not anhydrous. The tie lines, if drawn, would not terminate on the binodal curve because the percentage of water in the alcohol "component" would differ in the two phases. The alcohol dissolved in the hydrocarbon phase would be nearly anhydrous, and the water would be concentrated in the alcohol layer. There is no plait point.

It is for this reason that modification of solvent power by means of dilution should be tried with caution. Very often the material under extractive treatment will extract a mixed solvent selectively, making it a reagent of decidedly variable solubility characteristics, and complicating engineering calculations. This is especially true if there is more difference in miscibility for the components of the "solvent" than there is for those of the mixture to be extracted, as would usually be the case. This difficulty is diminished when there is strong affinity between the solvent and diluent, as with sulfuric acid and water.

Although glacial acetic acid is miscible with n-heptane, and would give no binodal curve at all with two light hydrocarbons, it has enough hygroscopicity to behave with water almost like a single component in the systems of 97% and 98.1% acetic acid with toluene and n-heptane (153) in giving normal-appearing binodal curves. Even in this case, however, the tie lines should not terminate on the curve. Assuming, as the authors did, that the heptane layer contained no water (although this is not quite accurate), the acid layer would contain all of the water and be more dilute, perhaps as low as 85%. This would dissolve very little heptane (cf. Fig. 4), and its composition would be close to the left side of their diagram (Fig. 1 of ref. 153). The composition of a phase in equilibrium with a saturated phase in such a system is not unique, but depends on the relative volumes of the phases. The same criticism applies to Fig. 2 of this chapter, but there is less discrepancy because of the much lower solubilities. Four component systems were considered by Brancker et al. (27), by Hunter (95), by J. C. Smith (211), and by Wiegand (240).

Figure 7a is an actual system (183), water-ethanol-succinonitrile (or ethylene cyanide, not "ethyl cyanide" (52)). As a system with two separate binodal curves for liquids it seems to be the only one published, and should be expected to be rare because the miscibility of succinonitrile with either water or ethanol is increased by addition of the other, although it is incompletely miscible with each. In fact, it is doubtful if such relations could exist in a system consisting of only three kinds of molecules, unless possibly the temperature is close to the critical point of one component. The unusual feature is due probably to the presence of solvate molecules, perhaps ternary ones, coupled with the proximity of the critical solution temperatures in both binary systems (31° and 55.5°C.) to the temperatures studied (18° and 31°C.).

If the system could be cooled without crystallizing any of the components, the two binodal curves probably would fuse together as in Fig. 7b (52, 83,

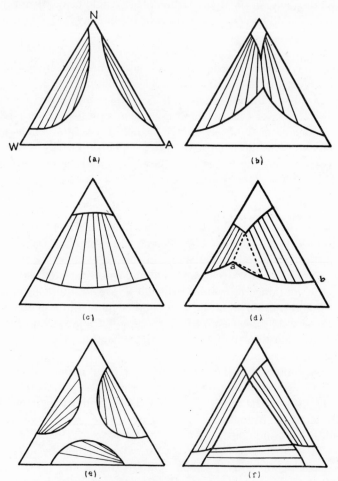

FIG. 7. Illustrative diagrams (see text).

(a) W   Water
     N   Succinonitrile
     A   Ethanol
(b), (c), (d) Supposed results on cooling (a).
(e) Supposed system with three binodal curves.
(f) Supposed diagram for three liquid layers.

94, 98) (no example of which has been published, however); but it is doubtful if they could merge gradually to a single band, Fig. 7c, as suggested (57, 69, 185, 186). It seems essential, as implied by Schreinemakers (184), that the first contact would be at both plait points, so that Fig. 7d (52, 83, 94, 98, 242) would be impossible. Hill's citation (83) of his own work (83a) and that with Miller (84) as exceptions is not pertinent, since in each case the three-phase area observed by them results from three binodal curves instead of two; and two of these three erupt from within the third, as in Fig. 8 of this chapter, to be discussed below (cf. 136).

Another objection to Fig. 7d is the continuous curve, *ab*, which bounds different two-phase areas without a break. Still another objection is the im-

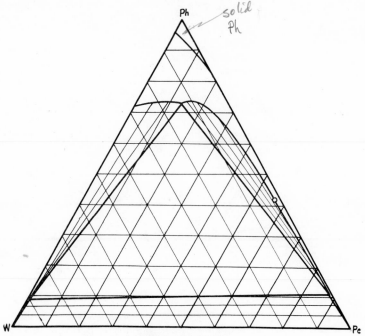

FIG. 8. (64) Three-liquid-phase system.
          W   Water
          Ph   Phenol
          Pe   Pentenes (mixed)

probability of three liquid phases in a ternary system two components of which are completely miscible and show no tendency to separate, as would be indicated by the proximity of a binodal curve (cf. Fig. 8).

Fig. 7d is also inconsistent with another rule of Schreinemakers (186) applicable to systems with three liquid layers, namely, "When two binodal curves intersect in a point (*a*, *b*, or *c*), their metastable extensions in the neighborhood of the intersection lie either both within (*a*) or both outside (*b* and *c*) the three-layer field." This is illustrated in Fig. 9. The "permissible"

graph is not an actual diagram, but shows the relations mentioned, somewhat exaggerated for clarity.

Schreinemakers did not make clear the theoretical basis for this apparently arbitrary rule, which however seems more reasonable on careful
reflection. Marsh (132, p. 128) emphasized it and expressed it in the form,
"The extensions of the one-phase boundaries must be either (1) both within the three-phase region . . . or (2) both within the two-phase region . . ." His
extension of it, eliminating the relations of e in the "erroneous" graph, is in
accordance with the well known principle of phase diagrams that no single
phase subtends an angle of more than 180° at any intersection. Case a is less
common than that of b (or c).

Figure 7e, with three separate binodal curves, proposed in three text
books (52, 57, 69), is possible, but the effect of each of three components, no

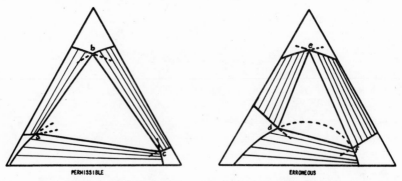

FIG. 9. Illustrative diagrams (see text) (132) (186).

pair of which is miscible, in increasing so greatly the mutual miscibility of the
remaining two would require exceptional relations. It would be contrary to a
principle stated in two of the books mentioned (57, p.97; 69, p.729), and
others (11, 223). Even the presence of ternary complex molecules would
hardly produce such relations unless binary complex molecules were practically excluded. A further requirement would be the substantial equality of
all three binary critical solution temperatures. No example of Fig. 7e has
been reported.* The excessive slopes of the tie lines has already been shown
to be inadmissable.

The same considerations make the form of Fig. 7f for three liquid layers
unusual unless solvate molecules are formed. This seems to be the explanation for the effect of each component in increasing mutual miscibility of the
other two in the system, water-ethyl ether-succinonitrile. A diagram pre-

* However, since submitting this manuscript the author has found experimentally
several systems with diagrams of the types of each of Figs. 7a, 7b, and 7e. These
systems will be described in a later paper.

sented for it by Schreinemakers (182) has been confirmed substantially (64), especially with respect to this feature, but not with respect to the concavity of some of the binodal curves, all of which were observed at 25°C. to be straight within experimental error. On raising the temperature to 55.5°C. the two-phase area on the water-nitrile side vanishes, and the system degenerates into one similar to Fig. 2, with ether as the nonconsolute component. The solvate forming tendency of succinonitrile, which gives it a unique diagram with water and ethanol (183 and Fig. 7a,) probably gives it an unusual one with ether also.

Illustrative diagrams similar to Fig. 7f are presented in nine or more citations (52, 57, 69, 83, 132, 172, 185, 186, 198) although they may not be typical. Some of these (132, 172) are inconsistent with Schreinemakers' abovementioned rule. In spite of such general interest, no diagram drawn to scale for a real system of three liquid phases at ordinary temperatures seems to be published except some complex ones for systems containing salts and giving solid phases (83a, 84). The only other one with three liquid phases found published, formamide-nitrobenzene-n-hexane, (103a) is of less theoretical interest because of the slight miscibilities of formamide. Graphs of both systems mentioned (103a, 182) show distortion from the tabulated data, presumably for clarity of certain parts.

A diagram, which is believed to be more typical, for a new three-liquid phase system is shown in Fig. 8 for water-phenol-mixed pentenes (64). An important difference from Fig. 7f is that two of the three two-phase areas have their wider bases on the triangle of three-phase area, rather than on the border lines of the system. One of these areas has its own plait point and fails to reach the border line because pentene and phenol as anhydrous liquids are completely miscible. A little water causes their separation. If n-pentane (C.S.T. with phenol 56.6°C.) had been used instead of pentene, this area would have extended to the border. The other two-phase area reaches the border at room temperature, but pentene decreases the miscibility of water and phenol, as is to be expected. At 66°C. (the C.S.T. of water and phenol) the area would recede from the border line and resemble the other loop. With rising temperature the base line of the internal triangle would rise until the three-phase area vanishes and the whole system degenerates into a simple one resembling Fig. 11. The short sloping line near the top of Fig. 8 represents solid phenol.

Another important difference between Figs. 7f and 8 is that two of the three components of the latter, water and pentene, are practically immiscible. This is usually a requirement for a three-liquid system because this pair must be very far apart in dipole moment or solubility characteristics in order to have a third liquid of intermediate properties with limited miscibility with each.

Hydrocarbons are so incompatible with water that it usually requires a concentration of 30 to 70% of a mutual solvent before the solubility of the hydrocarbon in the aqueous layer becomes appreciable (Figs. 4, 10, 11, 12). Soap solutions form an exception, however. Bailey (11) found that it required only 2.9% of sodium oleate to lower the C.S.T. of phenol and water from 65.3 to 0°C., and similar effects to a less extent are noted with hydrocarbons. A 0.4 N solution of sodium oleate dissolved up to 7.3% n-hexane (205), an increase of about five hundred fold; and hydrocarbon gases showed a four-fold increase in solubility (127, 128). McBain and O'Connor (126) proved

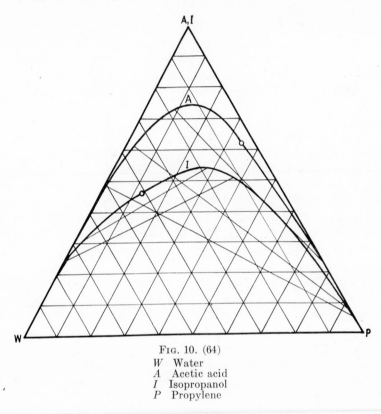

Fig. 10. (64)

W Water
A Acetic acid
I Isopropanol
P Propylene

that this was a true solution and not just an emulsion. However, soap solutions are practically nonselective for different hydrocarbons (205), and so are not useful in their separation. High solubilities of hydrocarbons in soap solutions were observed and discussed by Woodman (244), and by Palit and McBain (159). The phenomenon may be explained by considering the alkali metal ion as anchored in the aqueous layer, and the long organic portion of the soap molecule well rooted in the hydrocarbon layer, thus holding a considerable amount of the latter in the water. The detergency of sulfonates of large molecules is explained similarly.

Some systems are described in the literature with four (34, 103, 206) and even five (34b) liquid phases in equilibrium. Most of them include a soap as one component. This is paradoxical, since soap was just shown to be a good mixer, and now seems essential for a high degree of incompatibility. Probably the two observations are manifestations of the same properties. A typical five-phase liquid system contains two volumes each of n-hexane, ammonium hydroxide, and aniline to one each of aqueous solutions of sodium oleate and

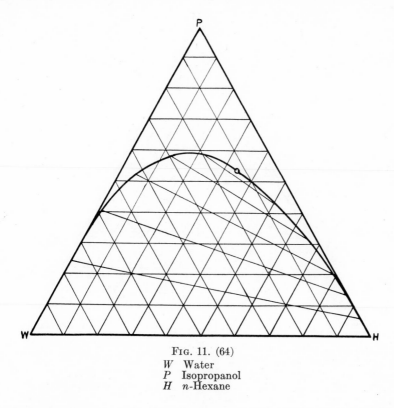

FIG. 11. (64)
W   Water
P   Isopropanol
H n-Hexane

potassium carbonate (34b). The dual nature of the soap molecule probably accounts for one extra phase. Presumably mercury would form a sixth layer.

Holmes (90) considered that mutual miscibility of liquids depends only on the ratio of radii of molecules, which must be greater than 1.618 to result in two layers. Similarly, to form three layers one liquid must have molecules with radii at least 1.618^2 or 2.62 times those of the smallest. He gave five examples of three-liquid phase systems (Table Ia and Ib). Although molecular size is certainly a factor, it is doubtful if miscibility can be simplified to such an extent, especially in view of low solubility of light hydrocarbons such as ethane in water.

The properties of a two-liquid phase system near the plait point are interesting. The vapor pressure and freezing point are almost independent of composition over a considerable range, and many other properties have a linear relation, as observed by Perrakis (161) and by Shükarev (199). The interfacial surface tension and the differences in density and refractive index and in all other properties for the two phases can be made as low as desired. Mondain-Monval and Quiquarez (144) made a study of many such

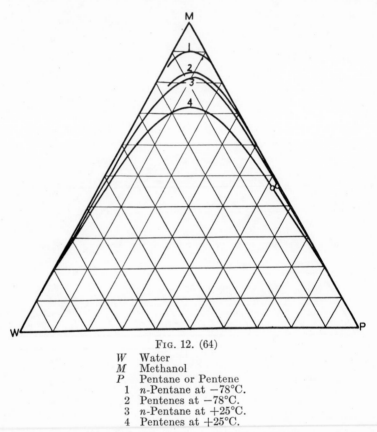

FIG. 12. (64)

W	Water
M	Methanol
P	Pentane or Pentene
1	n-Pentane at −78°C.
2	Pentenes at −78°C.
3	n-Pentane at +25°C.
4	Pentenes at +25°C.

systems, and found some with a high viscosity near the plait point, some with opalescence, and some with neither.

The opalescence sometimes shows beautiful colors, the most common ones being pale milky blue, greenish gold, and clear magenta. This is not analogous to the rainbow since the color is uniform and independent of the angle of observation. The colors appear only when the refractive indices of the two liquid phases near the plait point are practically equal. The colors are

(Continued on p. 265)

TABLE I

Ternary Systems with Two Liquid Layers, One or Two Components being
Hydrocarbons
(Literature Citations)

(a) Aqueous Systems

Nonhydrocarbon	Benzene	Toluene	Xylene
Acetaldehyde	153, 154	153	
Acetanilide	188 (p. 605)		
Acetic acid	16, 65, 99, 122, 144, 152, 154, 174, 188 (pp. 106–9), 198a, 216, 217, 233, 235	122, 144, 152, 188 (p. 106–12), 235	99, 122, 152, 188 (p. 112), 198a
Acetone	13, 23, 28, 72a, 101, 122, 151a, 155, 175, 188 (pp. 179–83), 233	101, 122, 155, 175, 188 (pp. 180–2)	122, 155, 175
Forty-four acids (organic, not mentioned otherwise)	67b, 150, 188, 198a, 207, 208	188, 207, 208	188, 207, 208
Twenty-four alkylamines	188, 207	188, 207	188, 207
Aniline	56b, 188 (p. 416)	188 (p. 416), 212	188 (p. 416)
Nineteen derivatives of Aniline	56b, 188		
p-Anisidine	188 (p. 560)		
Benzoic acid	67b, 188 (pp. 510–2), 198a, 207	6, 188 (pp. 511–2), 198a, 208	188 (pp. 510–2), 198a, 207
n-Butanol	23, 151a, 161, 188 (p. 267), 239a	66, 151a	
Iso-butanol	1, 90, 151a	151a	
sec-Butanol	151a	151a	
tert-Butanol	151a, 200a		
n-Butyric acid	122, 188 (pp. 253–4)	122, 188 (pp. 253-6)	122, 188 (p. 252)
Chloral hydrate	188 (p. 93)	188 (p. 93)	
Chloroacetic acid	67b, 109, 188 (pp. 88–9), 207	188 (pp. 89–90) 207	109
Chloroanilines	188 (p. 372)		
Collidine		188 (p. 616)	
Coniine			188 (p. 621)
m-Cresol	167	167	
Dichloroacetic acid	50a, 67b, 109, 188, (p. 77)	188 (p. 78)	109
Dioxane	19		
Ethanol	15, 23, 24, 90, 122, 141, 143, 144, 146, 151a, 154, 175, 188 (pp. 137–41), 213, 216, 217, 230, 233	40, 122, 142, 143, 144, 151a, 175, 188 (pp. 142–4, 542), 216, 217	122, 141, 143, 144, 175, 188 (pp. 145, 607)

TABLE I—*Continued*

Nonhydrocarbon	Benzene	Toluene	Xylene
Formic acid	188 (pp. 27–30)	188 (p. 30)	188 (p. 30)
Furfural		110	
Hydrazine	67b, 187 (p. 1028)		
Hydrogen chloride	187 (p. 575)		
Hydrogen cyanide	72a, 187 (p. 570)		
Hydroxyazobenzene	188 (p. 700)		
Iodine	187 (p. 666)	187 (p. 665)	
Mandelic acid	188 (pp. 594–6), 198a, 208		
Mercuric bromide	187 (p. 611)		
Mercuric chloride	124, 187 (p. 631)	29, 187 (p. 632), 198a	
Methanol	90, 122, 143, 144, 151a, 161, 175, 188 (pp. 46–7), 197a	122, 143, 151a, 175, 188 (p. 50)	122, 143, 175
β-Naphthol	188 (p. 660)		
Quinoline			188 (p. 624), 207
Phenol	167, 188 (p. 369–87)	188 (p. 386)	188 (p. 386)
Picric acid	188 (p. 330–1), 236	188 (p. 330–1), 198a	
Piperidine	67b, 188 (p. 308)		188 (p. 308)
n-Propanol	44, 90, 122, 151a, 175	122, 151a, 175	122, 175
Iso-propanol	122, 143, 151, 151a, 175, 188 (p. 206–7)	122, 143, 151a, 175, 237	122, 143, 175
Propionic acid	122, 188 (pp. 189–90), 198a	122, 188 (p. 190)	122, 188 (p. 191)
Pyridine	67b, 122, 188 (pp. 288–9), 209	122, 188 (p. 289), 198a	122, 188 (p. 288), 207
Resorcinol	188 (p. 396)		
Silver perchlorate[a]	83a (explosive)	84	
Sodium oleate	205	205	205
Stannic chloride			187 (p. 1491), 201
Toluidines	188 (p. 558)		
Trichloroacetic acid	3, 50a, 67b, 109, 150, 188 (p. 68), 198a	188 (p. 69)	109
n-Valeric acid	188 (pp. 301–2)	188 (p. 302)	
Iso-valeric acid	99, 188 (pp. 301–4)	188 (pp. 303–6)	99, 188 (pp. 303–5)

TABLE I—*Continued*

Nonhydrocarbon	Pentane	Hexane	Heptane	[*]Gasoline
Acetic acid		152		64 (Fig. 4), 152
Acetone	144, 175	144, 175	151a	151a
Benzoic acid				188 (p. 512), 198a
Benzyl amine			188 (p. 554)	
Four butanols			151a	151a
p-Chloroaniline			188 (p. 372)	
Ethanol	142, 144, 175, 188 (p. 146)	144, 175, 188, (pp. 146–9, 457), 216	151a, 188 (pp. 147–8, 562)	23, 39, 144, 151a, 188 (pp. 150–2), 229
Methanol	64 (Fig. 12), 144, 175	65, 169a, 175, 188 (p. 48)	188 (p. 48)	39, 154, 197a
o-Nitroaniline			188 (p. 402)	
Phenol[a]			188 (p. 563)	136
n-Propanol	175	175	151a	151a
Iso-propanol	175	64 (Fig. 11), 175	151a	151a
Soaps		126, 205		
p-Toluidine		188 (p. 558)		

Nonhydrocarbon	Cyclohexane	Mesitylene	Naphthalene	Petroleum ether
Acetic acid	106	122		188 (p. 113), 235
Acetone	144, 175	122	188 (p. 649)	
Acids (organic)			188 (p. 258)	188 (pp. 302, 306, 440, 513, 619)
Aniline[a]	180			
Four butanols	151a		223 (*tert* only)	
Butyric acid		122	223	188 (p. 257)
Ethanol	151a, 154, 175, 188 (p. 149), 216, 217	122, 188 (p. 136)		23, 39, 144
Formic acid				188 (p. 31)
Methanol	175, 188 (p. 52–4)	122		169a
Phenol			223	
n-Propanol	151a, 175, 238	122		
Iso-propanol	151a, 175, 238	122		
Propionic acid		122		188 (p. 193)
Pyridine		122		
Succinonitrile			223	
Triethylamine			223	

TABLE I—*Continued*

Nonhydrocarbon	Hydrocarbon
Acetic acid	Kerosene 188 (p. 113); propylene 64 (Fig. 10); tetralin or decalin 77.
Acetone	Isobutene or butadiene 203; trimethylethylene 151a; ethylbenzene 175.
Ammonia	1-Butene 163.
Aniline[a]	Petroleum (200–30°) 90.
sec-Butanol	Trimethylethylene 151a.
Caproic acid	Decalin 188 (p. 439).
Ethanol	Isopentane 188 (p. 146); paraffin oil (160–80°C) 92, 188 (p. 152); kerosene 23; trimethylethylene 151a; dimethylcyclohexane 188 (p. 607); cyclohexene 239; pinene 188 (p. 144); ethylbenzene 175; butyltoluene 143; turpentine 188 (p. 837).
Furfural	2-Butene, isobutene, or butadiene 89.
Hydrogen fluoride	Isobutane 29a.
Iodine	Tetralin or decalin 77
Mercuric chloride	Tetralin 77.
Methanol	Paraffin 39, 154; pentene 64 (Fig. 12); trimethylethylene 151a; cyclohexene 239; isobutene or butadiene 203; ethylbenzene 175; butyltoluene 143.
Methylethylketone	Isooctane or gasoline 147.
Nicotine[a]	Petroleum (200–30°C) 90.
Nitrobenzene[a]	Petroleum (200–30°C) 90.
Phenol[a]	2-Methylpentane 188 (p. 459); petroleum (200–30°C) 90; pentene 64 (Fig. 8); methylcyclohexane 188 (p. 563).
Picric acid	Tetralin 77.
Potassium oleate	Isobutane, petroleum ether, methylcyclopentane or butadiene 127.
n-Propanol	Ethylbenzene 175.
Iso-propanol	Propylene 64 (Fig. 10); cyclohexene 239; ethylbenzene 175; butyltoluene 143.
Trichloroacetic acid	Pentene 150, 198a; cumene 188 (p. 69).
Trichlorobutyric acid	Pentene 150, 198a.

(b) Nonaqueous Systems, One Hydrocarbon

Acetic acid	Aniline, methylaniline, or dimethylaniline with "benzine" (100–25°C.) 247.
Acetone	Acetic anhydride with hexane, petroleum ether, or gasoline 142, 144.
Acetone	Ethylene glycol with benzene, toluene, or xylene 188 (pp. 157–8) (components are interchanged), 228b.
Acetone	Ethylene glycol with butadiene or isobutene 203.
Acetonitrile	Seven acids with isooctane 202a.
Camphor	Sulfuric or phosphoric acid with ligroin (100–20°C.) 188 (p. 679).
Ethanol	Ethylene glycol with benzene, toluene, or xylene 188 (pp. 154–5), 228b.
Ethanol	Glycerol with benzene 188 (pp. 141, 155).
Ethanol	Lactic acid with benzene 188 (p. 141).
Ethanol	Salts with paraffin oil (b.p. 160–80°C) 92.

TABLE I—*Continued*

Nonhydrocarbon	Hydrocarbon
Ethanol (96%)	Ten solvents with gasoline 188 (p. 152).
Formic acid[b]	Bromoform with benzene 8.
Formic acid	Ethanol, n-propanol, or isoamyl alcohol with petroleum ether 198a.
Glycerol	Iodine with benzene 187 (p. 669).
Glycerol[a]	Nitrobenzene with petroleum (b.p. 200–30°C.) 90.
Glycerol	Iso-valeric acid with toluene 188 (p. 306).
Methanol	Acetic acid with isooctane 202a.
Methanol	Acetone with gasoline 197a.
Methanol	n-Butyric acid with isooctane 188 (p. 258), 202a.
Methanol	Ethylene glycol with 2-butene, isobutene, or butadiene 203.
Methanol	Ethylene glycol with nine hydrocarbons 204.
Methanol[b]	Formic acid with isooctane 188 (p. 31), 202a.
Methanol	Five other acids with isooctane 202a.
Methanol	Four fatty acids with hexane 188 (p. 53).
Methanol	Methyl esters of five fatty acids with isooctane 76a.
Methanol	Polystyrene with benzene 186a.
Methanol	Rapeseed oil with benzene 25.
Methanol[b]	Salts with hexane 92.
Methanol	Triethanolamine with isobutene or butadiene 203.
Methanol	Vaseline oil 188, with camphor (p. 679), carbon tetrachloride (p. 5), chloroform (p. 15), diethylamine (p. 280), naphthalene (p. 650).
β-Methoxyethanol	Eight fatty acids and four of their esters each with isooctane (12 systems) 76a, 188 (pp. 31, 114, 258, 620).
Nitrobenzene	Benzoic acid, butyric acid, o-nitrophenol, resorcinol, or valeric acid, each with hexane 188 (pp. 359, 458).
Nitrobenzene	m-Dinitrobenzene, hydroquinone, p-nitrobenzaldehyde, p-nitrophenol, m-nitrobenzoic acid, or resorcinol, each with hexane 223.
Nitrobenzene	Formamide with n-hexane 103a (three layers below 12.4°C.).
Oleic acid	Abietic acid with propane 87.
Oleic acid	Vegetable oils with propane 86.
Phenol	m-Phenylenediamine with benzene 248.
Picric acid	β-Naphthol with benzene 116.
Isopropanol	Ethylene glycol with isobutene or butadiene 203.
Propylene glycol	Soaps with benzene (six systems) 159.
Stearic acid	Palmitic acid with propane 50.
Sulfuric acid	Isopropyl acetate, petroleum ether 64 (Fig. 14).
Valeric acid	95.8% Sulfuric acid with benzene 188 (p. 301).

(c) Nonaqueous Systems, Two Hydrocarbons

Acetic acid (not glacial)	n-Heptane-toluene 153.
Aniline[b]	n-Hexane-methylcyclopentane 41, (Fig. 1).
Aniline[b]	Neohexane-cyclopentane 189.

TABLE I—*Continued*

Nonhydrocarbon	Hydrocarbon
Aniline[b]	*n*-Heptane-cetane 96.
Aniline[b]	*n*-Heptane-cyclohexane 96.
Aniline[b]	*n*-Heptane-methylcyclohexane 231.
Aniline	*n*-Heptane-benzene 228.
Aniline[b]	Cetane-cyclohexane 96.
Aniline	Cetane-benzene 96.
Aniline	Gasoline-benzene, toluene, or xylene 228.
Aniline	Cyclohexane-benzene 180, 228.
Antimony trichloride	Petroleum-toluene 215.
An aromatic amine (A)	A non-aromatic hydrocarbon (B) and an aromatic hydrocarbon (C), where A is aniline, *o*-anisidine, or *p*-phenetidine; B is isooctane, cyclohexane, or methylcyclohexane; and C is benzene, toluene, *o*-, *m*-, or *p*-xylene, ethylbenzene, biphenyl, naphthalene, or tetralin (75 systems) 5.
Dicyanoethylamine	Cyclohexane-benzene 33.
Dicyanoethylamine	Ethylbenzene-styrene 33.
Dicyanoethylamine	Toluene-"troluoil" (mostly heptanes) 33.
Dimethylsulfolane	Petroleum-toluene 215.
Ethanol (96%)	Gasoline-benzene 188 (p. 152).
Ethanol	Paraffin or ceresin-benzene 7.
Furfural	Butadiene-isobutene 203.
Furfural	Naphtha-butadiene or Isobutene[b] 203.
Furfural	Docosane-1,6-diphenylhexane 28.
Furfural	Petroleum-toluene 215.
Methanol	Gasoline-benzene 197a.
Methanol or ethanol	Benzene-paraffinic lubricating oil 64 (Fig. 6).
Methanol	Vaseline oil-naphthalene 188 (p. 650).
Methyl sulfate	*n*-Heptane-benzene 64 (Fig. 5).
Methyl sulfate	*n*-Pentane, *n*-hexane, or *n*-heptane-five aromatic hydrocarbons 160.
Nine solvents	*n*-Heptane-toluene 64 (Fig. 15).
Nine solvents	Straight run gasoline-xylene 64 (Fig. 16).
85% Phenol[b]	Pentane-pentene 64 (Fig. 2).
Polymethacrylic acid ester	Benzene-cyclohexane 186a.
Sulfolane	Petroleum-toluene 215.
Sulfur dioxide	Propane-propylene at −78°C. 64 (Fig. 13).
Sulfur dioxide	Petroleum-toluene 215.
Sulfur dioxide	Twelve pairs of hydrocarbons at −18°C. (two of them[b]) 145. (A thirteenth pair failed to separate into liquid layers.)

[a] Systems separate into three layers. Ten other ternary systems containing a hydrocarbon and giving three liquid layers are listed (223, p. 159), but no data are given.

[b] Double nonconsolute pair.

clear if the two indices are identical for some wavelength in the visible spectrum. Light of this wavelength passes through the emulsion without bending, and is eliminated from light transmitted at a slight angle. The latter light is not refracted, but reflected from surfaces of droplets. Since the two liquids usually differ in dispersion, the light of other wavelengths is so reflected, and shows the complementary color to that eliminated. The color appears only where direct light is cut out, as by a partition between window panes.

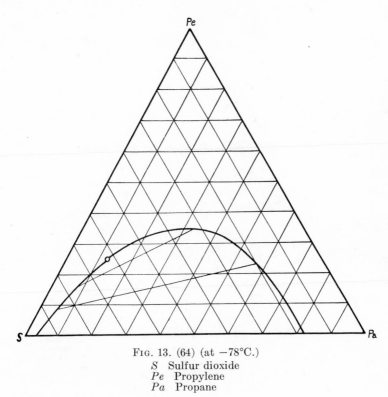

Fig. 13. (64) (at −78°C.)
S   Sulfur dioxide
Pe   Propylene
Pa   Propane

The only binary system showing colors which has been observed by the author is that of hydroxyethylethylenediamine with benzene (64). As the temperature falls with occasional agitation through a 20° range below the C.S.T., 60°C., there is a succession of opalescent colors. A trace of water, about 0.3%, is required to raise the C.S.T. to 80°C. in order to bring out the complete "opalescent spectrum," since no color appears above the C.S.T. With descending temperature the order of colors is then yellow, orange, red, magenta, violet, indigo, pale blue. The color at room temperature is pale milky blue because it is "minus orange," the long visible wavelengths being partly eliminated. The expected green is hard to observe.

II. COMPILATION OF TERNARY SYSTEMS

Table I is a compilation of nearly 600 ternary systems with two liquid layers involving hydrocarbons, most of which have been described in the literature, at least in part. Some of the listings cover only low concentrations of the consolute component or present only qualitative conclusions.

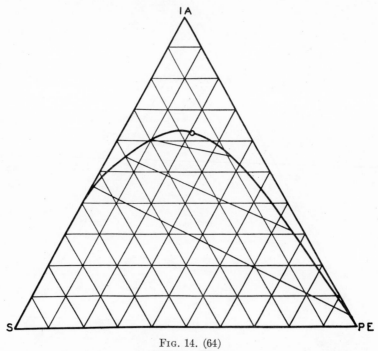

FIG. 14. (64)
S   Sulfuric acid
IA   Isopropyl acetate
PE   Petroleum ether

The list is presented since recent papers (e.g., 96) have indicated that very few ternary systems including a hydrocarbon have been published. About 140 of the systems include two hydrocarbons (Table Ic), but only ten of these have double nonconsolute pairs (like Fig. 2). The list is intended to be complete through 1947, but some systems may have been overlooked. Data for many of the systems are given in Seidell's books (187, 188), which are cited (with page number in parentheses when practicable) instead of about ninety original publications, in order to save space, and because some of the latter are available only with difficulty. A few of Seidell's references are repeated, so as to cover systems not mentioned by him, or if needed for discussion. Many of the citations listed are more recent papers. A compilation of ternary systems has been published already (210), but it includes only eighty-nine systems, of which only twenty-two involve a hydrocarbon.

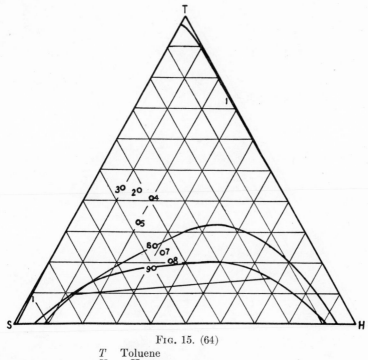

FIG. 15. (64)

T   Toluene
H n-Heptane
S   Solvent (as follows)
1   Triethylene glycol
2   Furfuryl alcohol
3   Maleic anhydride (at 60°C.)
4   Methyl sulfate
5   Dinitrochlorobenzene (at 55°C.)
6   Carbitol
7   Methyl Cellosolve
8   Acetic anhydride
9   Aniline

The new systems studied in this laboratory are shown in Figs. 2, 4, 5, 6, 8, and 10 to 16. With the exceptions indicated, these are at a temperature of approximately 25°C. In Figs. 15 and 16 several systems of solvents with two hydrocarbons are indicated only by plait points, since the binodal curves can be constructed approximately through these points. An exception is triethylene glycol, which is incompletely miscible with toluene so that in Fig. 15 its system has no plait point. The binodal curves with two other solvents, carbitol and aniline are shown.

In spite of the considerable number of systems listed in Table I, the number of possible combinations is so great that relatively few systems have been studied thoroughly. Since systems involving hydrocarbons are

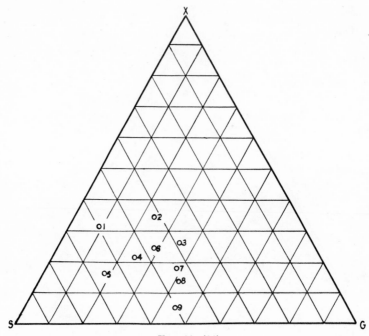

FIG. 16. (64)

X   Xylene
G   Straight-run gasoline (30°C. Aniline point)
S   Solvent (as follows)
 1   Methyl Carbitol
 2   Furfuryl alcohol
 3   Furfural
 4   Ethylene chlorohydrin
 5   Aldol
 6   Carbitol
 7   Methyl Cellosolve
 8   Acetic anhydride
 9   Aniline

relatively free from complex relations, however, it is possible to construct a diagram for such a system with considerable assurance and fair accuracy from the mutual solubilities of two pairs of components, provided the third pair is miscible.

When two pairs of components show limited miscibility, the diagram requires only two convex curves connecting the points on the sides of the triangle corresponding to the miscibilities (Fig. 2). When another pair is completely miscible, a single curve is drawn from the miscibility points on the base line. The curve is low and flat or parabolic if the miscibility is considerable (Figs. 1, 6, 13, 15); and it is high and hyperbolic if the miscibility is slight (Figs. 4, 10, 11, 12, 14). The plait point is near the middle in the former case, and usually far on one side in the latter case. It is usually near a composition of 50 to 60% of one of the nonconsolute components, namely the nonhydrocarbon if there are two hydrocarbons, and in most cases the hydrocarbon if there is only one. Figure 10 shows one exception to this.

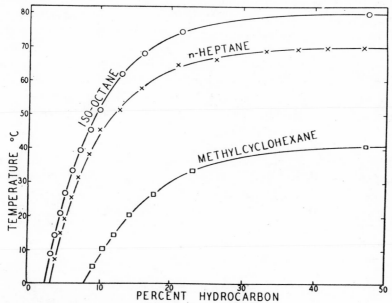

FIG. 17. (61) Solubilities of hydrocarbons in aniline.
Courtesy of *Industrial and Engineering Chemistry.*

III. BINARY SYSTEMS

The mutual solubilities of a large number of pairs of liquids are recorded in Seidell's book (188), but there are still many unobserved binary systems. It was with the purpose of greatly increasing the number of binary systems for which mutual solubilities of a hydrocarbon and a nonhydrocarbon might be estimated that investigations of the present author (61, 62, 64) were made. Instead of mutual solubilities at a uniform temperature, it seemed that the critical solution temperature (C.S.T.) of the system would be just as indicative broadly of the solubility relationships, and could be examined more expeditiously so as to cover a wide field. The qualitative relationship between these properties is illustrated in Fig. 17 (61). The solubilities at any temperature have an inverse relation to the C.S.T. (tops of the curves). The term "critical solution temperature" is sometimes used loosely in the literature meaning merely "solution temperature" or the temperature at which a dissolved liquid begins to precipitate out. This is no more accurate than to call a dew point or a boiling point a "critical temperature."

The curves of limited miscibility for binary systems are not quite symmetrical with respect to the 50% line, sometimes very unsymmetrical (197). However, by analogy with the ternary diagrams the curves are probably completely convex except when there is a third component such as salt in water (100) or methanol (51a), or water in acetic acid (105). Another exceptional condition would occur when there is no C.S.T. because of the intervention of the critical temperature of one of the components. An example of this is reported (Fig. 1 of 241) for thymol and water, although it is not clear why 270°C. is called a "critical temperature" (no C.S.T.), since it is more than 100° below the critical temperature of either component. In an experimental check on that system (64) 270°C. was found to be a C.S.T. and not a critical point. A real example lacking a C.S.T. would be the system, nitrobenzene-propane (60).

Bingham (20) observed qualitatively and recorded the mutual solubilities of fifty liquids in pairs (over 1000 observations), five of the liquids being hydrocarbons. Some C.S.T.'s were given. A few of Bingham's observations are questionable, particularly those of stannic chloride, which in the absence of water behaves like carbon tetrachloride, and is miscible with hydrocarbons, even lubricating oils, but is immiscible with water until it reacts vigorously with it. Bingham's low values for the C.S.T. of solvents with n-hexane were probably due to the presence of naphthenes in his sample.

Sulfur dioxide C.S.T. have been observed for sixty hydrocarbons. Those for saturated hydrocarbons are a nearly linear function of the boiling point (123), indicating a negligible selectivity for naphthenes (61), a conclusion contrary to that drawn from some early observations on hydrocarbon mixtures (145). Sulfur dioxide has a fair selectivity for aromatics and olefins (61, 62). Liquid ammonia has relatively a poor selectivity for all types of hydrocarbon (61, 62, 123).

IV. COMPILATION OF CRITICAL SOLUTION TEMPERATURES

The observed C.S.T. of individual hydrocarbons with nonhydrocarbons now number nearly 2400 (the majority being published from this laboratory). These are listed in Table II (see p. 273), which is intended to be complete for publications through 1947. The actual temperatures are given except that, in order to save space, observations listed in considerable numbers in a single reference which is readily available are cited in groups. If all points were given, the table would be nearly three times as long.

In order to present a direct comparison of all of the solvents, their C.S.T. with n-heptane are given in the second column, since this hydrocarbon is the one used most generally. Many of the temperatures in this column are estimated, as indicated by parentheses. Some of these estimates were made by adding 220° to the observed or estimated C.S.T. with benzene, since this is the average difference for heptane and benzene. This method gives a fictitious point in several cases because the critical temperature of n-heptane, 266.8°C., or the instability of reagents would prevent its realization. Some other estimates were made by subtracting 45° from C.S.T. with paraffin wax or oils of comparable miscibility, although these are unrealizable because of crystallization of reagents. The letter M in this column indicates that the reagent is completely miscible at all temperatures above −78°C. (or estimated to be so) with n-heptane and almost all other hydrocarbons (as liquids).

About 200 C.S.T. of solvents with lubricating oils (61) are omitted from Table II (unless such an observation is the only one with a certain solvent, or it is compared with the results of other observers) because the latter are not individual hydrocarbons. Similarly, some of those with lubricating oils listed (56c, 163a) with "greater than" or "less than" are omitted when the symbol is evident from the structure of the solvent or its C.S.T. with lighter hydrocarbons (cf. 61). Since the paraffin wax employed (61) was substantially equivalent to n-pentacosane, it is so designated. Some hydrocarbon mixtures of narrow boiling range are included. The lower boiling petroleum ether of Prins (164) was probably largely paraffinic, but the higher boiling cut very likely contained naphthenes, since its C.S.T. were all lower than those of the lighter cut.

When the same point has been observed by two or more investigators, a selected mean is recorded for observations showing fair agreement. In other cases both observations are given. A few question marks are applied when a reason for the discrepancy was suspected, such as water impurity in the solvent (25, 43, 114), or if the observation was inconsistent with several others.

The 422 solvents are listed alphabetically, thus providing an index for the solvents in the tables in the earlier papers (61, 62), which were arranged differently. The number of solvents could be increased still further, using temperatures preceded by "less than", by including the remaining solvents of Table II of a former paper (61), all of which are miscible as liquids with practically all hydrocarbons at available temperatures; and also by including pairs of solvents and hydrocarbons for which freezing curve data are listed in reference 100a and elsewhere. When the freezing curve has a very flat middle portion, the temperature is only slightly above the C.S.T. (cf. 199a). The list could also be extended indefinitely with "less than" or "more than" with the following considerations:

All hydrocarbons and practically all of their halogen derivatives are mutually completely miscible at all temperatures above the freezing curves, except in a few cases within about 30°C. below the critical temperature of one component. A C.S.T. of any solvent with an aromatic hydrocarbon is about 200°C. lower than that of the same solvent with a paraffin hydrocarbon of similar molecular weight. That of an olefin is usually 30 to 70°C. lower, and that of a napthene is 10 to 60°C. lower than that of the paraffin. The critical solution temperature in the same class of hydrocarbons increases with molecular weight except in some cases for hydrocarbons below C_6. A higher homologue of any nonhydrocarbon has a lower C.S.T. with the same hydrocarbon. The increment for such pairs is approximately 40°C. for each additional —CH_2 group. Introduction of an amino, hydroxyl, carboxyl, nitro, or cyano group into a solvent molecule raises the C.S.T. with a hydrocarbon substantially, of the order of 150 to 200°C. Halogen substituents, ether oxygen atoms, and carbonyl groups have relatively small effects. The quantitative effects of these and some other groups and their positions are presented in citations (61, 62).

The hydrocarbons taken with each solvent in Table II are arranged in ascending order of molecular weight for the classes, paraffins, olefins, naphthenes, and aromatics, respectively. No distinction is made between aniline points and C.S.T. with aniline because there is usually less than one degree difference (12), as should be expected considering the flatness of the curves of Fig. 17. Aniline points are the solution points for equal volumes of the components, which means about 40% by weight of the hydrocarbon in the system.

Care was taken to exclude demixing temperatures resulting from crystallization of a component, many of which are referred to as C.S.T. in other compilations, as discussed previously (62). Such a point can be a hundred degrees or more above the calculated C.S.T., and be misleading as to miscibility of the liquids. On the other hand the two points are coincident in some cases because in cooling the solution past the C.S.T. the sudden increase in mole fraction of one component in one of the resulting liquid phases is often sufficient to crystallize it.

Aniline and other aromatic solvents are very similar in selectivity characteristics, as illustrated by the parallelism of the lines in the graph of nitrobenzene and nitrotoluene points (60), so that missing C.S.T. with an aromatic solvent may be estimated from aniline points if a C.S.T. of one paraffin isomer is known with that solvent. Moreover, it was noted independently by Chavanne and Simon (36), by Francis (59), and by

(Continued on p. 301)

TABLE II

CRITICAL SOLUTION TEMPERATURES WITH HYDROCARBONS

Solvent	C.S.T. with n-Heptane	Hydrocarbon	C.S.T.	References
Acetal	(−61)	Two lubricating oils	<0	56c, 61
Acetamide	(363)	Benzene	142.5	62 (Table I)
		m-Xylene	79?	120, 188 (p. 121)
		m-Xylene	200	62
		Naphthalene	148.5	120, 188
		Biphenyl	167	120, 188
		Bibenzyl	185	120, 188
		α-Methylnaphthalene	169.5	120, 188
		Diphenylmethane	178	120, 188
		Indene	144	120
		Acenaphthene	178	120, 188
Acetanilide	204	Eight nonaromatics		61
Acetic acid	10.5	n-Hexane	−5	20, 61
		Isooctane	7	61, 140
		Petroleum (185–95°)	50.5	104
		Cyclohexane	5	61, 104
		Four other non-aromatics		61
		Five lubricating oils	153–201	56c, 61, 163a
Acetic anhydride	68	Isooctane	66	4, 61
		Petroleum (170–80°)	85.5	106
		Cyclohexane	52	4, 61, 62, 106
		Methylcyclohexane	56	4, 61, 62
		Decalin (cis)	83	4, 62
		Decalin (trans)	81.1	4
		Gasoline (n = 1.406)	54	144
		Five other nonaromatics		61
		Fifteen aromatics		62
		Five lubricating oils	143–172	56c, 61, 163a
Acetoacetanilide	(182)	Decalin	144	62
		Six aromatics		62
Acetone	−28	Isopentane	ca.−160	173b
		n-Octane	−5.5	165
		2,7-Dimethyloctane	18	225
		n-Dodecane	16.5	165
		n-Hexadecane	35.8	165
		n-Heptadecane	38	165
		Diisopentene	−3.8	75
		n-Pentacosane	65	61
		n-Pentacosane	>82	163a
		Seven other nonaromatics		61
		Seven lubricating oils	46 to >87	56c, 61, 158a, 163a
Acetone oxime	(5)	Cetane	35	64
Acetonitrile	84	n-Pentane	>60	64
		n-Hexane	77	64
		n-Heptane	84	37, 61

TABLE II—*Continued*

Solvent	C.S.T. with *n*-Heptane	Hydrocarbon	C.S.T.	References
Acetonitrile—*Cont.*		Triptane	73.5	64
		Isooctane	81	37, 61, 140
		1-Heptene	38	64
		Cyclohexane	76	61, 62
		Methylcyclohexane	78	61, 62
		Decalin	106	62
		Sixteen aromatics		62
		Lubricating oil	>82	56c
Acetonylacetone	68	Petroleum ether (42–62°)	>b.p.	164
		Petroleum ether (80–100°)	>b.p.	164
		Five other nonaromatics		61
		Methylcyclohexane	39	62
		Decalin	60	62
		Diamylbenzene	21	62
		Diamylnaphthalene	0	62
Acetophenone	4	*n*-Butane	10.6	60
		Isobutane	24.5	60
		n-Decane	10	20
		Seven other nonaromatics		61
		Three lubricating oils	13–47	56c, 61
Acetylacetone	(−14)	Lubricating oil	31.6	56c
Acetyl chloride	(−36)	Paraffinic lubricating oil	9	61
Acetyldiethylam-amine	6.25	Four heptanes		138
		Isooctane	46	140
Acetyldimethyl-amine	65	*n*-Heptane	65	64
Acetylsalicylic acid (see Aspirin)				
Adipic acid	(346)	Five aromatics		62
Aldol	36	Eight nonaromatics		61
Allyl alcohol	(M)	Two lubricating oils	86–91	56c
m-Aminoacetani-lide	(400)	Benzene	266?	200 (cf. 62)
p-Aminoacetani-lide	(408)	Benzene	188?	200
		Four other aromatics		62
p-Aminoaceto-phenone	(221)	Nine aromatics		62
m-Aminobenzoic acid	(320)	Benzene	100	64
p-Aminobenzo-phenone	(212)	Diamylbenzene	177	62
		Diamylnaphthalene	130	62
o-Aminobiphenyl	43	Five nonaromatics		61
p-Aminobiphenyl	125	Eight nonaromatics		61
p-Aminodiethyl-aniline	(0)	Isooctane	0–20	140
p-Aminodimeth-ylaniline	(100)	*n*-Heptane	>100	64

TABLE II—*Continued*

Solvent	C.S.T. with n-Heptane	Hydrocarbon	C.S.T.	References
1-Aminoethanol-(Aldehyde ammonia)	(320)	Naphthalene	100	64
p-Aminoethyl-acetanilide	(189)	Ten aromatics		62
2-Amino-2-methyl-1-propanol	89	n-Heptane	89	64
o-Aminophenol	(150)	Diamylnaphthalene	115	64
		Lubricating oil	<170?	56c
m-Aminophenol	(230)	Diamylnaphthalene	195	62
p-Aminophenol	(255)	Diamylnaphthalene	220	62
p-Aminophenyl-acetic acid	(100)			61
Ammonia	63	Propane	35	64
		Paraffins (C_6 to C_{12})	60–80	123
		Propylene	11	64
		1-Butene	20	163
		Seven other nonaromatics		61
		Ethylbenzene	<15	123
		Three xylenes	<15	123
		Six other aromatics		62, Tables I & II
		Twenty-seven hydrocarbons (mostly aromatic) (NH_3 probably not anhydrous)	>25?	43
Amyl acetate	(M)	Three lubricating oils	<0	56c, 163a
Four amyl alcohols	M	Five lubricating oils	<0 to 33	56c, 61, 163a
Isoamyl amine	(M)	Paraffinic lubricating oil	<0	61
Amyl furoate	−32	Seven nonaromatics		61
Amyl oleate	(M)	Propane (lower phase pt.)	None	86
Isoamyl nitrite	(M)	Paraffinic lubricating oil	<0	61
tert-Amylphenol	(M)	Paraffinic lubricating oil	<0	61
n-Amyl phthalate	(M)	Propane (lower phase pt.)	105	87
Isoamyl phthalate	(M)	Isooctane	<−40	64
		Decalin	<−35	64
Amyl stearate	(M)	Ethane (lower phase pt.)	19	86
Anethole	(M)	Lubricating oil	<0	56c
Aniline	70	About 295 observed and 40 estimated aniline points or C.S.T.		49
		Points for 121 hydrocarbons, 75 of them being additional		177–179
		About 295 observed and 100 estimated points		12

TABLE II—*Continued*

Solvent	C.S.T. with n-Heptane	Hydrocarbon	C.S.T.	References
Aniline—*Cont.*				
(Total observed		The following not in-		
hydrocarbons)		cluded in references 49		
111 Paraffins		and 179:		
41 Olefins		Nonacosane	*122	129
9 Diolefins		Propylene	47	64
146 Naphthenes		3-Ethyl-2-pentene	−40?	93
107 Aromatics		Diisobutene	42.8?	54
1 Acetylene		Diisobutene	36	61
—		1,10-Hendecadiene	23.6	12
415		Nineteen other olefins		148
		1-Hexadecyne	2	148
		1,1-Dimethylcyclo-	*45.4	12
		hexane		
		1-Propyl-1-cyclopen-	14.2	54
		tene		
		1-Butyl-1-cyclopen-	25	54
		tene		
		1,3,5-Trimethylcyclo-	56.9	123
		hexane		
		3-Cyclohexylpropene	8	148
		1-Methyl-3-butylcy-	*62.6	35
		clopentane		
		Camphene	30	118
		Turpentine	<17	125
		Octahydroindene,	32.2	51
		(C_9H_{16})		
		1-Cyclopentyl-2-	8.6	71
		cyclopentene		
		4-Cyclohexyl-2-pen-	37	148
		tene		
		Bicyclohexyl	*47.7	12
		4-Cyclohexyl-2-hep-	44	148
		tene		
		1,3-Dicyclopentyl-	54.8	71
		cyclopentane		
		1,3-Dicyclopentyl-	37.5	71
		cyclopentene		
		3-(Cyclopent-2-enyl)	21.5	71
		bicyclopentyl		
		3,3'-Dicyclopentyl-	67.8	71
		bicyclopentyl		
		2-Phenylheptane	*<−17	221
		Dodecylbenzene	*13.7	107
		Tetralin	*<−20	67
		sec- and iso-Butyl-	<0	162
		tetralin		
		Octyltetralin	10.8	162
		2,3-Dihexylnaph-	*−3.3	137
		thalene		
		1,1-Diphenyl-1-octa-	9.4	137
		decene		

* Improved value

TABLE II—*Continued*

Solvent	C.S.T. with *n*-Heptane	Hydrocarbon	C.S.T.	References
Aniline *Cont.*				
		1-Phenyl-1-α-naphthyl-1-octadecene	*−1.1	137
		Seven other dicyclics	*<0	62
		Four lubricating oils	75–115	56c, 61
Anisaldehyde	80	Petroleum ether (42–62°)	>b.p.	164
		Petroleum ether (80–100°)	55	164
		Isooctane	87	140
		Lubricating oil	91.2	56c
o-Anisidine	(70)	Isooctane	77	4
		Cyclohexane	31.4	4
		Methylcyclohexane	36.5	4
		Decalin (*cis*)	27.7	4
		Decalin (*trans*)	28.9	4
p-Anisidine	(130)	Decalin (*cis*)	87	4
		Decalin (*trans*)	89.2	4
Anisole	(M)	Lubricating oil	<0	56c
Anthranilic acid	204	Eight nonaromatics		61
Antimony bromide	(190)	Cyclohexane	175	135
Antimony chloride	(140)	Cyclohexane	125.5	135
		Cyclohexene	< m.p. curve	135
Antipyrine	(163)	Decalin	127	62
		Diamylbenzene	128	62
		Diamylnaphthalene	100	62
Arsenic bromide	(M)	Naphthalene	<20	100a (p. 190)
Aspirin	(255)	Decalin	115	64
		n-Pentacosane	>300	64
Azobenzene	(20)	Isooctane	<22	64
Benzalacetone	(50)	Petroleum ether (42–62°)	43	164
		Petroleum ether (80–100°)	25.5	164
Benzaldehyde	3	Petroleum ether (42–62°)	−1.5	164
		Petroleum ether (80–100°)	−13	164
		Isooctane	17	61, 140
		Seven other nonaromatics		61
		Four lubricating oils	14–45	56c, 61
Benzidine	(278)	Twelve aromatics		62
Benzoic anhydride	79	Seven nonaromatics		61
Benzoin	(89)	*n*-Pentacosane	134	64
Benzonitrile	8	Five heptanes		138
		Lubricating oil	26	56c
Benzoyl chloride	(M)	Paraffinic lubricating oil	<0	61
Benzoyl-α-naphthylamine	(213)	*n*-Pentacosane	258	64
		Decalin	<120	64
Benzyl acetate	−13.1	Petroleum ether (42–62°)	−11	164
		Petroleum ether (80–100°)	<−20	164
		n-Heptane	−13.1	140
		2,4-Dimethylpentane	−9.2	140
		Isooctane	9.5	140

* Improved value

TABLE II—*Continued*

Solvent	C.S.T. with n-Heptane	Hydrocarbon	C.S.T.	References
Benzyl alcohol	50.7	n-Butane	>60	64
(thirty-two non-		n-Pentane	68	64
aromatic hydro-		n-Hexane	50	61, 130, 148
carbons and one		Four other hexanes		130
aromatic)		Petroleum ether (42–62°)	>b.p.	164
		Petroleum ether (80–100°)	25.2	164
		n-Heptane	50.7	61, 138
		Five other heptanes		138
		n-Octane	54.5	131, 148
		Isooctane	73	61, 140, 148
		Nine other octanes		131
		2,7-Dimethyloctane	72	148
		Five other nonaromatics		61
		2-Phenylhexadecane	27.9	222
		Three lubricating oils	76–119	56c, 61
Benzyl benzoate	−2.05	Six heptanes		138
		Isooctane	16	140
Benzyl cyanide	(80)	Petroleum ether (42–62°)	>b.p.	164
		Petroleum ether (80–100°)	47	164
Benzyl-p-hy-	(206)	Decalin	92	62
droxybenzoate		Diamylbenzene	99	62
		Diamylnaphthalene	<80	62
o-Benzylphenol	67	Eight nonaromatics		61
Benzyl phthalate	(125)	Isooctane	132	64
		n-Pentacosane	173	64
		Methylcyclohexane	27	64
		Decalin	<25	64
Benzyl sulfide	(M)	Paraffinic lubricating oil	<0	61
o-Bromophenol	(−6)	2,2-Dimethylpentane	3.85	138
		2,4-Dimethylpentane	3.15	138
		Triptane	−3.80	138
		Isooctane	23	140
1,3-Butanediol	(295)	Benzene	75	64
		Naphthalene	89	64
		α-Methylnaphthalene	103	64
n-Butanol	M	Ethane (lower C.S.T.)	38.1	115
		Ethane (crit. pt., upper layer)	39.8	115
		n-Heptane	<−78	61
		n-Pentacosane	25	61
		Five lubricating oils	1–36	56c, 61, 163a
sec-Butanol	M	n-Heptane	<−78	61
		n-Pentacosane	25	61
		Four lubricating oils	9 to >40	61, 163a
Isobutanol	M	n-Heptane	<−78	61
		n-Pentacosane	38	61
		Six lubricating oils	14–80	56c, 61, 163a

TABLE II—*Continued*

Solvent	C.S.T. with *n*-Heptane	Hydrocarbon	C.S.T.	References
2-Butanone (Methyl ethyl ketone)	(M)	Cetane	<0	64
		Three lubricating oils	<0–57	56c, 163a
n-Butyl acetate	(M)	Three lubricating oils	<0	56c, 163a
"*n*-Butylalde-hyde"	(M)	Two lubricating oils	<10	163a
Butyl Carbitol	(0)	Two lubricating oils	22–47.5	56c
Butyl Cellosolve	(−38)	Paraffinic oil	7	64
		Three lubricating oils	<10	56c, 163a
Butyl formate	(M)	Two lubricating oils	<10	163a
Butyl furoate	−22	Seven nonaromatics		61
n-Butyl oxalate	−55	Four nonaromatics		61
p-tert-Butyl-phenol	(M)	Paraffinic lubricating oil	<0	61
n-Butyl phthalate	(20)	Propane (lower phase pt.)	106–7	87
		Two lubricating oils	<10–85	163a
Butyl tartrate	(20)	Isooctane	<25	64
n-Butyramide	178	Seven nonaromatics		61
Butyric acid	(−23)	Lubricating oil	22	56c
Carbitol (Dieth-ylene glycol monoethyl ether) (Observa-tions in ref. 63 and probably those in 56c and in 140 were made with impure Carbitol)	25	2,2-Dimethylpentane	20	63, 64
		2,3-Dimethylpentane	14	63, 64
		2,4-Dimethylpentane	20	63, 64
		Triptane	9	63, 64
		Isooctane	>90?	140
		Isooctane	28	61
		Seven other nonaromatics		61
		Three lubricating oils	109–133	56c, 61
Carbon dioxide	−51	Seven nonaromatics		61
Carbon disulfide	(M)	Two lubricating oils	<0	56c, 61
		Isopentane	ca.−160	173b
Carbon tetrabro-mide	(<15)	Cetane	<65	64
Carbon tetrachlo-ride	(<−40)	Three lubricating oils	<0	56c, 61, 163a
Castor oil	44.5	*n*-Hexane	35	20
		n-Heptane	44.5	64
Catechol	(181)	Diisobutene	162	64
		Cyclohexane	120	62
		Decalin	146	62
		Five aromatics		62
Cellosolve (β-Eth-oxyethanol)	−12	Six nonaromatics		61
		Six lubricating oils	61–106	56c, 61, 163a
Cellosolve acetate	(M)	Isooctane	<0	140
		Two lubricating oils	27–29.5	56c
Cetyl stearate	(M)	Propane (lower C.S.T.)	95.2	50
Chloral hydrate	(235)	*n*-Heptane	>102	64
		Benzene	<28	64
		Toluene	<45	64, 214

TABLE II—*Continued*

Solvent	C.S.T. with *n*-Heptane	Hydrocarbon	C.S.T.	References
Chloroacetic acid	137	Eight nonaromatics		61
		Four aromatics		62
Chloroacetone	(40)	Lubricating oil	85	56c
o-Chloroaniline	13	*n*-Butane	29.8	60
		Isobutane	50.5	60
		n-Pentane	23	64
		Seven other nonaromatics		61
p-Chloroaniline	80	*n*-Heptane	80	61
		Isooctane	86	61
o-Chlorobenzoic acid	(99)	Calcd. for *n*-heptane and benzene	99 −52	199a
m-Chlorobenzoic acid	(75)	Calcd. for *n*-heptane and benzene	75 −36	199a
p-Chlorobenzoic acid	(123)	Calcd. for *n*-heptane and benzene	123 −13	199a
β-Chloroethanol (Ethylene chlorohydrin)	113	*n*-Heptane	113	37, 61
		Isooctane	116	37, 61
		Four other noncyclics		61
		Three naphthenes		61, 62
		Eleven aromatics		62
		Three lubricating oils	141–171	56c, 61
β-Chloroethyl acetate	(10)	Isooctane	16	140
Chloromaleic anhydride	150	*n*-Heptane	150	64
		Cyclohexane	115	64
		Methylcyclohexane	124	64
		Tetraisopropylbenzene	122	64
		α-Methylnaphthalene	< −30	64
o-Chlorophenol	6	Seven nonaromatics		61
p-Chlorophenol	67	Seven nonaromatics		61
Chloropicrin	M	*n*-Heptane	< −60	64
Cineole	< −20	Isooctane	< −20	64
		Lubricating oil	<0	56c
Cinnamic acid	(70)	*n*-Pentacosane	<120	64
Cinnamic aldehyde	65	Petroleum ether (42–62°)	>b.p.	164
		Petroleum ether (80–100°)	50.5	164
		Isooctane	82	140
		Lubricating oil	87	56c
Cinnamyl alcohol	102	Petroleum ether (42–62°)	>b.p.	164
		Petroleum ether (80–100°)	56.5	164
		Eight other nonaromatics		61
α-Citral	<0	Isooctane	<0	140
Citronellal hydrate	(40)	Petroleum ether (42–62°)	20.5	164
		Petroleum ether (80–100°)	9.5	164
Citronellal hydrate oxime	(80)	Petroleum ether (42–62°)	>b.p.	164
		Petroleum ether (80–100°)	>b.p.	164
Cottonseed oil (refined)	(M)	Propane (lower C.S.T.)	66.2	50, 86
		Isobutane (lower phase pt.)	126	86

TABLE II—*Continued*

Solvent	C.S.T. with *n*-Heptane	Hydrocarbon	C.S.T.	References
o-Cresol	9	Seven nonaromatics		61
		Three lubricating oils	19–76	56c, 61
m-Cresol	14	Eight nonaromatics		61
		Three lubricating oils	40.5–93	56c, 61
p-Cresol	12	Seven nonaromatics		61
		Three lubricating oils	42.5–98	56c, 61
Cresylic acid	0	*n*-Butane	14.2	60
		Isobutane	45.5	60
		Isooctane	20	61, 140
		Seven other nonaromatics		61
		Three lubricating oils	23–74	56c, 61
Crotonaldehyde	−14	Seven nonaromatics		61
		Four lubricating oils	<21–69	61, 163a
Cyanoacetic acid	(320)	Benzene	>90	64
Cyclohexanol	(M)	Two lubricating oils	<0	56c, 61
Cyclohexylamine	(M)	Isooctane	<0	140
o- and *p*-Cyclo-hexylphenols	(M)	Paraffinic lubricating oil	<0	61
Diacetone alcohol (4-Hydroxy-4-methyl-2-pentanone)	8	Isooctane	4	61
		Isooctane	21.5	140
		n-Pentacosane	94	61, 163a
		Four lubricating oils	65–96	61, 163a
		Seven other nonaromatics		61
2,4-Diaminotoluene	(220)	Tetraisopropylbenzene	185	64
Diamylhydroquinone	(M)	Paraffinic lubricating oil	<0	61
Dianisidine	(150)			61
Dichloroacetic acid		Lubricating oil	<0	56c
2,5-Dichloro-aniline	(−10)	*n*-Pentacosane	<40	64
β,β-Dichloroethyl ether (Chlorex)	16	*n*-Butane	13.1	64
		n-Pentane	11	64, 243
		n-Hexane	12	61, 243
		n-Heptane	16	61, 243
		n-Octane	20.67	243
		n-Nonane	24.0	243
		n-Hexadecane	47.93	243
		Three lubricating oils	34–68	61, 158a
		Six other nonaromatics		61
β,β-Dichloroethyl sulfide (Mustard gas)	(20)	Ligroin	19	220
		Gasoline	20.4	220
		Kerosene	25.6	220
		R.R. light oil	37	220
2,4-Dichloro-phenol	(0)	Lubricating oil	<40	56c
Dicroton	−24	Eight nonaromatics		61
Dicyclohexylamine	(M)	Isooctane	0	140

TABLE II—*Continued*

Solvent	C.S.T. with n-Heptane	Hydrocarbon	C.S.T.	References
Diethanolamine	(381)	Thirteen aromatics		62
Diethylamine	M	n-Heptane	< −60	64
Diethylaniline	(M)	Lubricating oil	<0	56c
Diethylcyclo-hexylamine	(M)	Isooctane	<0	140
Diethylene glycol	(312)	α-Methylnaphthalene	125	62, 121
		Thirty-three other aromatics		62
		Lubricating oil	>235	56c
Diethylene glycol monoethyl ether (see Carbitol)				
Diethylene glycol monomethyl ether (Methyl Carbitol)	104	Eight nonaromatics		61
Diethylene triamine	>110	n-Heptane	>110	64
		Methylcyclohexane	98	64
		Kerosene	150	64
Diethylformamide	66	n-Heptane	66	64
Di(β-hydroxyethyl)aniline	(165)	α-Methylnaphthalene	<20	64
Diisoamylamine	(M)	Isooctane	<0	140
Dimethoxymethane (Methylal)	(−45)	Cetane	<10	64
		Crystal oil	0	64
Dimethoxytetramethylene glycol	(5)	Kerosene	35	64
Dimethylamino-1,2-propanediol	134	n-Heptane	134	64
Dimethylaniline	(M)	Two lubricating oils	<0	56c, 61
Dimethyldihydroresorcinol	(205)	n-Pentacosane	250	64
		Decalin	<115	64
m-Dinitrobenzene	(193)	Four nonaromatics		61
		Three lubricating oils	169–230	56c, 61
		Four aromatics		62
Each Dinitrobenzene		Five polycyclic aromatics	<m.p.	100a (p. 176)
2,4-Dinitrobenzoyl chloride	(150)			61
2,4-Dinitrochlorobenzene	187	Eight nonaromatics		61
		Three lubricating oils	151–206	56c, 61
		Three aromatics		62
2,4-Dinitrophenol	(186)	Diamylbenzene	151	62
		Diamylnaphthalene	117	62
Five dinitrophenols		Benzene	<m.p. curves	188 (p. 351)
Dioxane	−4	Six nonaromatics		61

TABLE II—*Continued*

Solvent	C.S.T. with *n*-Heptane	Hydrocarbon	C.S.T.	References
)iphenylamine	26	Isopentane	44.9	31
		Four other nonaromatics		61
)iphenyl disulfide	(M)	Paraffinic lubricating oil	<0	61
)iphenylethylene-diamine	103	Eight nonaromatics		61
)ipropylene gly-col	120	*n*-Heptane	120	64
		Cyclohexane	72	64
		Methylcyclohexane	84	64
		α-Methylnaphthalene	<−40	64
)i-*n*-propyl-ketoxime	(M)	Isooctane	<0	140
ξ-Dithiodiglycol	(400)	Naphthalene	180	64
)itolylthiourea	(M)	*n*-Heptane	<−78	64
Σpichlorohydrin	(0)	Lubricating oil	53.2	56c
Σthanol	−60	Ethane	<−78	113, 115
		Ethane (lower C.S.T.)	31.9	115
		Ethane (crit. pt., upper layer)	40.67	115
		n-Butane	37.5?	114
		n-Butane	<−78	64
		n-Pentane	<−78	64
		Isopentane	−30?	114
		Paraffins (160–80°)	33.5?	92
		n-Decane	−15	20
		Biisooctyl	38.72	245
		"Paraffin oil"	89.7	39
		n-Pentacosane	112	20, 61, 163a
		Three other non-aromatics		61
		Five other oils	108–128	56c, 61, 163a
Σthanolamine	(323)	Thirteen aromatics		62
β-Ethoxyethanol (see Cellosolve)			.	
Σthyl abietate	(M)	Paraffinic lubricating oil	<0	61
Σthylacetanilide	(30)	Isooctane	<33	64
		Cetane	43	64
		n-Pentacosane	69	64
Σthyl acetate	M	*n*-Heptane	<−78	61
		n-Pentacosane	12	61, 163a
		Five lubricating oils	−2 to 68	56c, 61, 163a
Σthyl acetoace-tate	43	Propane	32	64
		n-Butane	25	64
		Isobutane	37.7	64
		Isooctane	35	61, 140
		Petroleum ether (42–62°)	29	164
		Petroleum ether (80–100°)	28.5	164
		Three lubricating oils	100–130	56c, 61
		Seven other nonaromatics		61

TABLE II—*Continued*

Solvent	C.S.T. with n-Heptane	Hydrocarbon	C.S.T.	References
Ethyl acetyl gly-colate	(60)	Isooctane	67.5	140
Ethylaniline	(−30)	n-Hexane	−47.8	219, 188 (p. 615)
		2-Methylpentane	−40.8	219, 188 (p. 615)
		2,2-Dimethylbutane	−33.7	219, 188 (p. 615)
Ethyl bromide	(M)	Isopentane	ca.−160	173b
Ethyl benzoate	(M)	Paraffinic lubricating oil	<0	61
Ethyl carbamate (Urethane)	(M)	Benzene	<30	100a (p. 112)
		Toluene	<30	214, 100a (p. 112)
Ethyl carbonate	M	Kerosene	<0	64
		Three lubricating oils	<0	56c, 163a
Ethyl chlorocar-bonate	(M)	Two lubricating oils	<10	163a
Ethyl cyanoace-tate	(>90)	Isooctane	>93	140
Ethyldiethanol-amine	135	n-Heptane	135	64
Ethylene cyano-hydrin (see β-Hydroxypro-pionitrile)				
Ethylene diace-tate	58	n-Hexane	47	64
		n-Heptane	58	64
		Isooctane	57	64, 140
		n-Pentacosane	137	64
		1-Heptene	11	64
		Three naphthenes		62
		Twelve aromatics		62
Ethylenediamine	108	n-Heptane	108	37, 64
		Isooctane	112	37, 64
		Lubricating oil	<0?	56c
Ethylene difor-mate	(190)	Twenty-nine Aromatics	(subtract 25°, see text)	62
Ethylene glycol	(400)	Ten aromatics		62
Ethyl ether	M	Chrysene (lower C.S.T.?)	207–18	(cf. 62)
Ethyl formate	−34	Seven nonaromatics		61
		Four lubricating oils	41–71	61, 163a
Ethyl furoate	20	Seven nonaromatics		61
Ethyl glycolate	>80	Isooctane	>91	140
Ethyl isothiocya-nate	(M)	Lubricating oil	<0	56c

TABLE II—*Continued*

Solvent	C.S.T. with *n*-Heptane	Hydrocarbon	C.S.T.	References
Ethyl lactate	21	Isooctane	17	61, 140
		Pinene	19.15	120
		Seven other nonaromatics		61
Ethyl methyl carbamate	(45)	Isooctane	52	140
Ethyl methyl xanthate	<−30	*n*-Heptane	<−30	64
Ethyl oxalate	23.5	Eight nonaromatics		61
Ethylphenylethanolamine	84	*n*-Heptane	84	64
		Isooctane	88	64
		Diamylbenzene	<27	62
Ethyl-β-phenyl glycolate	(80)	Petroleum ether (42–62°)	>b.p.	164
		Petroleum ether (80–100°)	60	164
Ethyl phthalate	28.2	Propane (lower phase pt.)	100.5	87
		Five hexanes		139
		Six heptanes		138
		Petroleum ether (42–62°)	20.5	164
		Petroleum ether (80–100°)	8	164
Ethyl propionate		Two lubricating oils	<10 to 45?	163a
Ethyl salicylate	M	Paraffinic lubricating oil	<0	61
Ethyl sulfate	75	*n*-Heptane	75	63, 64
		2,2-Dimethylpentane	65	63
		2,3-Dimethylpentane	61	63
		2,4-Dimethylpentane	65	63
		Triptane	56	63
		Nineteen other nonaromatics		148
		Lubricating oil	136	56c
Ethyl tartrate	125	*n*-Heptane	125	64
		Cyclohexane	82	64
		Methylcyclohexane	92	64
Ethyl thiocyanate	−7	*n*-Heptane	−7	64
		Lubricating oil	30.4	56c
Eugenol	3	*n*-Butane	23	60
		Isobutane	43	60
		Isooctane	24.5	140
		Isooctane	11	61
		Seven other nonaromatics		61
		Three lubricating oils	21–63	56c, 61
Formamide	(470)	Naphthalene	230	62
		Hexane (crit. pt., upper layer)	250	103a
Formanilide	228	*n*-Heptane	228	64
		Cyclohexane	131.5	64
		Methylcyclohexane	150	64
		Lubricating oil	>100	56c
Formic acid	(185)	*n*-Pentane	28? or 34.2?	120
		n-Hexane	180	20
		n-Decane and paraffin	200	20
		Benzene	74	(cf. 62, Table I)

TABLE II—*Continued*

Solvent	C.S.T. with *n*-Heptane	Hydrocarbon	C.S.T.	References
Furfural	95	2,4-Dimethylpentane	98	64
(Ninety-seven		Triptane	90	64
nonaromatics,		Camphene	48	118, 120
thirty-nine aro-		Pinene	62.4	120
matics)		Docosane	144.3	28
		Eight other nonaromatics		61, 62
		Eighty-five other non-aromatics		179
		Toluene	<-60.7	169
		m-Xylene	-55	169
		Three other aromatics		62
		Thirty-four other aromatics		179
		Six lubricating oils	122–165	56c, 61, 163a
Furfuryl alcohol	115	Decalin	88	62
		Eight nonaromatics		61
		Seventeen aromatics		62
		Three lubricating oils	148–183	56c, 61
Furoic acid	168	Diisobutene	107	64
		Six other nonaromatics		61
Glycerol	(520)	Naphthalene	>250	62
Glycerol dichloro-hydrin	(20)	Pinene	43.3	120
Glycerol-α-mono-chlorohydrin	(352)	Five aromatics		62
		Lubricating oil	>100	56c
Glycerol-α-iso-amyl ether	(−45)	Kerosene	<-25	64
Glycerol-α-methyl ether	(220)	Benzene	<1	64
		α and β-methylnaph-thalenes	57	64
Glycerol-α-phenyl ether	(100)	Methylcyclohexane	>100	64
Glyceryl furfural	(215)	Benzene	<-5	64
Glyceryl oleate	(−18)	Isooctane	−18	64
Glycolic acid	(320)	Benzene	>90	64
Hexachlorophenol	(<55)	*n*-Pentacosane	<100	64
Hydrazobenzene	(150)			61
Hydrogen bromide	(M)	*n*-Heptane	<-78	64
Hydrogen chloride	M	Ethane	<-134.5	100a (p. 212)
		Propane	<20	70
		n-Butane	<21	157
		n-Heptane	<-91	64
Hydrogen fluoride	(280)	Benzene	>15	108a
Hydrogen sulfide	M	Propane	<-78	64
		n-Butane	<-78	64
		Crystal oil	−29	64
		Crystal oil (lower phase pt.)	>100	64

TABLE II—*Continued*

Solvent	C.S.T. with *n*-Heptane	Hydrocarbon	C.S.T.	References
Hydroquinone	(370)	Naphthalene	ca. 154	100a (p. 140)
		Phenanthrene	ca. 164	19a
		Diphenylmethane	ca. 160	100a (p. 140)
		Triphenylmethane	177	100a (p. 140)
		Eight other aromatics		62
o-Hydroxybenzoic	(90)	*n*-Heptane	(90)	199a
acid		Benzene	(17)	199a
m-Hydroxyben-	(339)	Benzene	(119)	199a
zoic acid				
p-Hydroxyben-	(370)	Benzene	(150)	199a
zoic acid				
o-Hydroxybi-	28	Three nonaromatics		61
phenyl				
m-Hydroxybi-	121	Seven nonaromatics		61
phenyl				
p-Hydroxybi-	(120)	*n*-Pentacosane	165	64
phenyl				
Hydroxyethyl-	(280)	Benzene (colored opal-	60	64
ethylenediamine		escence)		
2-Hydroxy-3-	113	*n*-Heptane	113	64
methoxybenz-				
aldehyde				
β-Hydroxypro-	(318)	Benzene	98	64
pionitrile (Eth-				
ylene cyano-				
hydrin)				
Five hydroxy-		Calcd. for heptane and		199a
toluic acids		benzene		
Lactic acid	(286)	Diisobutene	>160	64
		Benzene	66	62
		Toluene	100	62
		m-Xylene	124	62
Lauric acid	(M)	Propane (lower phase pt.)	111	86, 87
Limonene	(M)	Lubricating oil	95?	56c
Linoleic acid	(M)	Propane (lower phase pt.)	79.8	86
Maleic acid	(250)			61
Maleic anhydride	(200)	Decalin	211	62
		Twenty-one aromatics		62
		Lubricating oil	>100	56c
Mesityl oxide (4-	(−45)	Paraffinic oil	0	61
Methyl-3-pen-		Two lubricating oils	<10	163a
tene-2-one)				
Methanol	51	Ethane (crit. pt., upper	35.37	115
		layer)		
		Propane	−32	64
		Propane	+22?	112a
(18 Paraffins		*n*-Butane	17?	114, 225
3 Olefins		*n*-Butane	−17	64
6 Naphthenes		Isobutane	20.1	225
18 Aromatics		*n*-Pentane	14.75	37, 64, 114, 144
—				
45 Total)				

TABLE II—*Continued*

Solvent	C.S.T. with n-Heptane	Hydrocarbon	C.S.T.	References
Methanol—*Cont.*		Isopentane	10.5	114
		n-Hexane	32 to 43.8	20, 245, 61 (table on p. 766)
		3-Methylpentane	26.8	64
		n-Heptane	51	37, 61, 63
		2,2-Dimethylpentane	40	63
		2,3-Dimethylpentane	37	63
		2,4-Dimethylpentane	40	63
		Triptane	32	63
		Isooctane	42.5	37, 61
		Isooctane	54	140
		n-Decane	76	20
		2,7-Dimethyloctane	86.8	225
		n-Pentacosane	187	61
		"Paraffin oil"	166	39
		Propylene	<-78	64
		1-Heptene	12	61
		Diisobutene	0	61
		Cyclopentane	15	64
		Methylcyclopentane	30.4	64
		Cyclohexane	45 to 57.8	51a, 61 (table p. 766) 242a
		Methylcyclohexane	46	61, 119
		Decalin	101	62
		Pinene	-64	120
		Tetralin	30	64, 77
		Seventeen other aromatics		62
		Three lubricating oils	188–204	56c, 61
β-Methoxyethanol (Methyl Cellosolve)	48	n-Heptane	48	37, 61
		Isooctane	46	37, 61
		Six other nonaromatics		61
		Six lubricating oils	95–123	56c, 61, 163a
Methyl acetate	(<15)	Isooctane	<15	64
		n-Pentacosane	>50	163a
		Three lubricating oils	40–70	56c, 163a
Methylal (see Dimethoxymethane)				
Methylaniline	0	n-Hexane	−18.6	219
		2-Methylpentane	−14	219
		3-Methylpentane	−17.25	219
		2,2-Dimethylbutane	−7.65	219
		n-Heptane	0	61
		Isooctane	9.5	61
		Isooctane	5.5	140
		n-Pentacosane	46	64
		Methylcyclopentane	−47.4	219
		Ethylcyclopentane	−49.4	219
		Propylcyclopentane	−43.0	219
		Two lubricating oils	12–46	56c, 61

TABLE II—*Continued*

Solvent	C.S.T. with *n*-Heptane	Hydrocarbon	C.S.T.	References
Methyl anthranilate	46	Petroleum ether (42–62°)	2	164
		Petroleum ether (80–100°)	<−20	164
		Eight other nonaromatics		61
Methylanthranilic acid	<100	Paraffinic lubricating oil	<170	61
Methylcyclohexanol	(−61)	Paraffinic lubricating oil	−16	61
Methylene iodide (10 Paraffins 4 Naphthenes)	97	*n*-Pentane	>100	64
		n-Hexane	100	20, 64
		n-Hexane	105.4	225
		2,2-Dimethylbutane	>100	64
		n-Heptane	97	64
		Triptane	100	64
		2-Methylheptane	96	64
		n-Octane	96	64
		Isooctane	112	64
		n-Decane	90	20
		2,7-Dimethyloctane	119.5	225
		Paraffin	128	20
		Cyclopentane	30.5	64
		Methylcyclopentane	44	64
		Cyclohexane	28.1	64
		Cyclohexane	34.5	225
		Methylcyclohexane	45	64
Methyl ethyl ketone (see 2-Butanone)				
Methyl formate	6	*n*-Heptane	6	64
Methyl furoate	57	Seven nonaromatics		61
Methyl hydrogen adipate	127	*n*-Heptane	127	64
Methyl isothiocyanate	(M)	Lubricating oil	<29.2	56c
Methyl malonate	(70)	Pinene	54.5	120
		Camphene	55.4	118, 120, 219
Methyl nitrate	(5)	Lubricating oil	49.5	56c
2-Methyl-2-nitropropanediol	(343)	Benzene	123	64
Methyl oxalate	(75)	Camphene	62.6	118, 120, 219
2-Methyl-2,4-pentanediol	7	*n*-Heptane	7	64
Methyl phthalate	89	*n*-Heptane	89	64
Methyl ricinoleate	(M)	Propane (lower phase pt.)	91.3	86
Methyl sulfate	154	*n*-Heptane	154	64
		Three naphthenes		62
		Seventeen aromatics		62
		Turpentine	108.2	188 (p. 159)
		Two lubricating oils		56c, 61
Methyl thiocyanate	44	*n*-Heptane	44	64
		Lubricating oil	77.8	56c

TABLE II—*Continued*

Solvent	C.S.T. with n-Heptane	Hydrocarbon	C.S.T.	References
Methyl-o-tolyl ketone	(M)	Isooctane	<0	140
Michler's ketone (p,p'-Bisdimethylaminobenzophenone)	(150)	n-Heptane	>100	61
Monoacetin (Glycerol monoacetate)	(313)	Five aromatics		62
Morpholine	5.3	n-Heptane	5.3	140
		2-Methylhexane	5.1	140
		2,2-Dimethylpentane	6.1	140
		2,3-Dimethylpentane	0.1	140
		2,4-Dimethylpentane	6.3	140
		Triptane	0	140
		Isooctane	13	140
		Isooctane	29	64
		n-Pentacosane	79	64
Myristic acid	(M)	Propane (lower phase pt.)	104.5	86
β-Naphthol	130	Six nonaromatics		61
α-Naphthonitrile	67	Eight nonaromatics		61
		Three lubricating oils	42–91	56c, 61
β-Naphthonitrile	74	Seven nonaromatics		61
α-Naphthylamine	113	Eight nonaromatics		61
β-Naphthylamine	131	Seven nonaromatics		61
		Cetane	189	64
m-Nitroacetophenone	178	n-Heptane	178	64
		Methylcyclohexane	110	62
		Decalin	106	62
		Diamylbenzene	93	62
		Diamylnaphthalene	56	62
3,4-Nitroaminotoluene	173	Eight nonaromatics		61
o-Nitroaniline	206	Seven nonaromatics		61
p-Nitroaniline	(260)	Decalin	239	62
		Fourteen aromatics		62
Nitroanisole		Lubricating oil	>100	56c
Nitrobenzene	18	Propane	None	60
(36 Paraffins		n-Butane	40	60
1 Olefin		n-Butane	28.3	225
2 Naphthenes)		Isobutane	61	60
		n-Pentane	24.5	25a, 47, 53, 60, 226, 243
		Isopentane	32	25a, 53, 60, 110a, 224–7
		Neopentane	54 (calcd.)	60
		Petroleum ether (42–62°)	20.5	164
		Petroleum ether (80–100°)	5	164

TABLE II—*Continued*

Solvent	C.S.T. with *n*-Heptane	Hydrocarbon	C.S.T.	References
Nitrobenzene (*cont.*)		*n*-Hexane	20.4	25a, 47, 60, 61, (Table p. 766) 103a, 110a, 139, 144, 223 to 227, (cf. 20)
		2-Methylpentane	25	53, 130, 139, 243
		3-Methylpentane	21	64, 130, 139
		2,2-Dimethylbutane	33	60, 130, 139, 243
		2,3-Dimethylbutane	24	130, 139
		n-Heptane	18	25a, 47, 60, 61, 138, 243
		2-Methylhexane	22	47, 53, 138
		Triptane	22	138, 243
		Three other heptanes		138
		n-Octane	20	25a, 47, 131, 227, 243
		2-Methylheptane	23.6	131
		2-Methylheptane	10.6?	47
		3-Methylheptane	21.2	131
		4-Methylheptane	20.5	131
		3-Ethylhexane	18.9	131
		2,3-Dimethylhexane	19	131
		2,4-Dimethylhexane	22.8	131
		2,5-Dimethylhexane	28	47, 131, 226
		3,4-Dimethylhexane	16.7	131
		2-Methyl-3-ethylpentane	17.2	131
		Isooctane	29	61, 138, 140, 243
		n-Nonane	21.78	243
		2-Methyloctane	19.4	47
		n-Decane	27.5	20
		2,7-Dimethyloctane	18.2?	47
		2,7-Dimethyloctane	28.37	25a, 225,
		n-Dodecane	27.0	47
		n-Tetradecane	25.2?	47
		n-Hexadecane	33.3	47
		n-Hexadecane	38.52	243
		n-Pentacosane	54	61
		Diisobutene	−25	61
		Cyclohexane	−4	61
		Methylcyclohexane	−3	61
		Five lubricating oils	14–53	56c, 61, 158a
o-Nitrobenzoic acid	(248)	Decalin	218	62
		Eight aromatics		62

TABLE II—*Continued*

Solvent	C.S.T. with n-Heptane	Hydrocarbon	C.S.T.	References
Three nitroben-zoic acids		Calcd. for benzene		199a
p-Nitrobenzyl chloride	103	Eight nonaromatics		61
o-Nitrochloroben-zene	41	Seven nonaromatics		61
m-Nitrochloro-benzene	(40)	Lubricating oil	<79.8	56c
p-Nitrochloro-benzene	(<70)	Isooctane	<74	64
Nitrodiphenyl-amine	84	n-Heptane	84	64
Nitromethane	115	n-Hexane	60?	121
		n-Heptane	115	64, 148
		Isooctane	107	64, 148
		Cyclohexane	79	62, 148
		Methylcyclohexane	90	62, 148
		Decalin	116	62, 148
		Forty-one other non-aromatics		148, 149
		Twelve aromatics		148, 149
		Seventeen other aro-matics		62
		Lubricating oil	>100	56c
2-Nitro-4-methyl-phenol	18	Five nonaromatics		61
Nitronaphthalene	(58)	n-Pentacosane	103	32
o-Nitrophenol	43	Seven nonaromatics		61
m-Nitrophenol	(100)	Methyldiisopropylben-zene	115	62
p-Nitrophenol	(100)			61
Nitroso - β - naph-thol	(100)			61
o-Nitrotoluene	−1	Propane	65	60
		n-Butane	12.5	60
		Isobutane	32.8	60
		n-Pentane	2	60
		Isopentane	9	60, 76, 225
		n-Hexane	1	60, 61
		Neohexane	11 (calcd.)	60
		Triptane	−1	64
		Six other nonaromatics		61
		Four lubricating oils	−4 to 35	56c, 61
m-Nitrotoluene	(0)	Isopentane	7.05	76
		n-Hexane	−30 (calcd.)	45
p-Nitrotoluene	(0)	Lubricating oil	<45	56c
Nitrous oxide	M	n-Heptane	<−91	64
Octadecyl stearate	(M)	Propane (lower phase pt.)	94.9	86
Octyl phthalate	(M)	Propane (lower phase pt.)	105+	87

TABLE II—*Continued*

Solvent	C.S.T. with *n*-Heptane	Hydrocarbon	C.S.T.	References
Oleic acid	(M)	Propane (lower C.S.T.)	91.1	87
		Isobutane (lower phase pt.)	None	86
		Lubricating oil	123?	56c
Oxalic acid	(400)	Naphthalene	>200	64
Palmitic acid	(M)	Propane (lower C.S.T.)	96.9	50
Paraldehyde	−54	Four nonaromatics		61
		Five lubricating oils	<0 to 40	56c, 61, 163a
o-Phenetidine	28	Cyclohexane	−2	4, 61
		Decalin (*cis*)	−6.3	4
		Decalin (*trans*)	−6.8	4
		Seven other nonaromatics		61
p-Phenetidine	83	Isooctane	91	4, 61
		Five other noncyclics		61
		Cyclohexane	45	4, 61
		Methylcyclohexane	53	4, 61
		Decalin (*cis*)	47.3	4
		Decalin (*trans*)	48.1	4
Phenol	52.9	Isobutane	121	64
		n-Pentane	56.6	234
		Isopentane	63.5, 66.2	32
		Isopentane	69.05	234
		n-Hexane	51	61, 234
		n-Hexane	42.5	32
		2-Methylpentane	57.2	234
		n-Heptane	52.9	61, 234
		n-Heptane	23.5?	32
		n-Octane	49.5	32
		Isooctane	66	61
		n-Pentacosane	117	61
		Petroleum (240–5°, d 0.822)	54.3	234
		1-Pentene	<20	64
		Di-isobutene	0	61
		Methylcyclohexane	11	61
		Methylcyclohexane	18	234
		Four lubricating oils	74–112	56c, 61
Phenylacetalde- hyde	(30)	Petroleum ether (42–62°)	17.5	164
		Petroleum ether (80–100°)	6.5	164
Phenyl acetate	7.45	Petroleum ether (42–62°)	2.5	164
		Petroleum ether (80–100°)	−4.5	164
		Six heptanes		138
		Isooctane	26.5	140
		Lubricating oil	50	56c
Phenylacetonitrile	71.3	Six heptanes		138
		Isooctane	73	140
Phenyl Cellosolve (*β*-Phenoxy- ethanol)	(60)	Methylcyclohexane	47	64

TABLE II—*Continued*

Solvent	C.S.T. with *n*-Heptane	Hydrocarbon	C.S.T.	References
o-Phenylenedi-amine	(206)	Diisopropylbenzene	111	62
		Triphenylmethane	91	100a (p. 143), 111
m-Phenylenedi-amine	(289)	Benzene	69	62, 200
		Triphenylmethane	98	100a (p. 143), 111, 168
p-Phenylenedi-amine	(292)	Eleven aromatics		62
β-Phenylethanol	27	Petroleum ether (42–62°)	30.5	164
		Petroleum ether (80–100°)	6	164
		n-Heptane	34	61
		n-Heptane	20.7	138
		Five other heptanes		138
		Isooctane	50	61, 140
		Five other nonaromatics		61
Phenylethanol-amine	(133)	Eleven aromatics		62
Phenylhydrazine	(114)	Three naphthenes		62
		Eight aromatics		62
		Lubricating oil	148	56c
Phenyl isocyanate	<−40	*n*-Heptane	<−40	64
		Lubricating oil	<0	56c
Phenyl isothio-cyanate	<−60	*n*-Heptane	<−60	64
		Lubricating oil	13	56c
Phenyl-α-naph-thylamine	63	Six nonaromatics		61
Phenyl phosphite (The triphenyl-phosphite of ref. 61 may have contained wa-ter.)	(22)	*n*-Pentacosane	67	64
		Diisobutene	8	64
		Three other nonaromatics		61
		Decalin	25	62
		Diamylbenzene	<31	62
Phenyl phthalate	135	Four noncyclics		61
		Three naphthenes		61, 62
		Three aromatics		62
Phenylpropanol	(40)	Petroleum ether (42–62°)	31.5	164
		Petroleum ether (80–100°)	4.5	164
Phenyl salicylate	(−11)	Paraffinic lubricating oil	34	61
Phenylstearic acid	(M)	Paraffinic lubricating oil	<0	61
Phenylthiourea	(150)	*n*-Heptane	>100	64
Phosgene	(M)	Four hydrocarbons in-cluding lubricating oil	<15.6	7a
Phosphorus	(230)	*n*-Hexane	210	20
		n-Decane	250?	20
		n-Decane	>390? or >300	79, 80
		Benzene	190	20

TABLE II—*Continued*

Solvent	C.S.T. with n-Heptane	Hydrocarbon	C.S.T.	References
Phosphorus (*cont.*)		Naphthalene	202.7	79, 80
		Anthracene	198	79
		Phenanthrene	200	79, 80
Phosphorus oxychloride	(M)	Isooctane	<0	64
Phosphorus tribromide	(M)	Lubricating oil	<0	56c
Phthalic anhydride	186	Eight nonaromatics		61
α-Picoline	(M)	Lubricating oil	30?	56c
Picric acid	(400)	Triphenylmethane	140.3	51b
		Triphenylmethane	144.5	111, 168
		Eleven other aromatics	<m.p. curve	100a (pp. 11! - 21)
Picryl chloride	(M)	Seven polycyclic aromatics	<m.p.	51b, 100a (p. 117)
Pinacol	<12	n-Heptane	<12	64
n-Propanol	M	Ethane (lower C.S.T.)	38.67	115
		Ethane (crit. pt., upper layer)	41.7	115
		n-Heptane	<−78	61
		n-Pentacosane	65	61
		Paraffinic oil	82	61
		"Paraffin oil"	13.5	39
		"Paraffin oil" (d 0.8723)	35.2	246
		Five lubricating oils	36.5–75	56c, 61, 163a
Isopropanol	M	Ethane (crit. pt., upper layer)	44	115
		n-Heptane	<−78	61
		n-Pentacosane	68	61
		Dotriacontane	88	165
		"Paraffin oil" (d 0.8723)	39.7	246
		Five lubricating oils	40–83	56c, 61, 163a
Propionaldehyde	(0)	Isooctane	<0	140
Propionamide	(295)	Camphene	145	120
		Naphthalene	75	118
Propionic acid	M	n-Heptane	<−70	61
		Isooctane	<0	140
		n-Pentacosane	8	61
		Three lubricating oils	−31 to 55?	56c, 61
Propionitrile	(20)	n-Decane	40	20
		2,7-Dimethyloctane	55.1	225
		Cyclohexane	12.2	75
p-Isopropylbenzaldehyde	(M)	Isooctane	<0	140
Propylenediamine	34	n-Heptane	34	64
		2,4-Dimethylpentane	35.5	64
		Triptane	30	64
Propylene glycol	(300)	Benzene	80	62, 64, 159
		Naphthalene	100	62, 64
		α- and β-Methylnaphthalenes	119	62

TABLE II—*Continued*

Solvent	C.S.T. with n-Heptane	Hydrocarbon	C.S.T.	References
Propylene glycol monomethyl ether	(M)	Isooctane	<0	140
Propyl furoate	−24	Seven nonaromatics		61
Propyl phosphate	(4)	n-Pentacosane	49	64
Propyl phthalate	(M)	Propane (lower phase pt.)	106–7	87
Pyridine	−22	n-Heptane	−22	37, 61
		Isooctane	−15	37, 61
		Five lubricating oils	−10 to 25.7	56c, 61, 163a
		Five other nonaromatics		61
Pyrogallol	(350)	Diphenylmethane	122.9	100a (p. 141), 111
		Triphenylmethane	178.5	100a (p. 141), 111
Pyruvic acid (2-Oxopropionic acid)	(245)	m-Xylene	83.5	121
Quinoline	(−30)	Lubricating oil	14	56c
Quinone	108	Three nonaromatics		61
		Five polycyclic aromatics	<m.p. curves	100a (p. 127)
Resorcinol	(339)	n-Hexane (lower C.S.T.?)	250	20
		Decane	260	20
		Diisobutene	>235	64
		Benzene	109	62 (Tables I & II) 225, 245
		Toluene	131	20, 62
		Ethylbenzene	151.5	225
		m-Xylene	148.7	31
		Diphenylmethane	115.4	100a (p. 139)
		Triphenylmethane	142	100a (p. 139)
		Phenanthrene	111	19a, 62
		Seven other aromatics		62
Resorcinol dimethyl ether	<0	Isooctane	<0	140
Salicyl alcohol	(208)	Ten aromatics		62
Salicylaldehyde	34	n-Butane	59	64
		n-Pentane	41	64
		Three lubricating oils	35–78	56c, 61
		Eight other nonaromatics		61
Salicylic acid	(90)	n-Heptane (extrapolated)	(90)	199a
		n-Pentacosane	140	64
		Benzene (extrapolated)	(17)	199a
Sebacic acid	(100)	Decalin	122	62
		Diisopropylbenzene	<120	62
Stannic bromide	(M)	Paraffin oil	<0	64
Stannic chloride	(M)	Paraffin oil	<0	64

TABLE II—*Continued*

Solvent	C.S.T. with n-Heptane	Hydrocarbon	C.S.T.	References
annic iodide (Eighteen non-aromatics, one aromatic)	136.4	n-Pentane (probably no C.S.T.)	>199.8	22
		Isopentane (probably no C.S.T.)	>215	22
		n-Hexane	148.5	22, 46, 79
		2-Methylpentane	185.4	22
		3-Methylpentane	147.8	22
		2,2-Dimethylbutane	200±	22
		2,3-Dimethylbutane	166.8	22
		n-Heptane	136.4	22, 46, 64, 79
		2-Methylhexane	160.3	22
		3-Methylhexane	144.1	22
		Triptane	163	64
		n-Octane	132	22, 46, 79
		3-Methylheptane	138.3	22
		Isooctane	195.1	22, 46, 64, 79
		Dotriacontane	194	79, 81
		Diisobutene	129.0	22
		Cyclohexane	115.4	22
		Methylcyclohexane	119.7	22
		Benzene	115.8	22
tearic acid typhnic acid (see Trinitroresor-cinol)	(M)	Propane (lower C.S.T.)	91.4	50
uccinonitrile (Ethylene cya-nide)	(272)	Benzene	52	64
		Lubricating oil	>100	56c
ulfur (Two nonaro-matics ten aromatics)	(383)	n-Decane	220?	20
		Paraffin	None	81, 112
		Benzene	163	2, 20, 81, 100 (p.394), 112, 245
		Benzene (lower C.S.T.)	226	79, 112
		Toluene	179	2, 20, 79, 112, 100 (p. 394), 245
		Toluene (lower C.S.T.)	222	79, 112
		Ethylbenzene	189	79, 112
		m-Xylene	None	79, 112
		p-Xylene (Sλ)	190	73, 187 (p. 1452)
		p-Xylene (S, equilibrium)	None	73
		Naphthalene	<82	64
		Biphenyl	ca. 113	64
		Phenanthrene	<86	64

TABLE II—*Continued*

Solvent	C.S.T. with n-Heptane	Hydrocarbon	C.S.T.	References
Sulfur (*cont.*)		Fluorene	<100	64
		Triphenylmethane	147	79, 112, 202
		Triphenylmethane (lower C.S.T.)	199	79, 112, 202
Sulfur bromide	(M)	n-Heptane	<−56	64
Sulfur chloride	(M)	n-Heptane	<−70	64
		Isooctane	−40	64
		Lubricating oil	<0	56c
Sulfur dioxide	19.2	Propane	−24	64
		n-Butane	−4.7	197
(19 Paraffins,		Isobutane	−1	64
6 Olefins		n-Pentane	2	130
11 Naphthenes		n-Hexane	11	20, 61, 123
24 Aromatics				193, 197,
—				225
60 Total)		2-Methylpentane	10	123
		n-Heptane	19.2	61, 123
		2-Methylhexane	18	123
		n-Octane	26	123, 192, 197
		2-Methylheptane	24	123
		Isooctane	18.7	61
		n-Nonane	32	123
		n-Decane	37	20, 123, 197
		2,7-Dimethyloctane	34.1	225
		n-Hendecane	42	123
		n-Dodecane	47.1	123, 197
		n-Tetradecane	55.5	197
		n-Pentacosane	95	61
		n-Dotriacontane	110	197
		Propylene	<−78	64
		Pentene	<−80	130, 194
		Pentene	>25?	43
		1-Heptene	−21	61
		Octene	−16.5	194
		Octene	>25?	43
		Diisobutene	−35	61
		Cetene	42.7	43, 195
		Methylcyclopentane	8	123
		Cyclohexane	13	61, 62, 123
				191, 196
				225
		Methylcyclohexane	15.5	61, 62, 123
		Ethylcyclohexane	25	123
		Dimethylcyclohexane	>25	43
		Nonanaphthene	27	123
		Hexahydromesitylene	30.5	123
		Decalin	42	43, 61, 190
		Cyclohexene	<−80	196

TABLE II—*Continued*

Solvent	C.S.T. with n-Heptane	Hydrocarbon	C.S.T.	References
Sulfur dioxide (*cont.*)		Pinene	>25	43
		Carvene (*d*-Limonene)	<25	43
		Styrene	<−60	133
		Three other aromatics		62
		Twelve other liquid aromatics	<25	43
		Eight solid aromatics	<m.p.	43
Tetrahydrofurfuryl alcohol	82	Isooctane	93	61
		Isooctane	87	140
		Three naphthenes		61, 62
		Five noncyclics		61
		Three aromatics		62
Tetramethylthiuram disulfide	(150)	n-Heptane	>100	64
		Naphthalene	<65	64
Thiocarbanilide	(134)	n-Pentacosane	179	61
Thiourea	(200)			61
Thymol	(M)	Paraffinic oil	<0	61
Titanic chloride	(M)	n-Heptane	<0	64
		Isooctane	<0	64
Tolidine	>100	n-Heptane	>100	61
o-Toluidine	22	n-Hexane	21.1	75, 188 (p. 457, 559), 219
		n-Hexane	25	61
		2-Methylpentane	25.5	188 (p. 559), 219
		n-Heptane	25	61
		n-Heptane	19.7	138
		Five other heptanes		138
		Isooctane	35	61
		Isooctane	31	140
		Methylcyclopentane	−10.9	219
		Ethylcyclopentane	−8.3	219
		Methylcyclohexane	−6.6	75, 219
		Methylcyclohexane	−3	61
		Four more non-aromatics		61
		Three lubricating oils	34–69	56c, 61
m-Toluidine	19	n-Hexane	21.3	45, 219
		Six heptanes		138
		Isooctane	30	140
		n-Decane	32	20
		2,7-Dimethyloctane	38.5	225
		Cyclohexane	−18 (calcd.)	45
		Methylcyclohexane	−8.3	45, 188 (p. 559), 219

TABLE II—Concluded

Solvent	C.S.T. with n-Heptane	Hydrocarbon	C.S.T.	References
p-Toluidine	(18)	2-Methylpentane	36	188 (p. 559), 219
		3-Methylpentane	32.4	188 (p. 559), 219
		Isooctane	<35	61
		n-Pentacosane	63	61
m-Toluylene-diamine	(>150)			61
Triamylamine stearate	(M)	Paraffinic oil	<0	61
Tricaprylin	(M)	Propane (lower C.S.T.)	100.5	86
Trichloroacetic acid	(<7)	Isooctane	<46	64
		n-Pentacosane	<52	64
Triethanolamine	(380)	Fifteen aromatics		62
Triethylene glycol	(240)	Thirty-one aromatics		62
Triethylene-tetramine	(210)	Tetraisopropylbenzene	174	64
Trimethylene gly-col	(375)	Isooctane	>90	140
		Naphthalene	155	64
Trinitroaniline (Picramide)		Six polycyclic aromatics	<m.p. curves	51b, 100a (p. 127)
Trinitrobenzene		Six polycyclic aromatics	<m.p. curves	100a (pp. 118–9)
Trinitroresorcinol (Styphnic acid)	(360)	Diphenylmethane	>144.6	100a (p. 122)
		Triphenylmethane	>167.4	100a (p. 122)
		Ten other polycyclics	<m.p. curves	100a (p. 122)
Trinitrotoluene		Six polycyclic aromatics	<m.p. curves	100a (p. 146)
Triolein	(M)	Propane (lower phase pt.)	64.5	86
Tripalmitin	(M)	Propane (lower C.S.T.)	73.5	86
Triphenylguani-dine	(106)	Paraffinic lubricating oil	151	61
Tristearin	(M)	Propane (lower C.S.T.)	69.2	86
Valeric acid	(M)	n-Decane	−20	20
Water	(540)	Benzene	>300	102
		Toluene	250?	152
		Toluene	>300	102
		Xylene	>250	102
		Tetralin	>250	102
2,4-Xylenol-1	−60	Four nonaromatics		61
2,5-Xylenol-1	(M)	Paraffinic lubricating oil	<0	61
Xylidines (mixed)	−23	Seven nonaromatics		61
		Three lubricating oils	−14 to +29	56c, 61

Schiessler and coworkers (177) that for isomeric paraffins of widely various boiling ranges the aniline points are related inversely and linearly to the density. Combination of these two relations means that for any aromatic nonhydrocarbon solvent the denser paraffin hydrocarbon isomers are more soluble. This distinction is not of much use in segregating antiknock quality, however, because the latter among paraffin isomers is related mostly to the number of branches, which is unrelated to density. The solubility (or C.S.T.) of triptane in aniline, for example, is not much different from that of n-heptane, although some heptanes of intermediate antiknock value have higher C.S.T. and some have lower than either. Wiener (240a) has shown relations of aniline C.S.T. to structure for paraffin isomers.

On the other hand a different class of solvents, those with high dielectric constants, most of which are water soluble, have moderate selectivities for highly branched paraffins. Methanol, for example, has C.S.T. with heptanes which are lowered an average of 6°C. for each branch. These solvents can be used to concentrate paraffins of high antiknock value (63), although they are relatively unselective for other classes of hydrocarbons. They should be used preferably on wholly paraffinic products such as alkylates from isoparaffins. Since these solvents are also sensitive to molecular weight, it is necessary to use a charge stock of narrow boiling range.

Stannic iodide (m.p. 144°C.) is a solvent which is even more sensitive to branching of an aliphatic chain, but in the opposite direction. One branch in a 2-position may raise the C.S.T. by 24 or 37°C., but branches in other positions and an additional one in the 2-position have relatively slight effects. By contrast, stannic iodide is very unselective to more fundamental differences in structure. It shows no selectivity between benzene and cyclo-hexane although with other solvents there is an average difference in C.S.T. of 180°C. for this pair. Stannic iodide is not practical for concentrating antiknock value because of its high cost, and the high temperatures and pressures required for the separation.

V. Lower Critical Solution Temperatures

Most of the temperatures of Table II are "upper critical solution temperatures," above which the two liquids are completely miscible. The "lower C.S.T." below which the two liquids are completely miscible (so marked for sixteen cases) result usually from the proximity of the critical point of one component (32.27°C. for ethane, 96.8°C. for propane, 234.8°C. for n-hexane, and 193.8°C. for ethyl ether). Sixteen other points are marked "lower phase pt.," and are similar, indicating the temperature below which a single phase existed. The latter were not necessarily obtained with the ratio of component to give the lowest possible temperature of change, and therefore the lower C.S.T. might be a little lower. It can be considered that in the critical region such a component partakes partly of the nature of a gas and so becomes less miscible with other liquids. The use of propane as a selective solvent in the temperature range 70 to 100°C. has been found convenient for refining certain vegetable oils (50, 86, 87). Although its selectivity is only a function of "effective molecular weight" (50), the usual means of applying that distinction, fractional distillation, is less applicable to oils of such low volatility.

The solubility of hexachloroethane in liquid and vapor ethane was studied by Holder and Maass (88) near the critical temperature of the saturated solution, 44.85°C. In Table II the critical temperatures of the ethane layers are listed for five two-phase systems (with alcohols) although these are not C.S.T.

Upper C.S.T. also can be affected substantially, in this case raised, by proximity of a critical temperature. Ethane and propane have no C.S.T. with aniline and nitrobenzene, and the butanes have much higher aniline points than do the pentanes and hexanes. This effect may persist even down to the vicinity of the boiling point, as illustrated by the higher C.S.T. of the butanes than of the pentanes and hexanes with o-nitrotoluene (60).

In two previous papers (61, 62) some evidence was presented supporting the opinion that no wholly hydrocarbon mixture would separate into two liquid layers. The result of an upper C.S.T. was meant. However, an earlier publication (232) which seems to present an exception had been overlooked. It is related to a lower C.S.T. To a mixture of propane and crude oil was added methane at about 1400 pounds pressure. Not only was asphalt (nonhydrocarbon) precipitated, but two liquid hydrocarbon layers were observed and analyzed, showing mostly methane and propane in somewhat different proportions. Presumably these two layers would still fail to mix if isolated from the asphalt; although the investigations of Sage and coworkers (173) have not shown a similar separation into two liquid phases under similar conditions with methane and either propane or crystal oil or both (172, p. 138) in absence of nonhydrocarbons. If a binary system did separate into two liquids and a vapor phase, the phase rule indicates that it could have only one pressure at any temperature. The discussion of Wilson et al. (242) defines the conditions under which propane near its critical temperature forms two liquid layers with heavy naphthenic oils. One such case has been confirmed by the present author, a "minimum phase point" (lower C.S.T.) of 80°C. being found for propane with a naphthenic oil of 144 S. U. S. viscosity at 99°C. No system containing only two hydrocarbons that separates into two liquid layers seems to be described in the literature.

When propane is used for refining oils at ordinary temperatures, it should not be considered as a primary selective solvent (108), but as an auxiliary one. It can precipitate asphalts (containing nonhydrocarbons) which may carry down with them some cyclic hydrocarbons; but the main purpose of the propane is to decrease the viscosity of the oil by dilution so as to facilitate crystallization of wax or extraction with another solvent such as cresylic acid.

"Lower C.S.T." for other reasons are rare, and probably would not normally occur with a hydrocarbon as a component because of its nonpolar character. Timmermans (223) suggested that any two liquids should theoretically have both an upper and lower C.S.T. These cannot usually be realized because either a freezing or a critical point intervenes, or else (according to him) the "lower C.S.T." is above the "upper C.S.T." so that there is no range of limited liquid miscibility. On the other hand the allotropy of sulfur permits realization of this anomaly in a different sense in the case of three aromatic hydrocarbons (79, 112, 202).

Dolgolenko (48) believed that a lower C.S.T. results only by formation of a third molecular species, such as hydrates. Some support for his idea comes from the analogous and somewhat anomalous observation that acetic acid is more miscible with hydrocarbons than is acetic anhydride. Consequently, a two-phase system of some hydrocarbons with acetic anhydride would become homogeneous on adding a limited amount of water and shaking until the anhydride was hydrated. Probably this is due to associated acetic acid molecules. This is similar to the quasichemical reaction suggested to account for the only published ternary diagram with two binodal curves (183, and Fig. 7a). Hirschfelder et al. (85) explained lower C.S.T. by postulating the breaking by kinetic energy of the hydrogen bonds needed for mixing. This seems to be equivalent in modern terms to Dolgolenko's explanation.

VI. Supersaturation

The existence of supersaturated liquid mixtures is indicated in only a few cases. None has been observed by the present author. In fact many C.S.T. were observed below the freezing point of one component by rapid cooling so as to get separation of liquid phases before crystallization took place. Davis (42) investigated this point and found some systems with definite supersaturation, of the order of 1°, but not in the region of the C.S.T. Palit and McBain (159) found no super-cooling of C.S.T. with soap solutions; but E. L. Smith (205) observed some hydrocarbon solubilities in soap solutions three times as high by an indirect procedure as by the direct one. Flaschner (58) observed a supersaturated solution of methylpiperidine in water near the center of a large two-phase area.

VII. Use of C.S.T. in Analysis

Critical Solution Temperatures are usually nearly linear functions of composition for a mixture of two similar substances with a common solvent. This relation has been used frequently as a means of analysis for water (65, 92, 104, 105, 169a) and for aromatic hydrocarbons using aniline points (228) or C.S.T. with aniline (36) or nitrobenzene (53, 130, 131) or benzyl alcohol (7b, 130, 131). The use of two such solvents separately, aniline and benzyl alcohol (7b), to get independent equations, would have been more efficient if one of the solvents had been nonaromatic.

For highly aromatic hydrocarbon mixtures the aniline points are below the freezing point of aniline, preventing the observation. To meet this difficulty "mixed aniline points" are used, a further application of the linear relation mentioned. This requires dilution of the sample with an equal volume of straight run gasoline of 60°C. aniline point (125a, 198b) or with n-heptane (12). Unfortunately, the relation is not very reliable in this respect, as shown by Ball (12) and by Rice and Lieber (169) so that at best mixed aniline points give only a control test. The resulting uncertainties induced Rice and Lieber (169) to propose furfural as a solvent for analysis of highly aromatic oils since its lower freezing point largely removes that limitation, and its C.S.T. are about 32°C. higher than those of aniline. Even this increase is not enough for lower aromatics because of the very low temperatures involved, and the instability of the solvent to light and oxidation has retarded its general acceptance.

Ethylene diformate, which has C.S.T. with aromatic hydrocarbons about 100°C. higher than those of furfural, was suggested (62) for this purpose. It is colorless and stable to light, but must be kept anhydrous because it hydrolyzes gradually to glycol and formic acid, both of which would raise C.S.T. greatly. Its C.S.T. with aromatic hydrocarbons recorded previously (62) are now considered about 25°C. too high because of the presence of a little glycol in the reagent.

No single solvent will cover wide ranges of aromaticity of oils satisfactorily; but for control purposes a solvent can be selected from Table II to give the C.S.T. in a convenient temperature range for any oil. This is much more reliable than any "mixed solvent point." Nitromethane, for example, has a C.S.T. with aromatic hydrocarbons intermediate between those of furfural and those of ethylene diformate. Going in the other direction, methylaniline has been found convenient (67a) for testing high molecular weight paraffinic oils because it has solvent points about 77°C. lower than those of aniline.

Critical solution temperatures have been used recently in analysis for individual paraffin isomers (60, 138, 139). The linear relation was used also (61) to estimate some C.S.T. unattainable because of crystallization. On the other hand Boutaric and Corbet (25) estimated the C.S.T. of methanol and benzene at 29°C. by extrapolation from results after dilution with rapeseed oil to increase the difference in refractive index. Their result seems much too high according to four other investigators (cf. 62), possibly because of water in their sample of methanol. Fuoss (66) used a trace of hydrochloric acid to facilitate determination of a C.S.T.

VIII. Miscibility Relations

Effects of structure on miscibility of organic compounds were discussed by Ewell *et al.* (56a), employing the concept of hydrogen bonding. Mutual solubility of liquids was summarized graphically in Fig. 4 of a recent paper (62) (cf. also 103, 103a), which has been quoted and sometimes called the "octagon figure." In this figure eight typical liquids were assigned to the corners of an octagon, and the type of diagonal indicated qualitatively the miscibility of any pair. It was suggested there how a much larger number of liquids could be included, as follows:

Beginning with water at one extreme all liquids (except molten metals), including solids which can be melted at applicable temperatures, are arranged according to miscibility relations, with high paraffin hydrocarbons at the other extreme. However, the arrangement cannot be absolute. The solvents differ considerably in selectivity because of effect of molecular weight (90), internal pressure (82), and other factors. Acetone, for example, is miscible with both water and light hydrocarbons, while aniline is only slightly soluble in either. By contrast with water, glycerol mixes with aniline but not with acetone. If miscibility relations were known accurately for all of the more than 88,000 possible pairs of the 422 liquids which have been tested in some binary mixture with a hydrocarbon (or over 260,000 if the 415 hydrocarbons were included), it might be possible to make a comprehensive diagram by arranging the reagents in a rough semicircle, and assigning different radial positions to compensate for the other factors. Limiting miscibility might then be determined by linear distance instead of difference in arc, but such a diagram is premature.

REFERENCES

1. Alberty, R. A. and Washburn, E. R. *J. Phys. Chem.*, **49**, 4 (1945).
2. Alekseev, V. *Ann. physik. Chem.*, (2) **28**, 305 (1886); through ref. 100 (p. 394).
3. Andreasov, L. M. *Ukrain. Khem. Zhur.*, **3**, 463 (1928); *Chem. Abstracts*, **23**, 3145.
4. Angelescu, E. and coworkers. *Bull. sect. sci. acad. roumaine*, **23**, 515 (1941); *Chem. Abstracts*, **37**, 6180.
5. Angelescu, E. and coworkers. *Bull. sect. sci. acad. roumaine*, **24**, 106, 167, 483 (1942); **25**, 337, 421, 473, 515, (1943); **26**, 25, 123 (1944); *Chem. Abstracts*, **38**, 2557, 3189, 5135; **39**, 3998, 3999.
6. Appel, F. J. and Elgin, J. C. *Ind. Eng. Chem.*, **29**, 451 (1937).
7. Armani, G. and Rodano, G. A. *J. Soc. Chem. Ind.*, **31**, 912 (1912).
7a. Atkinson, R. H., Heycock, C. T., and Pope, W. J. *J. Chem. Soc.*, **117**, 1422 (1920).

7b. Aubert, M. and Aubreé, E. *Compt. rend.*, **182**, 577 (1926).

8. Avenarius, A. M. and Tarasenkov, D. N. *J. Gen. Chem. U.S.S.R.*, **16**, 1777 (1946); *Chem. Abstracts*, **41**, 5372.

9. Bachman, I. *J. Phys. Chem.*, **44**, 446 (1940).

10. Bachman, I. *Ind. Eng. Chem. Anal. Ed.*, **12**, 38 (1940).

11. Bailey, C. R. *J. Chem. Soc.*, **123**, 2579 (1923).

12. Ball, J. S. *U. S. Bur. Mines, Repts. Investigations*, 3721 (1943).

13. Bancroft, W. D. *Proc. Am. Acad. Art. Sci.*, **30**, 324 (1894); *Brit. Chem. Abstracts*, **68**, ii 158; *Phys. Rev.*, **3**, 21 (1895).

14. Bancroft, W. D. *J. Phys. Chem.*, **1**, 403, 647 (1897).

15. Bancroft, W. D. and Hubard, S. S. *J. Am. Chem. Soc.*, **64**, 347 (1942).

15a. Beech, D. G. and Glasstone, S. *J. Chem. Soc.*, **1938**, 67.

16. Belton, J. W. *Trans. Faraday Soc.*, **35**, 1354 (1939).

17. Benedict, M. and Rubin, L. C. *Trans. Am. Inst. Chem. Engrs.*, **41**, 353 (1945).

18. Bergelin, O., Lockhart, F. J., and Brown, G. G. *Trans. Am. Inst. Chem. Engrs.*, **39**, 173 (1943).

19. Berndt, R. J. and Lynch, C. C. *J. Am. Chem. Soc.*, **66**, 282 (1944).

19a. Bernoulli, A. L. and Sarasin, A. *Helv. Chim. Acta*, **13**, 520–1 (1930).

20. Bingham, E. C. *Am. Chem. J.*, **37**, 549 (1907).

21. Bingham, E. C. and Spooner, L. W. *Physics*, **4**, 387 (1933).

22. Bocharov, A. A. and Obolentsev, R. D. *J. Applied Chem. U.S.S.R.*, **19**, 492 (1946); U. O. P. Survey Foreign Petroleum Litt., Nov. 8–15, 1946.

23. Bogin, C. D. *Ind. Eng. Chem.*, **16**, 380 (1924).

24. Bonner, W. D. and Williams, M. B. *J. Phys. Chem.*, **44**, 404 (1940).

25. Boutaric, A. and Corbet, G. *Compt. rend.*, **184**, 1446 (1927).

25a. Brahme, J. S. S. and Hunter, T. G. *J. Inst. Petroleum Technol.*, **13**, 798 (1927).

26. Brancker, A. V., Hunter, T. G., and Nash, A. W. *Ind. Eng. Chem. Anal. Ed.*, **12**, 35 (1940).

27. Brancker, A. V., Hunter, T. G., and Nash, A. W. *J. Phys. Chem.*, **44**, 683 (1940). *Ind. Eng. Chem.*, **33**, 880 (1941).

28. Briggs, S. W. and Comings, E. W. *Ind. Eng. Chem.*, **35**, 411 (1943).

29. Brown, O. W. *J. Phys. Chem.*, **2**, 51 (1898); *Brit. Chem. Abstracts*, **76**, ii, 83.

29a. Butler, E. B., Miles, C. B., and Kuhn, C. S. Jr. *Ind. Eng. Chem.*, **38**, 147 (1946).

30. Campbell, J. A. *Ind. Eng. Chem.*, **36**, 1158 (1944).

31. Campetti, A. *Atti accad. sci. Torino*, **52**, 114 (1917); *Chem. Abstracts*, **11**, 3150.

32. Campetti, A. and del Grosso, C. *Mem. reale accad. sci. Torino (II)*, **61**, 187 (1911); *Nuovo cimento*, **6**, 379 (1913); *Chem. Abstracts*, **8**, 2294.

33. Carbide and Carbon Chemicals Corp., through Elgin, J. C. *Ind. Eng. Chem.*, **40**, 53 (1948); Wilkes, B. G. Jr., U. S. Patent 2,439,534 (1948).

34. Carrière, J. F. *Chem. Weekblad*, (a) **26**, 570 (1929); (b) **41**, 58 (1945); *Chem. Abstracts*, **24**, 3701; **40**, 794.

35. Chavanne, G. and Miller, O. *Bull. soc. chim. Belg.*, **39**, 287 (1930); *Chem. Abstracts*, **24**, 5027.

36. Chavanne, G. and Simon, L. J. *Compt. rend.*, **168**, 1111 (1919); *Chem. Abstracts*, **13**, 2125.

37. Cornish, R. E., Archibald, R. C., Murphy, E. A., and Evans, H. M. *Ind. Eng. Chem.*, **26**, 399 (1934).

38. Cosby, J. N. and Sutherland, L. H. *Refiner Natural Gasoline Mfr.*, **20**, 471 (1941).

39. Crismer, L. *Bull. soc. chim. Belg.*, **18**, 18 (1904); *Chem. Centr.*, **1904** I, 1480.

40. Curtis, C. B. *J. Phys. Chem.*, **2**, 371 (1898); *Brit. Chem. Abstracts*, **76**, ii, 185.

41. Darwent, B. de B. and Winkler, C. A. *J. Phys. Chem.*, **47**, 449 (1943).
42. Davis, H. S. *J. Am. Chem. Soc.*, **38**, 1166 (1916).
43. DeCarli, F. *Gazz. chim. ital.*, **57**, 347 (1927); *Chem. Abstracts*, **21**, 3047.
44. Denzler, C. G. *J. Phys. Chem.*, **49**, 358 (1945).
45. Dessart, A. *Bull. soc. chim. Belg.*, **35**, 9 (1926); *Chem. Centr.*, **1926 II**, 157.
46. Dice, M. E. and Hildebrand, J. H. *J. Am. Chem. Soc.*, **50**, 3023 (1928).
47. Dobryanskii, A. F. and Khesin, I. *Neftyanoe Khoz.*, **1929**, No. 8–9, 80.
48. Dolgolenko, V. I. *J. Russ. Phys. Chem. Soc.*, **39**, 841 (1907); *Chem. Abstracts*, **2**, 1374; *Z. physik. Chem.*, **62**, 499 (1908).
49. Doss, M. P. Physical Constants of Principal Hydrocarbons, 4th ed., The Texas Co., 1943.
50. Drew, D. A. and Hixson, A. N. *Trans. Am. Inst. Chem. Engrs.*, **40**, 675, 690 (1944).
50a. Drucker, K. *Z. physik. Chem.*, **49**, 563 (1904).
51. D'yakova, M. K. and Lozovoi, A. V. *J. Gen. Chem. U.S.S.R.*, **9**, 261 (1939); *Chem. Abstracts*, **33**, 6254.
51a. Eckfeldt, E. L. and Lucasse, W. W. *J. Phys. Chem.*, **47**, 169 (1943).
51b. Efremov, N. N. *J. Russ. Phys. Chem. Soc.*, **50 I**, 372, 421, 441 (1918); *Chem. Abstracts*, **17**, 3327–8; ref. 100A, p. 121.
52. Elgin, J. C. in Perry's Chemical Engineers' Handbook. McGraw-Hill, New York, 1941, pp. 1223–4.
53. Erskin, A. M. *Ind. Eng. Chem.*, **18**, 694 (1926).
54. Evans, E. B. *J. Inst. Petroleum Technol.*, **23**, 222 (1937).
55. Evans, T. W. *Ind. Eng. Chem.*, **26**, 439, 860 (1934).
56. Evans, T. W. *Ind. Eng. Chem. Anal. Ed.*, **6**, 408 (1934).
56a. Ewell, R. H., Harrison, J. M., and Berg, L. *Ind. Eng. Chem.*, **36**, 871 (1944).
56b. Farmer, R. C. and Warth, F. J. *J. Chem. Soc.*, **85**, 1713 (1904).
56c. Ferris, S. W., Birkhimer, E. R., and Henderson, L. M. *Ind. Eng. Chem.*, **23**, 753 (1931).
57. Findlay, A. The Phase Rule, 6th ed., Longmans, Green, New York, 1927, pp. 97, 216–8.
58. Flaschner, O. *Z. physik. Chem.*, **62**, 493 (1908).
59. Francis, A. W. *Ind. Eng. Chem.*, **33**, 554 (1941).
60. Francis, A. W. U. S. Patent 2,303,265 (1942); *Ind. Eng. Chem. Anal. Ed.*, **15**, 447 (1943).
61. Francis, A. W. *Ind. Eng. Chem.*, **36**, 764 (1944).
62. Francis, A. W. *Ind. Eng. Chem.*, **36**, 1096 (1944).
63. Francis, A. W. U. S. Patent 2,402,954 (1946).
64. Francis, A. W. Unpublished work in this laboratory.
65. Freed, M. *Trans. Roy. Soc. Canada*, III, **27**, 179 (1933); *Chem. Abstracts*, **28**, 2982.
66. Fuoss, R. M. *J. Am. Chem. Soc.*, **65**, 78 (1943).
67. Garner, F. H. *J. Inst. Petroleum Technol.*, **14**, 715 (1928).
67a. Geddes, B. W., Wilcox, L. Z., and McArdle, E. H. *Ind. Eng. Chem. Anal. Ed.*, **15**, 487 (1943).
67b. Georgievics, G. v. *Z. physik. Chem.*, **90**, 47 (1915).
68. Getman, F. H. and Daniels, F. Outlines of Physical Chemistry, 7th ed., Wiley, New York, 1941, p. 339.
69. Glasstone, S. Textbook of Physical Chemistry, 2nd ed., Van Nostrand, New York, 1946, pp. 729, 792–9.
70. Glockler, G., Fuller, D. L., and Roe, C. P. *J. Chem. Phys.*, **1**, 714 (1933).

71. Goheen, G. E. *J. Am. Chem. Soc.*, **63**, 748 (1941).
72. Griffin, C. W. *Ind. Eng. Chem. Anal. Ed.*, **6**, 40 (1934); **8**, 358 (1936).
72a. Gross, Philipp, Schwarz, K., and Iser, M. *Monatsh.* **55**, 287, 329 (1930); *Chem. Abstracts*, **24**, 3943.
73. Hammick, D. L. and Holt, W. E. *J. Chem. Soc.*, **1926**, 2002.
74. Hand, D. B. *J. Phys. Chem.*, **34**, 1961 (1930).
75. Hartenberg, W. Thesis, Brussels, 1926; through ref. 188, pp. 180, 433, 457.
76. Hennaut-Roland, Mme. *Bull. soc. chim. Belg.*, **42**, 80 (1933); *Chem. Abstracts*, **27**, 3920.
76a. Henriques, H. J. *J. Am. Chem. Soc.*, **55**, 3284 (1933).
77. Herz, W. and Schuftan, P. *Z. physik. Chem.*, **101**, 281–284 (1922).
78. Hibshmann, H. J. *Ind. Eng. Chem.*, **41**, 1366, 1369 (1949).
79. Hildebrand, J. H. Solubility of Non-Electrolytes, 2nd ed., especially Chapter IX. Reinhold, New York, 1936.
80. Hildebrand, J. H. and Buehrer, T. F. *J. Am. Chem. Soc.*, **42**, 2216 (1920).
81. Hildebrand, J. H. and Wachter, A. *J. Am. Chem. Soc.*, **57**, 870 (1935).
82. Hildebrand, J. H. and coworkers *J. Am. Chem. Soc.*, **38**, 1452 (1916); **39**, 2297 (1917); **41**, 1067 (1919); **43**, 500 (1921).
83. Hill, A. E. in Taylor's Treatise on Physical Chemistry, Vol. I, Van Nostrand, New York, 1931, pp. 574–5.
83a. Hill, A. E. *J. Am. Chem. Soc.*, **44**, 1163 (1922); Cf. **62**, 3524 (1940).
84. Hill, A. E. and Miller, F. W. Jr. *J. Am. Chem. Soc.*, **47**, 2702 (1925).
85. Hirschfelder, J. O., Stevenson, D. P., and Eyring, H. *J. Chem. Phys.*, **5**, 896 (1937).
86. Hixson, A. W. and Bockelmann, J. B. *Trans. Am. Inst. Chem. Engrs.*, **38**, 891 (1942).
87. Hixson, A. W. and Hixson, A. N. *Trans. Am. Inst. Chem. Engrs.*, **37**, 927 (1941).
88. Holder, C. H. and Maass, O. *Can. J. Research*, **18B**, 293 (1940).
89. Holloway, C. Jr. and Thurber, S. H. *Ind. Eng. Chem.*, **36**, 980 (1944).
90. Holmes, John, *J. Chem. Soc.*, **113**, 263 (1918).
91. Horsley, L. H. *Anal. Chem.*, **19**, 508 (1947).
92. Howard, E. J. and Patterson, W. H. *J. Chem. Soc.*, **1926**, 2787.
93. Howes, D. A. *J. Inst. Petroleum Technol.*, **19**, 319 (1933).
94. Hunter, T. G. in Science of Petroleum, Vol. III, Oxford Univ. Press, London, 1938, p. 1819.
95. Hunter, T. G. *Ind. Eng. Chem.*, **34**, 963 (1942).
96. Hunter, T. G. and Brown, T. *Ind. Eng. Chem.*, **39**, 1343 (1947).
97. Hunter, T. G. and Nash, A. W. *J. Soc. Chem. Ind.*, **51**, 285T (1932); *Ind. Eng. Chem.*, **27**, 836 (1935); *J. Inst. Petroleum Technol.*, **22**, 49 (1936).
98. Hunter, T. G. and Nash, A. W. *J. Soc. Chem. Ind.*, **53**, 96T (1934).
99. Il'insky, T. F. and Ivanov, M. N. *Trudy Voronezh. Gosudarst. Univ.*, **10**, No. 2, 185 (1938); *Chem. Abstracts*, **33**, 5257.
100. International Critical Tables, Vol. III, McGraw-Hill, New York, 1928, pp. 394–417.
100a. International Critical Tables, Vol. IV, McGraw-Hill, New York, 1928, pp. 105–213.
101. Jacobs, W. Thesis, Leiden, 1914, through ref. 100, p. 401.
102. Jaeger, A. *Brennstoff-Chem.*, **4**, 259 (1923); *Chem. Abstracts*, **18**, 459.
103. Jänecke, E. *Z. Elektrochem.*, **38**, 583, 860 (1932).

03a. Jänecke, E. *Z. physik. Chem.*, **184,** 59 (1939).

04. Jones, D. C. *J. Chem. Soc.*, **1923,** 1374.

05. Jones, D. C. and Amstell, S. *J. Chem. Soc.*, **1930,** 1316.

06. Jones, D. C. and Betts, H. F. *J. Chem. Soc.*, **1928,** 1180.

07. Ju, T. Y., Shen, G., and Wood, C. E. *J. Inst. Petroleum Technol.*, **26,** 519 (1940).

08. Kalichevsky, V. A. Modern Methods of Refining Lubricating Oils, Reinhold, New York, 1938, (especially p. 155).

08a. Klatt, W. *Z. anorg. allgem. Chem.*, **234,** 189 (1937).

09. Knaus, C. Thèse Bâle 1923; through *Z. physik. Chem.*, **169A,** 471 (1934).

10. Knight, O. S. *Trans. Am. Inst. Chem. Engrs.*, **39,** 439 (1943).

10a. Kohnstamm, P. and Timmermans, J. *Proc. Koninkl. Acad. Wetenschap.*, **1911,** 865; *Chem. Abstracts,* **5,** 3532.

11. Kremann, R. and coworkers *Monatsh.* **41,** 631 (1920); **42,** 117 (1921); *Chem. Abstracts,* **15,** 3638; **16,** 89; *Monatsh.* **43,** 321 (1922); *Brit. Chem. Abstracts,* **124,** i, 332.

112. Kruyt, H. R. *Z. physik. Chem.*, **65,** 486, 497 (1909).

112a. Kuenen, J. P. *Phil. Mag.*, (6) **6,** 642 (1903), through ref. 172, p. 118.

113. Kuenen, J. P. *Proc. Acad. Sci. Amsterdam*, **5,** 473 (1903); *Brit. Chem. Abstracts,* **84,** ii, 410.

114. Kuenen, J. P. *Proc. Acad. Sci. Amsterdam*, **14,** 644 (1912); *Chem. Abstracts,* **7,** 2507.

115. Kuenen, J. P. and Robson, W. G. *Z. physik. Chem.*, **28,** 356 (1899); *Brit. Chem. Abstracts,* **76** ii, 356.

116. Kuriloff, B. *Z. physik. Chem.*, **24,** 441 (1897).

117. Laddha, G. S. and Smith, J. M. *Ind. Eng. Chem.*, **40,** 494 (1948).

118. Lecat, M. *Ann. soc. sci. Bruxelles*, **45,** 169 (1926); *Chem. Abstracts,* **22,** 3561.

119. Lecat, M. *Rec. trav. chim.*, **45,** 623 (1926).

120. Lecat, M. *Rec. trav. chim.*, **47,** 13 (1928); *Ann. soc. sci. Bruxelles*, **49B,** 17, 109 (1929); *J. chim. phys.*, **27,** 75 (1930).

121. Lecat, M. *Compt. rend.*, **222,** 734 (1946).

122. Leikola, E. *Suomen Kem.*, **13B,** 13 (1940); *Brit. Chem. Abstracts,* **1942** i, 170

123. Leslie, R. T. *J. Research Natl. Bur. Standards*, **13,** 595 (1934).

124. Linhart, G. A. *J. Am. Chem. Soc.*, **37,** 258 (1915).

124a. Lloyd, B. A., Thompson, S. O., and Ferguson, J. B. *Can. J. Research*, **15B,** 101 (1937).

125. Louise, E. *Compt. rend.*, **150,** 526 (1910); *Chem. Abstracts,* **4,** 1368.

125a. McArdle, E. H. *Chem. & Met. Eng.*, **44,** 601 (1937).

126. McBain, J. M. and O'Connor, J. J. *J. Am. Chem. Soc.*, **62,** 2855 (1940).

127. McBain, J. W. and O'Connor, J. J. *J. Am. Chem. Soc.*, **63,** 875 (1941).

128. McBain, J. W. and Soldate, A. M. *J. Am. Chem. Soc.*, **64,** 1556 (1942).

129. Mair, B. J., Willingham, C. B., and Streiff, A. J. *J. Research Natl. Bur. Standards*, **21,** 597 (1938).

130. Maman, A. *Compt. rend.*, **198,** 1324 (1934).

131. Maman, A. *Compt. rend.*, **205,** 320 (1937).

132. Marsh, J. S. Principles of Phase Diagrams, McGraw-Hill, New York, 1935, pp. 122–170.

133. Marvel, C. S. and Glavis, F. J. *J. Am. Chem. Soc.*, **60,** 2622 (1938).

134. Mayer, J. E. Paper presented before the "Symposium on Liquid Phenomena" of the Division of Physical Chemistry at the 111th Meeting of the American Chemical Society, Atlantic City, April, 1947.

135. Menshutkin, B. N. *Mem. inst. polytechnique*, **13,** 1 (1910); **14,** 251 (1911); through ref. 100, p. 394.

136. Mertslin, R. V. *J. Gen. Chem. U. S. S. R.,* **8,** 1742 (1938); *Brit. Chem. Abstracts*, **1939** i, 265; *Chem. Abstracts,* **33,** 4859. The latter erroneously says "C_6H_6" instead of "benzine" (4 times).

137. Mikeska, L. A. *Ind. Eng. Chem.,* **28,** 970 (1936).

138. Miller, V. A. *Ind. Eng. Chem. Anal. Ed.,* **17,** 5 (1945).

139. Miller, V. A. *Ind. Eng. Chem. Anal. Ed.,* **17,** 566 (1945).

140. Miller, V. A. Private communication to the author (1945).

141. Mochalov, K. I. *Bull. inst. reserches biol. Perm.,* **11,** 25 (1937); *Chem. Abstracts*, **32,** 2417.

142. Mondain-Monval, P. and Quiquarez, J. *Compt. rend.,* **210,** 246 (1940); *Chem. Abstracts,* **34,** 2665.

143. Mondain-Monval, P. and Quiquarez, J. *Bull. soc. chim.,* (5) **7,** 240 (1940); *Chem. Abstracts,* **34,** 4651.

144. Mondain-Monval, P. and Quiquarez, J. *Bull. soc. chim.,* (5) **11,** 26 (1944); **12,** 380 (1945); *Chem. Abstracts,* **39,** 8; **40,** 270.

145. Moore, R. J., Morrell, J. C., and Egloff, G. *Met. Chem. Eng.,* **18,** 396 (1918).

146. Mossler, G. and Markus, F. *Pharm. Post,* **47,** 291 (1914); *Chem. Abstracts,* **8,** 3216.

147. Moulton, R. W. and Walkey, J. E. *Trans. Am. Inst. Chem. Engrs.,* **40,** 695 (1944).

148. Mulliken, S. P. and Wakeman, R. L. *Rec. trav. chem.,* **54,** 367 (1935).

149. Mulliken, S. P. and Wakeman, R. L. *Ind. Eng. Chem. Anal. Ed.,* **7,** 276 (1935).

150. Nernst, W. and Hohmann, C. *Z. physik. Chem.,* **11,** 370 (1893).

151. Olsen, A. L. and Washburn, E. R. *J. Am. Chem. Soc.,* **57,** 303 (1935).

151a. Ormandy, W. R., Pond, T. W. M., and Davies, W. R. *J. Inst. Petroleum Technol.,* **20,** 308 (1934).

152. Orton, K. J. P. and Jones, David C. *J. Chem. Soc.,* **115,** 1055, 1060 (1919).

153. Othmer, D. F. and Tobias, P. E. *Ind. Eng. Chem.,* **34,** 690 (1942).

154. Othmer, D. F. and Tobias, P. E. *Ind. Eng. Chem.,* **34,** 693, 696 (1942).

155. Othmer, D. F., White, R. E., and Trueger, E. *Ind. Eng. Chem.,* **33,** 1240 (1941).

156. Othmer, M. E. *Chem. & Met. Eng.,* **43,** 325 (1936).

157. Ottenweller, J. H., Holloway, C. Jr., and Weinrich, W. *Ind. Eng. Chem.,* **35,** 207 (1943).

158. Pacini, D. *Nuovo cimento,* **10,** 131 (1915); *Chem. Abstracts,* **10,** 310.

158a. Page, J. M. Jr., Buchler, C. C., and Diggs, S. H. *Ind. Eng. Chem.,* **25,** 419 (1933).

159. Palit, S. R. and McBain, J. W. *Ind. Eng. Chem.,* **38,** 741 (1946).

160. Pascal, P. and Quinet, M. L. *Compt. rend.,* **211,** 193 (1940); *Ann. chim. anal. chim. appl.,* **23,** 5 (1941); *Chem. Abstracts,* **36,** 368, 3120.

161. Perrakis, N. *J. chim. phys.,* **22,** 280 (1925); *Chem. Abstracts,* **20,** 1544.

162. Petrov, A. D. and Andreev, D. N. *J. Gen. Chem. U. S. S. R.,* **12,** 95 (1942); *Chem. Abstracts,* **37,** 2006.

163. Poffenberger, N., Horsley, L. H., Nutting, H. S., and Britton, E. C. *Trans. Am. Inst. Chem. Engrs.,* **42,** 820 (1946).

163a. Poole, J. W. *Ind. Eng. Chem.,* **21,** 1098 (1929); **23,** 170 (1931).

164. Prins, H. J. *Rec. trav. chim.,* **42,** 25 (1928).

165. Ralston, A. W., Hoerr, C. W., and Crews, L. T. *J. Org. Chem.,* **9,** 319 (1944).

166. Randall, M. and Longtin, B. *Ind. Eng. Chem.,* **31,** 1295 (1939).

167. Rathmann, F. H. *J. Applied Chem. U. S. S. R.,* **10,** 1233 (1937); *Chem. Abstracts,* **32,** 1426.

168. Rheinboldt, H. and Kircheisen, M. *J. prakt. Chem.*, (ii) **112,** 187 (1926); *Brit. Chem. Abstracts*, **1926A,** 476.
169. Rice, H. T. and Lieber, E. *Ind. Eng. Chem. Anal. Ed.*, **16,** 107 (1944).
169a. Rising, M. M. and Hicks, J. S. *J. Am. Chem. Soc.*, **48,** 1931 (1926).
170. Rushton, J. H. *Ind. Eng. Chem.*, **29,** 309 (1937).
171. Saal, R. N. J. and Dijck, W. J. D. van. *Proc. World Petroleum Congr.*, London, **2,** 352 (1933).
172. Sage, B. H. and Lacey, W. N. Volumetric and Phase Behavior of Hydrocarbons, Stanford Univ. Press, California, 1939, pp. 118, 138, 170.
173. Sage, B. H., Lacey, W. N., and Schaafsma, J. G. *Ind. Eng. Chem.*, **26,** 214, 874 (1934).
173a. Sage, B. H., Backus, H. S., and Lacey, W. N. *Ind. Eng. Chem.*, **27,** 686 (1935).
173b. Sapgir, S. *Bull. soc. chim. Belg.*, **38,** 392 (1929); *Chem. Abstracts*, **24,** 2109.
174. Sasaki, T. *Bull. Chem. Soc. Japan*, **14,** 3 (1939); *Chem. Abstracts*, **33,** 3230.
175. Sata, N. and Kimura, O. *Bull. Chem. Soc. Japan*, **10,** 409 (1935); *Chem. Abstracts*, **30,** 350.
176. Scatchard, G. Paper presented before the "Symposium on Liquid Phenomena" of the Division of Physical and Inorganic Chemistry at the 111th Meeting of the American Chemical Society, Atlantic City, April, 1947.
177. Schiessler, R. W., Cosby, J. N., Clarke, D. G., Rowland, C. S., Sloatman, W. S., and Herr, C. H. *Petroleum Refiner*, **21,** 383 (1942).
178. Schiessler, R. W., Clarke, D. G., Rowland, C. S., Sloatman, W. S., and Herr, C. H. *Petroleum Refiner*, **22,** 390 (1943).
179. Schiessler, R. W., Herr, C. H., Rytina, A. W., Weisel, C. A., Fischl, F., McLaughlin, R. L., and Kuehner, H. H. *Proc. Am. Petroleum Inst.*, **26** III, 260 (1946).
180. Schlegal, Helene. *J. chim. phys.*, **31,** 517 (1934); *Chem. Abstracts*, **29,** 1704.
181. Schreinemakers, F. A. H. *Z. physik. Chem.*, **23,** 417; **26,** 237; **30,** 460 (1897–9).
182. Schreinemakers, F. A. H. *Z. physik. Chem.*, **25,** 543 (1898).
183. Schreinemakers, F. A. H. *Z. physik. Chem.*, **27,** 95 (1898).
184. Schreinemakers, F. A. H. *Z. physik. Chem.*, **29,** 577–8 (1899).
185. Schreinemakers, F. A. H. *Z. physik. Chem.*, **33,** 92 (1900).
186. Schreinemakers, F. A. H. Die heterogenen Gleichgewichte, edited by Roozeboom, Friedr. Vieweg u. Sohn, Braunschweig, 1911, Drittes Heft, Zweiter Teil, pp. 6–17.
186a. Schulz, G. V. and Jirgensons, B. *Z. physik. Chem.*, **B46,** 105 (1940); *Chem. Abstracts*, **35,** 953.
187. Seidell, A. Solubilities of Inorganic and Metal-Organic Compounds, 3rd ed., Vol. I, Van Nostrand, New York, 1941.
188. Seidell, A. Solubilities of Organic Compounds, Vol. II, Van Nostrand, New York, 1941.
189. Serijan, K. T., Spurr, R. A., and Gibbons, L. C. *J. Am. Chem. Soc.*, **68,** 1763 (1946).
190. Seyer, W. F. and Cornett, W. F. *Ind. Eng. Chem.*, **29,** 91 (1937).
191. Seyer, W. F. and Dunbar, V. *Trans. Roy. Soc. Canada, III*, **16,** 307 (1922); *Chem. Abstracts*, **17,** 2072.
192. Seyer, W. F. and Gallaugher, A. F. *Trans. Roy. Soc. Canada, III*, **20,** 343 (1926); *Chem. Abstracts*, **21,** 2592.
193. Seyer, W. F. and Gill, A. F. *Trans. Roy. Soc. Canada, III*, **18,** 209 (1924); *Chem. Abstracts*, **19,** 917.
194. Seyer, W. F. and Hodnett, L. *J. Am. Chem. Soc.*, **58,** 997 (1936).

195. Seyer, W. F. and Hugget, J. L. *Trans. Roy. Soc. Canada, III,* **18,** 213 (1924); *Chem. Abstracts,* **19,** 917.

196. Seyer, W. F. and King, E. G. *J. Am. Chem. Soc.,* **55,** 3140 (1933).

197. Seyer, W. F. and Todd, E. *Ind. Eng. Chem.,* **23,** 325 (1931).

197a. Shepherd, F. M. E. *J. Inst. Petroleum Technol.,* **20,** 294 (1934).

198. Sherwood, T. K. Absorption and Extraction, McGraw-Hill, New York, 1937, pp. 242–4.

198a. Shilov, H. and Lepin, L. *Z. physik. Chem.,* **101,** 353 (1922).

198b. Shoemaker, B. H. and Bolt, J. A. *Ind. Eng. Chem. Anal. Ed.,* **14,** 200 (1942).

199. Shükarev, A. *Z. physik. Chem.,* **71,** 90 (1910).

199a. Sidgwick, N. V. and Ewbank, E. K. *J. Chem. Soc.,* **119,** 992 (1921).

200. Sidgwick, N. V. and Neill, J. A. *J. Chem. Soc.,* **123,** 2813 (1923).

200a. Simonsen, D. R. and Washburn, E. R. *J. Am. Chem. Soc.,* **68,** 235 (1946).

201. Smirmov, V. I., *Z. physik. Chem.,* **58,** 373 (1907).

202. Smith, Alexander, Holmes, W. B., and Hall, E. S. *J. Am. Chem. Soc.,* **27,** 806 (1905); *Z. physik. Chem.,* **52,** 613 (1905).

202a. Smith, Albert E. and Norton, J. W. *J. Am. Chem. Soc.,* **54,** 3812 (1932).

203. Smith, A. S. and Braun, T. B. *Ind. Eng. Chem.,* **37,** 1047 (1945).

204. Smith, A. S. and Funk, J. E. *Trans. Am. Inst. Chem. Engrs.,* **40,** 211 (1944).

205. Smith, E. Lester *J. Phys. Chem.,* **36,** 1401 (1932).

206. Smith, E. Lester *Nature,* **127,** 91 (1931); **131,** 167 (1933).

207. Smith, Homer W. *J. Phys. Chem.,* **25,** 204 (1921); **26,** 256 (1922); through citation 188.

208. Smith, Homer W. and White, T. A. *J. Phys. Chem.,* **33,** 1953 (1929).

209. Smith, Julian C. *J. Phys. Chem.,* **46,** 376 (1942).

210. Smith, Julian C. *Ind. Eng. Chem.,* **34,** 234 (1942).

211. Smith, Julian C. *Ind. Eng. Chem.,* **36,** 68 (1944).

212. Smith, Julian C. and Drexel, R. E. *Ind. Eng. Chem.,* **37,** 601 (1945).

213. Spausta, F. *Erdöl u. Teer,* **8,** 282 (1932); *Chem. Abstracts,* **26,** 6095.

214. Speyers, C. L. *Am. J. Sci.,* (4) **14,** 294 (1902), through ref. 188, p. 92, and ref. 100a (p. 112).

215. Staaterman, H. G., Morris, R. C., Stager, R. M., and Pierotti, G. J. *Chem. Eng. Progress,* **43,** 148 (1947).

216. Tarasenkov, D. N. and Paul'sen, I. A. *J. Gen. Chem. U. S. S. R.,* **7,** 2143 (1937); **8,** 76 (1938); *Chem. Abstracts,* **32,** 33, 5288.

217. Tarasenkov, D. N. and Paul'sen, I. A. *Acta Physicochim. U. R. S. S.,* **11,** 75 (1939); *Chem. Abstracts,* **34,** 1238.

218. Thiele, E. W. *Ind. Eng. Chem.,* **27,** 392 (1935).

219. Thiry, R. Thesis, Brussels, 1925, through ref. 188, pp. 457, 553, 559, 615.

220. Thompson, T. G. and Odeen, H. *J. Ind. Eng. Chem.,* **12,** 1057 (1920).

221. Tilicheev, M. D. *Khim. Tverdogo Topliva* **9,** (2) 181 (1938); *Chem. Abstracts,* **34,** 926.

222. Tilicheev, M. D. and Kuruindin, K. S. *Neftyanoe Khoz.,* **19,** 586 (1930); *Chem. Centr.,* **1931** I, 2561.

223. Timmermans, J. *Z. physik. Chem.,* **58,** 145, 159, 186, 196 (1907).

224. Timmermans, J. *Proc. Acad. Sci. Amsterdam,* **13,** 523 (1910); Thesis, Brussels, 1911.

225. Timmermans, J. *J. chim. phys.,* **20,** 502–506 (1923); *Chem. Centr.,* **1924** I, 1734.

226. Timmermans, J. and Hennaut-Roland, Mme. *J. chim. phys.,* **29,** 529¦ (1932); **32,** 501, 589 (1935); *Chem. Abstracts,* **27,** 2079; **30,** 2072.

227. Timmermans, J. and Martin, F. *J. chim. phys.*, **23**, 733 (1926); **25**, 411 (1928); *Chem. Abstracts*, **21**, 1038; **22**, 4024.

228. Tizard, H. T. and Marshall, A. G. *J. Soc. Chem. Ind.*, **40**, 20T (1921).

228a. Trimble, F. and Dunlop, A. P. *Ind. Eng. Chem. Anal. Ed.*, **12**, 721 (1940).

228b. Trimble, H. M. and Fraser, G. E. *Ind. Eng. Chem.*, **21**, 1064 (1929).

229. Vandam, L. *Bull. soc. chim. Belg.*, **20**, 374 (1906); *Chem. Centr.*, **1907** I, 1810.

230. Vartaressian, K. A. and Fenske, M. R. *Ind. Eng. Chem.*, **28**, 928, 1353 (1936).

231. Vartaressian, K. A. and Fenske, M. R. *Ind. Eng. Chem.*, **29**, 270 (1937).

232. Vink, D. J., Ames, A. M., David, R. A., and Katz, D. L. *Oil Gas J.*, **39**, No. 28, Nov. 21, 1940, p. 34.

233. Vlček, A. K. *Chem. Obzor.*, **8**, 198 (1933); **10**, 88 (1935); *Chem. Abstracts*, **28**, 3646; **31**, 3771.

234. Vondracek, R. *Collection Czechoslov. Chem. Commun.*, **9**, 168 (1937); *Chem. Abstracts*, **31**, 5232.

235. Waentig, P. and Pescheck, G. *Z. physik. Chem.*, **93**, 540 (1919).

236. Walden, P. *Ber.*, **34**, 4191 (1901).

237. Washburn, E. R. and Beguin, A. E. *J. Am. Chem. Soc.*, **62**, 579 (1940).

238. Washburn, E. R., Brockway, C. E., Graham, C. L., and Deming, P. *J. Am. Chem. Soc.*, **64**, 1886 (1942).

239. Washburn, E. R., Graham, C. L., Arnold, G. B., and Transue, L. F. *J. Am. Chem. Soc.*, **62**, 1454 (1940).

239a. Washburn, E. R. and Strandskov, C. V. *J. Phys. Chem.*, **48**, 241 (1944).

240. Wiegand, J. H. *Ind. Eng. Chem. Anal. Ed.*, **15**, 380 (1943).

240a. Wiener, H. *J. Phys. Colloid Chem.*, **52**, 1082 (1948).

241. Wilcox, K. W. and Bailey, C. R. *J. Phys. Chem.*, **33**, 706 (1929).

242. Wilson, R. E., Keith, P. C. Jr., and Haylett, R. E. *Trans. Am. Inst. Chem. Engrs.*, **32**, 364, 375 (1936).

242a. Wood, S. E. *J. Am. Chem. Soc.*, **68**, 1963 (1946).

243. Woodburn, H. M., Smith, K., and Tetewsky, H. *Ind. Eng. Chem.*, **36**, 588 (1944).

244. Woodman, R. M. *J. Soc. Chem. Ind.*, **52**, 185T (1933).

245. Wratschko, F., *Pharm. Presse*, **34**, 143 (1929); *Chem. Abstracts*, **23**, 3539.

246. Zepalova-Mikhailova, L. A. *Trans. Inst. Pure Chem. Reagents (U. S. S. R.)*, No. 15, 3 (1937); *Chem. Centr.*, **1939** I, 4914.

247. Zhuravlev, E. F. *J. Phys. Chem. U. S. S. R.*, **12**, 639 (1938); **13**, 679 (1939); *Chem. Abstracts*, **34**, 315, 1544.

248. Zhuravlev, E. F. and Bychkova, M. N. *J. Gen. Chem. U. S. S. R.*, **17**, 1577 (1947); *Chem. Abstracts*, **42**, 3652.

CHAPTER 8

SOLID-LIQUID EQUILIBRIA OF HYDROCARBONS

By M. R. CINES

Phillips Petroleum Company, Research Department, Bartlesville, Oklahoma

CONTENTS

INTRODUCTION

Solid-liquid equilibria play two roles in the physical chemistry of hydrocarbons. In the first, they are important in themselves as a physical property of individual compounds. As such they are salient points in developing an understanding of solid-phase behavior in regard to molecular size and shape. Associated properties, e.g., heats of fusion, solid-phase transi-

315

(5), integrating and neglecting terms containing $\dfrac{T_0 - T}{T_0}$ to powers higher than the second in the expanded integral, we find

$$-\ln x_1 = \frac{\Delta H_f}{RT_0^2}\,(T_0 - T) + \frac{\Delta H_f(T_0 - T)^2}{RT_0^3} - \frac{C_p^l - C_p^s}{2RT_0^2}\,(T_0 - T)^2. \quad (7)$$

For hydrocarbons, when the value of $T_0 - T$ is small, the last two terms are of second-order importance and they can generally be neglected. It should be noted carefully that, in this derivation of the melting-point-lowering relation, no assumption has been made as to the nature of the components other than those already mentioned.

I. MELTING POINTS, SOLID-PHASE TRANSITIONS AND ASSOCIATED HEAT EFFECTS

In view of the longstanding emphasis which organic chemists have placed on the melting point as a means of identification and characterization of organic compounds, it seems hardly necessary to stress the importance of this particular physical property. Among hydrocarbons, the melting point assumes even greater significance. In fact, a recent survey (2) of physical properties determined on hydrocarbons shows clearly that the melting point is the property most frequently reported for any new synthetic or newly isolated hydrocarbon. With the accumulation of data on hydrocarbons, efforts have been made to correlate structure with melting point in order to be able to predict values for unknown members in a given series and to obtain some insight into the melting process. Certainly, with the wide variation in molecular structure and with the nature of the intermolecular forces remaining the same for all molecules, these melting point data should be of great value for ultimate tests of hypotheses on the melting process.

1. MELTING POINTS OF HOMOLOGOUS SERIES

When the melting points of a series of hydrocarbons are to be compared, it is important to find out as much as possible about the method of measurement and the quality of the samples studied in order to evaluate the precision and probable accuracy of the results. From the freezing-point-depression equation (equation 7), it is obvious that the purity of the sample will have a pronounced effect on the melting point so that the purification of the samples is an important criterion of the validity of the results. When a melting point is reported on the basis of results on a sample which shows a considerable melting range, it should be examined carefully to determine whether or not it has been corrected to the value for zero impurity. Since the formation of solid solutions may actually raise the melting point of a sample above that of the pure material, particular caution is necessary in evaluating data on hydrocarbon types which are known to tend to form solid solutions with the probable impurities, e.g., those hydrocarbons with low entropies of fusion and the long-chain members of homologous series. The formation of solid solutions among hydrocarbons will be discussed in later sections of this chapter.

Of all hydrocarbon types, more attention has been given to the melting points of n-alkanes than to those of any other class of hydrocarbons. Values for numerous members of this homologous series have been reported from methane up to n-heptacontane, $C_{70}H_{142}$. Although the results on the higher members of the series have not been verified, they have been included in Fig. 1 to show the relation between melting point and chain length. Data on other homologous series are not nearly as complete as can be seen by the curves in Fig. 2 for the 2-methylalkanes and the n-1-alkenes. Similar presentations of melting points of alkylcyclopentanes, alkylcyclopentenes, alkylcyclohexanes and alkylbenzenes are available in the literature (3, 4).

It is clearly indicated by the curve for the n-alkanes that the melting point is asymptotically approaching a maximum value, the so-called convergence temperature. Similar behavior has been noted for other long-chain homologous series, e.g., n-monobasic acids, dibasic acids, n-primary alcohols (5). Not only are the shapes of the temperature versus chain-length curves similar but they all appear to be approaching similar maximum values, about 400°K. (6). Garner et $al.$ (7) have calculated from the heats of fusion and the setting points of the C_{22}, C_{26}, C_{30}, and C_{34} n-paraffins that the convergence temperature is roughly 408°K. A theoretical explanation for the identity of the convergence temperature for all long-chain, polymethylene molecules was developed by Eyring (8). On the basis that all long-chain molecules act in segments, the magnitudes of entropy and heats of fusion for these molecules would be those corresponding to the attainment of new equilibrium positions for these segments. Thus, with long chains, the melting point, which is the ratio $\Delta H_f / \Delta S_f$, will approach a limiting value. Since the nature of the end groups becomes unimportant in very long chains, the limiting melting point should be the same for all long-chain homologous series. Assuming a convergence temperature of 395°K., Eyring calculates that these long chains act in segments of approximately twenty methylene groups. In contrast to the polymethylenes which are more or less free to rotate about the carbon-carbon single bonds and hence can act in segments, the polyenes, which are more rigid by virtue of the double-bonded carbons and cannot act in segments, have melting points much higher than the alkanes and do not show any convergence at approximately 400°K. (9).

The smooth melting-point versus chain-length curve for the n-alkanes (Fig. 1) has stimulated numerous attempts to develop analytical expressions

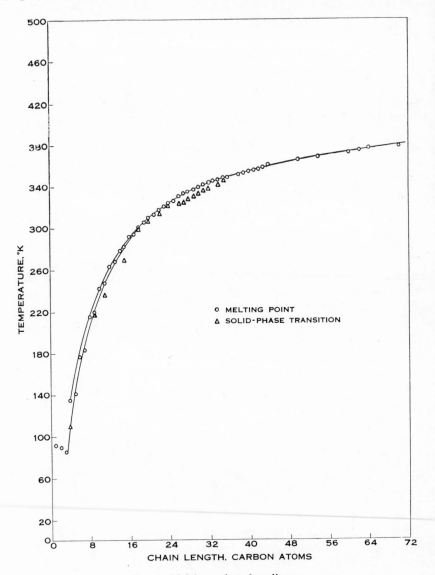

FIG. 1. Melting point of n-alkanes.

to represent the melting point as a function of the number of carbon atoms. These efforts date back to 1906 when Tsakalotos (10) developed an equation to calculate the melting point of a normal paraffin from the value of the next lower member of the series. The calculated results fit the data available at

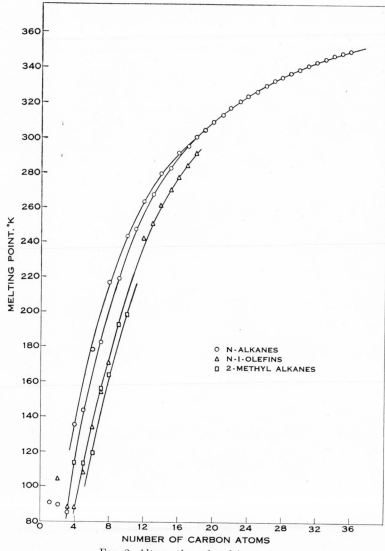

FIG. 2. Alternation of melting points.

that time fairly well. Since then there have been numerous other efforts at such correlations. Unfortunately some (11, 12) are of dubious value since they have been based on data obtained from the International Critical

Tables in which undue weight seems to have been given to the values of
Levene et al. (13) which are probably too high (14). Garner et al. (7) developed an equation which fits the data for the melting points of n-paraffins
above n-eicosane with fair accuracy. The best relation developed to date
is that of Etessam and Sawyer (15) which is based on molecular weight
rather than the number of carbon atoms in the chain as in previous correlations. Their equation

$$T = 414.5M/(M + 94.4), \qquad (8)$$

where T is the melting point in degrees Kelvin, and M is the molecular
weight, represents the experimental data from n-heneicosane ($C_{21}H_{44}$) to
n-heptacontane ($C_{70}H_{142}$) within $\pm 0.5°K$. This equation predicts the convergence temperature of $415°K$., which is slightly higher than other values.
Until more precise values for the higher members of the normal paraffin
series are available, it would seem likely that the equation of Etessam
and Sawyer would suffice for most purposes.

2. ALTERNATION OF MELTING POINTS

The melting point of the normal alkanes from C_1 to C_{20} are plotted as a
function of the chain length in Fig. 2 on a scale large enough to show clearly
that the paraffins with odd chain lengths, up to C_{18}, melt lower than the
even members of the series. This phenomenon of alternation of melting
points between odd and even members of homologous series was first noted
in 1877 by Baeyer (16) and has since been observed in a large number of
homologous series of long-chain molecules, e.g., mono- and dicarboxylic
acids, methyl esters, nitriles, glycols, diamines, halides. However, in the
case of n-paraffins the alternation seems to disappear above C_{18}; a behavior apparently unique to the n-paraffins series. One possible way to
account for the disappearance of alternation is that actually the melting
points of the higher homologues are in error as a result of solid-solution formation with the probable impurities and/or as a result of complications in
phase behavior arising from the solid-phase changes which, for some long-
chain paraffins, occur quite close to the melting point (Fig. 1). On the other
hand, since several investigators have reported freezing points on different
samples of the same long-chain hydrocarbons, and since most of the values
give reasonable agreement, it would seem probable that the true melting
points could not be very different from the reported values. Precision calorimetric measurements of the melting point of long-chain paraffin molecules
in which the purity and the melting point can be obtained simultaneously
would provide the best type of data to give dependable and precise results.
However, lacking information to the contrary, it appears improbable that
alternation in melting points of the normal alkanes persists beyond C_{18}.

This phenomenon of alternation in long-chain homologous series has stimulated various investigators to propound theories to explain it. The earlier hypotheses asssumed that alternation was a general property exhibited by other physical constants, e.g., boiling point, solubility, refractive index. However, in a careful investigation of physical properties related to the liquid state for mono- and dibasic acids, Verkade et al. (17) proved conclusively that alternation was restricted to properties of the solid phase. Thus, the explanation of alternation must be associated with the solid state and probably does not arise as a property of the individual molecules themselves. On this basis, it is possible to discount Hinrich's theory (18) postulating that the difference in properties arises from the symmetry of even members about their axis of rotation which results in higher moments of inertia and therefore greater stability for even than for odd-carbon-atom molecules. Similarly, Biach's (19) explanation based on alternating weak and strong carbon to carbon bonds, and Cuy's (20) and Pauly's (21) assumption that alternation resulted from alternating positive and negative carbon atoms must all be discarded as they would suggest differences in liquid-state properties as well. On the basis of a zig-zag chain structure, Pauly (21) has also suggested that the difference in melting points might arise from the fact that the terminal groups of the odd series would be in "cis" relation to each other whereas in the even series they would be in the "trans" position. The possibilities of cis and trans structure were further elaborated by Nikrassov (22) and Müller (23). The latter pointed out that, in a crystal of the even series, the pattern of the end groups repeats with every molecule while in the odd series two molecular layers are encountered before the pattern repeats so that a difference in lattice energy of the two series would be expected. Malkin (24) has pointed out that not all long-chain homologous series show alternation, i.e., n-alkanes, C_{18} and above, primary alcohols, ethyl esters, etc. From x-ray data on alternating and nonalternating series, it has been found that, for members of an alternating series, the stable crystal form at the melting point is one in which the chains are tilted at an angle with respect to the basal 001 plane while nonalternating homologues had forms, stable at the melting point, consisting of chains which were vertical, that is, perpendicular to the basal 001 plane. Malkin points out that, for crystals with vertical chains, there is no difference in packing, but with tilted chains there is an obvious difference. The influence of chain tilting on intermolecular-layer spacing is shown clearly in Fig. 3. It can be seen that for the vertical chains, the intermolecular-layer spacing for the even molecules, I_{EV}, is identical with that for the odd membered, I_{OV}. However, on tilting the chains, for the even series, the intermolecular spacing, I_{ET}, is constant and less than that for the vertical chain. In the case of the odd series, there are two alternating spacings, I_{OT_1} and I_{OT_2}.

From the comparison of the intermolecular spacings in the lower left hand corner of Fig. 3, it can be seen that spacing I_{OT_1} is the same as I_{ET} and less than I_{EV} and I_{OV}. However the second of the tilted-odd-series spacings, I_{OT_2}, is larger than all the other spacings including the vertical type. Thus, because this increased spacing represents decreased density of packing, the tilted-odd-series will melt at lower temperatures.

In view of Malkin's theory, the data of Müller (25) on the long spacing of the n-paraffin crystals is particularly interesting. He shows that the stable form at the melting point for the even series from hexane to hexadecane is the tilted-chain type. Above n-hexadecane there is a solid-phase transition from the shorter spacing of the tilted form to the longer spacing

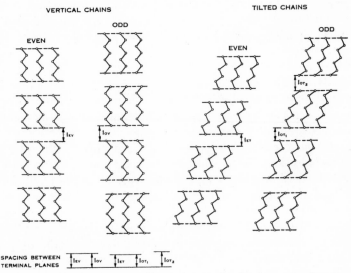

FIG. 3. Effect of chain tilt on intermolecular-layer spacing.

of the vertical chain. This transition occurs just a few degrees below the melting point. On the other hand, in the odd-membered series, below tridecane, the stable form at the melting point is the tilted chain while above undecane it is the vertical-chain crystal form. Thus, Malkin's theory would account, in straightforward fashion, for the alternation up to n-undecane. Above this member of the series, the stable form of the odd members is the vertical chain while the even ones remain tilted up to n-hexadecane. Since the tilted form provides denser packing and hence greater lattice stability, it would be expected that the even members with the tilted structure would melt at higher temperatures than the more loosely packed vertical-chain odd members. Above n-hexadecane all n-alkanes are in the vertical form. Since there is no difference in packing density, no alternation in melting points should be expected.

More recently on the basis of theoretical calculations made in an effort to account for the barrier hindering the rotation of methyl groups in ethane molecules, Eyring (26) has proposed an explanation for alternation of the normal paraffins involving resonance with double-bonded structures. According to this hypothesis, double-bond resonance in the even-carbon-atom series can result in double bonds at both ends of the molecule simultaneously while for odd members only one terminal double bond is possible. Therefore, the hydrogen atoms of the terminal groups of the even-carbon-atom chains are more free to form coordination type bonds with neighboring molecules which results in greater intermolecular forces in the crystals of the even series and therefore higher melting points. On melting, the expansion results in breaking these coordination bonds so that alternation would not be observed in the physical constants of the liquid state. Since this theory is based on resonance with double-bonded structure, which in the ethane molecule requires the opposed configuration of the hydrogen atoms to be the stable form, and since there appears to be considerable spectroscopic evidence that the staggered rather than the opposed is the stable form, Eyring's hypothesis would seem to need further substantiation before it can be considered as a replacement for Malkin's interpretation of alternation.

As has already been pointed out, the melting-point data for other homologous series are much less complete than for the n-alkane series. For the 2-methyl alkanes, the available data to 2-methyl nonane (27) show alternation just as in the normal series. In this case, it should be noted that the alternation shows the even-carbon-atom molecules melting lower than the odd-membered ones which appears to be a contradiction of the previous observations. However, when the number of atoms in the chain is considered rather than the total number in the molecule, the behavior for this series is in line with the others. For other paraffin series, there are insufficient data to reach any conclusions about alternation. The data for the n-1-olefins up to 1-heptadecene (27, 28) do not show alternation. Likewise, on the basis of the available data, the alkylnaphthenes and alkylbenzenes do not show alternation (3, 4).

3. MELTING POINT AND MOLECULAR STRUCTURE

It has been suggested that because of their unique character the study of the melting-point behavior of hydrocarbons might give valuable information for the understanding of the solid state and the melting process. Thus, among the paraffins, with the same intermolecular forces, the isomers with their differences in molecular symmetry and crystal structure show marked differences in melting points. Through the sponsorship of the American Petroleum Institute, several research projects have been established to synthesize hydrocarbons and to determine the physical properties of the highly purified products. Although the data compiled by API Research Project 44 are still limited for the more complex isomers and therefore do not permit any generalized picture as yet, certain correlations between molecular structure and melting points are possible. In general, the n-alkanes melt higher than other isomeric branched paraffins. The reason for the high melting point is undoubtedly the closer packing possible with straight chains which increases the heat of fusion and the lattice stability. However, there is one general class of paraffins, the high symmetry isomers, which does melt even higher than the normal alkanes. Thus, 2,2-dimethylpropane has spherical symmetry and melts at 256.56°K. whereas

TABLE I

EFFECT OF MOLECULAR SYMMETRY ON SOLID PHASE BEHAVIOR

Hydrocarbon	Melting point °K.	Heat of fusion cal./mole	Transition temperature °K.	Heat of transition cal./mole
n-Pentane	143.44	2011	None	
2,2-Dimethylpropane	256.56	778	140.02	616
n-Heptane	182.57	3358	None	
2,2,3-Trimethylbutane	248.20	526	121.0	567
n-Octane	216.36	4931	None	
2,2,3,3-Tetramethylbutane	373.85	1702	148.2	480
n-Nonane	219.56	5280[a]		
2,2,3,3-Tetramethylpentane	263.3	—		
3,3-Diethylpentane	242	—		
2,3-Dimethylbutane	145.19	191.4	136.07	1552
2,2-Dimethylbutane	174.28	138.4	140.79 / 126.81	68.2 / 1293
Cyclohexane	279.83	635	186.09	1605
Cyclopentane	179.69	144	138.07 / 122.39	83 / 1165

[a] Includes heat of transition which occurs 2.4° below m.p.

normal pentane melts at 143.44°K. or about 113 degrees below the high symmetry isomer. Several examples of similar behavior are shown in Table I. In each case, the spherical or nearly spherical molecule melts at temperatures considerably above those for the n-paraffins. It is noteworthy that all these high-melting paraffins have solid-phase transitions. As further illustration of the influence of spherical symmetry raising melting points, it should be noted that methane melts much higher than would be predicted by extrapolation of the melting-point vs. chain-length curve in Fig. 1.

Just as was found for the paraffins, among other hydrocarbon classes there are some individual compounds which have abnormally high melting points in comparison with other members of the same group. Thus, cyclopentane, cyclohexane, 1,1-dimethylcyclopentane, 1,1-dimethylcyclohexane, cis-1,2-dimethylcyclohexane and cis-1,2-dimethylcyclopentane all melt considerably higher in comparison with other naphthenes than would be predicted on the basis of their molecular weights. Of these high-melting naphthenes, four are known to be enantiotropic just as the highly symmetric paraffins. It has been suggested (26) that the cyclic alkanes show alternation of melting points similar to the long-chain paraffins. The available data, most of which have been reported by Ruzicka (29), show marked fluctuations rather than the smooth alternation of the long-chain molecules. These fluctuations are so erratic that no definite conclusion can be reached. It might be of some significance that the melting point of cyclotetratriacontane, $C_{34}H_{68}$, is about 340°K. while n-tetratriacontane, $C_{34}H_{70}$, melts at 346°K. perhaps indicating convergence of these cyclic compounds at approximately the same temperature as the straight-chain paraffins.

Among the aromatic hydrocarbons, the unsubstituted parent molecules, e.g., benzene, naphthalene, anthracene, melt at much higher temperatures than the methylated or alkylated homologues, e.g., toluene, α-methylnaphthalene. The high symmetry and planar structure of these parent hydrocarbons is responsible for the high melting points. It is obvious that closer packing is possible with the planar molecules than with the alkyl aromatics. The resulting greater lattice stability accounts for the higher melting point. In the case of alkyl aromatics, with increasing length of the side chain the melting point approaches more and more closely that of the chain itself.

When the long-chain paraffins were discussed, it was pointed out that they appear to act in segments, made possible by the hindered-rotation about the carbon-carbon bond, and hence have a maximum melting point or convergence temperature. As in the case of the polyenes which do not have the same degree of freedom of intramolecular rotation as the polymethylenes, the parent polynuclear aromatics cannot act in segments; all intermolecular bonds must break simultaneously in order to melt. Therefore, it is easily understandable that the melting point of these polynuclear aromatics would not approach a convergence temperature, except possibly the melting point of graphite itself. The marked contrast between n-paraffin and polynuclear aromatics can be seen by comparing two 34-carbon-atom molecules, n-tetratriacontane, $C_{34}H_{70}$, and tetrabenzo-(de, hi, op, st)-pentacene, $C_{34}H_{18}$. The paraffin melts at 346°K.; the aromatic at 853°K. (30).

Further, more-detailed correlations between structure, symmetry and melting point will undoubtedly be possible when more precise and accurate data are available on more of the isomers of higher molecular-weight hydrocarbons.

4. SOLID-PHASE TRANSITIONS

In calorimetric studies and x-ray crystallography of hydrocarbons, it has been shown that some possess solid-phase transitions from one crystal form to another. Once again, more investigations have been carried out on the enantiotropism of n-paraffins than on that of any other hydrocarbon class. The known transition temperatures for this series have been indicated in Fig. 1. In the lower-molecular-weight members of this series, transitions have been observed calorimetrically in n-butane, n-nonane,

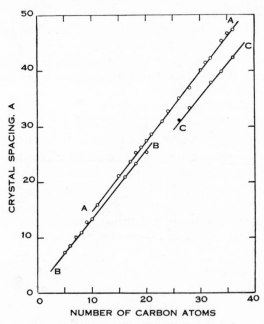

FIG. 4. Long spacing of n-alkane crystals.

n-undecane and n-pentadecane (31, 32, 33). X-ray measurements by Müller (34) and Piper *et al.* (35) have extended the range of n-paraffins known to have more than one crystal form up to n-tetratetracontane ($C_{44}H_{90}$). The results of Müller's research (34) on the long spacings of the normal-paraffin crystals from C_5H_{12} to $C_{30}H_{62}$ are shown in Fig. 4. Above n-eicosane, the long spacings of both the odd- and even-carbon-atom chains fall on the same curve when measured near the melting point. In the even series from C_6H_{14} to $C_{16}H_{34}$, only the shorter spacing of the curve BB, Fig. 4, is observed. From $C_{16}H_{34}$ to $C_{22}H_{46}$ the long spacing, AA, is observed near the melting point while the shorter spacing, BB, is the stable crystal form at lower temperatures. In contrast, the odd-carbon-atom chains containing 11 to 19 carbon atoms crystallize only with the long spacing AA. Piper *et al.* (35) report a third spacing, shown by line CC in the figure, from $C_{26}H_{54}$ to $C_{36}H_{74}$. Parks *et al.* (32) and Ubbelohde (33) report transitions for *n*-undecane and *n*-pentadecane but the solid-phase transformations occur at temperatures so close to the melting point that Müller may not have observed them. Müller indicates that the difference in spacing AA and BB is the result of tilting of the chain with respect to the basal 001 plane. As has been pointed out previously these results offer strong support to Malkin's theory for the alternation of the melting points of the *n*-paraffins. In later work, Müller (36) extended his observations on crystal transitions to $C_{31}H_{64}$, $C_{34}H_{70}$ and $C_{44}H_{90}$. With increasing molecular weight, from $C_{24}H_{50}$ to $C_{44}H_{90}$, the difference between melting and transition points passes through a maximum value and then diminishes until at $C_{44}H_{90}$ the difference is only one-half degree. This general trend, which indicates that these solid-phase transitions will probably disappear in chains containing more than 44 carbon atoms, was also noted by Seyer *et al.* (37) in their dilatometric measurements of the transitions of *n*-paraffins.

Those solid-phase transformations of the *n*-paraffins which have been observed in calorimetric measurements were found to have heat effects which are much smaller than the heat of fusion. On the other hand, the enantiotropism of spherically symmetric hydrocarbons which have been studied calorimetrically shows that the heat and entropy of transition is usually much greater than similar values for the fusion (Table I). By analogy with the measurements of 2,2-dichloropropane (38) (a molecule similar in size and shape with 2,2-dimethylpropane) at the solid-transition point the crystal form of these spherical molecules changes from a low-temperature anisotropic to a high-temperature isotropic form. One notable characteristic of all these spherically symmetric hydrocarbons is that the volume change from liquid to solid is small, e.g., for cyclohexane, the change is only half that measured for benzene (1); correspondingly, the crystals stable between the melting and transition points are of soft and waxy texture. In contrast the low-temperature crystal form is hard, brittle, and opaque; this opacity results from the cracks and imperfections accompanying the large volume change of the transformation of the isotropic to anisotropic crystal. In addition to those highly symmetric alkanes with melting points higher than the straight-chain compounds, the nearly spherical molecules, 2,2-dimethylbutane and 2,3-dimethylbutane, also show these so-called rotational transitions. As with the alkanes, the high-melting cyclanes also have transitions in the solid phase involving entropy changes which are much greater than the entropy of fusion. Two of these symmetric hydrocarbons, cyclopentane and 2,2-dimethylbutane have a second solid-phase transition, involving only very small entropy changes. They are observed between the melting point and the large rotational transition of these two compounds.

5. HEAT EFFECTS AND ENTROPY CHANGES

With all phase changes there are, of course, associated heat effects and entropy changes which are important. The data on these thermodynamic properties for hydrocarbons is much more limited than on the equilibrium temperatures. Of the available thermodynamic data, only those for the lower boiling compounds have been obtained in precision calorimeters. Since the purity of the materials used for the determination of the thermodynamic properties is of prime importance, the only reliable measurements are those made in calorimeters where it was possible to determine the purity of the samples as well as the thermodynamic properties (see section on purity determinations by melting points). The calorimetric data for paraffins up to n-hexadecane are shown in Fig. 5. The values for the paraffins above hexadecane have not been obtained by the calorimetric method and the purities of the samples were not well known, so that it is not surprising to find that they do not correlate very well with the values for the lower homologues. It would be very valuable to have calorimetric measurements on the paraffins which are solid above room temperature. To illustrate the difference between the calorimetric and other data, Ubbelohde (33) calculated the heats of fusion for normal tetra-, hexa- and octadecanes from the equation

$$q = 0.61n - 1.06, \quad Kcal/mole \quad (9)$$

where q is the heat of fusion in calories per gram, and n is the number of carbon atoms in the molecule. This relation was obtained by Garner and King (39) on the basis of their measurements on four normal alkanes containing from 24 to 34 carbon atoms. The actual values which Ubbelohde obtained from his calorimetric measurements were considerably higher than those predicted by the equation. If the results of Garner and King were correct, even though the calculation does involve an extrapolation, it would be expected that the heats of fusion of the hydrocarbons $C_{14}H_{30}$ to $C_{18}H_{38}$ would be closely related to those found for the higher homologues.

In Fig. 5, for the enantiotropic paraffins, e.g., n-butane, the sum of the transition and fusion values agree much more closely with the smooth curves than do the fusion data alone. This behavior is an example of the fairly general rule that the sum of the transition and fusion heats and entropies for enantiotropic molecules is equal to the normal values for fusion of monotropic molecules of the same type and molecular weight (40).

As an example of fairly universal behavior of the heats and entropies of isomeric hydrocarbons, the available data on seven-carbon-atom hydrocarbons are given in Table II. It is apparent that with increasing branching of the chain the heat and entropy of fusion decreases; the highest values are obtained with the straight-chain n-heptane. The decrease in the heat of fusion with branching can be understood when the density of packing of molecules in the crystal lattice is taken into account. In the n-alkanes, the hydrogen atoms that envelope the carbon chains are all uniformly spaced

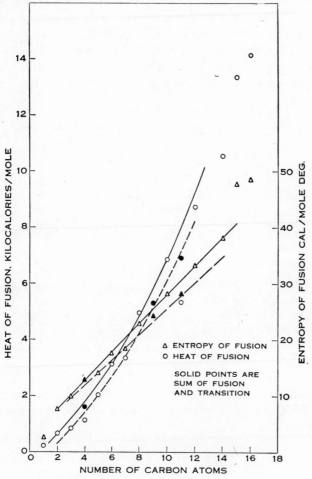

FIG. 5. Heat and entropy of fusion of n-paraffins.

with respect to the envelopes of neighboring chains so that all the hydrogen atoms are equally active in the intermolecular bonding. When the chain begins to branch the hydrogen envelope begins to bulge, preventing the uniformly close approach found in the n-paraffins and thereby reducing the total lattice energy which in turn results in lower heats of fusion and lower melting points. Surprisingly enough, when the branching reaches the state of spherical molecules, the heat of fusion becomes abnormally low but the melting point rises considerably above the values for the straight-chain molecules. Not only is this behavior true for the alkanes, but also for the highly symmetric naphthenes as well. Thus, for the seven-carbon-atom hydrocarbons listed in Table II, the entropy of fusion generally lies in the range of 9 to 14 e.u. n-Heptane has the appreciably higher value of 18.39 e.u. while, in marked contrast, for 2,2,3-trimethylbutane the value is only 2.12 e.u. Similarly, the values for 1,1-dimethylcyclopentane and cis-1,2-dimethylcyclopentane are quite low. In general, all spherically or

TABLE II

HEAT AND ENTROPY OF FUSION OF SOME C$_7$ HYDROCARBONS

Hydrocarbon	Melting point °K.	Heat of fusion cal./mole	Entropy of fusion e.u.
n-Heptane	182.57	3358	18.39
2-Methylhexane	154.89	2120	13.69
3-Ethylpentane	154.57	2260	14.62
2,2-Dimethylpentane	149.37	1401	9.38
2,4-Dimethylpentane	153.93	1600	10.41
3,3-Dimethylpentane	138.70	1689	12.18
2,2,3-Trimethylbutane	248.20	526	2.12
Toluene	178.17	1582	8.88
Ethylcyclopentane	134.73	1640	12.17
1,1-Dimethylcyclopentane	203.43	258	1.27
cis-1,2-Dimethylcyclopentane	219.31	380	1.7
$trans$-1,2-Dimethylcyclopentane	155.59	1540	9.90
$trans$-1,3-Dimethylcyclopentane	139.48	1760	12.6
Methylcyclohexane	146.56	1613	11.01

nearly spherically symmetric molecules which have high melting points have very low entropies of fusion, 2 e.u. being a fairly average value.

6. ENANTIOTROPISM AND THE HIGH MELTING POINT OF SPHERICALLY SYMMETRIC MOLECULES

Not only do these highly symmetric molecules have low heats and entropies of fusion and high melting points but equally characteristically the solid phases are enantiotropic. While crystal transitions are observed in other types of hydrocarbons, for this particular class, the entropy of transformation is always greater than the entropy of melting. All these characteristic features of the spherical molecules must be borne in mind in order to account for the high melting points observed. In the melting process of normal crystals, as the temperature is increased the amplitude of the vibrations of the molecules in their lattice positions increases. As the thermal energy increases, the amplitude of the vibrations approaches a critical value beyond which rotation occurs. Since the crystal structure is not adapted to permit rotation of the molecules, the crystal disintegrates, or melts, when the thermal energy of the molecules reaches the rotational level. However, with highly symmetric molecules, the process is different. In 1930, Pauling (41) postulated that certain molecules with low moments of inertia would be able to rotate in the solid phase, that actual thermal effects would be observed at the transition from vibration to rotation and that, for polar molecules, the dielectric constant of the high-temperature (rotating) solid phase would be like that for a polar liquid. These predictions were later confirmed by measurements on the hydrogen halides. The investigations of White and Morgan (42) and Smyth et al. (43) have shown that similar rotational transitions can occur in the solid phase of organic molecules with large moments of inertia.

Support for the proposal that rotation can occur in solid hydrocarbons is obtained from a study of data on all five members of the methylchloromethane series (tetramethylmethane to tetrachloromethane), all of which have the same symmetry and size since the methyl group and the chlorine substituent are nearly equal in size; all five have more than one solid crystalline form. Since the two end members of the series do not have any dipole moment, dielectric constant measurements are only possible for the three intermediate members, t-butyl chloride, 2,2-dichloropropane, and methyl chloroform. Smyth et al. (43) found that for these three compounds there was no decrease in dielectric constant on freezing but that a large and abrupt decrease did occur on transformation from the high-temperature crystal form to the lower temperature one. Thus, these three compounds probably possess the same degree of rotational freedom of the individual molecules in the high-temperature solid form as in the liquid state, while, in the low-temperature stable crystal form, the molecules undergo only normal librations. Since the end members of this series are similar in all respects (low heat of fusion, high melting point, high symmetry, etc.) to these intermediate members, it is very likely that they too possess rotational transitions and that the molecules rotate in the high temperature crystalline state. Similar investigations on polar analogues of cyclohexane and cyclopentane indicate that these hydrocarbon molecules can also rotate in the crystal.

If spherically symmetric molecules can rotate in the solid phase, their melting behavior will differ from normal hydrocarbons and their higher melting points are more easily understandable. Thus, with the highly symmetric molecules, the interaction between neighbors in the lattice does not depend on their orientation so that even with the molecules rotating there is still sufficient molecular interaction to maintain the lattice. When the thermal energy of the molecules is sufficient to cause rotation, the crystal can rearrange to accommodate the rotation and need not disintegrate. Actual melting is postponed until the energy of the molecules reaches such a level as to result in movement of the molecules from the equilibrium lattice positions. The uniform low value of the entropy of fusion of these crystals in which molecular rotation occurs has been accounted for by Eyring (44) solely on the basis that in the liquid phase all the molecules can share the total free volume. The result of such sharing is to produce a "communal" entropy change which Eyring calculates to be equal to about 2 e.u., which is in accord with actual experimental values (Tables I and II).

7. LITERATURE SOURCES OF MELTING POINT AND ASSOCIATED DATA

The data on melting points and heats of fusion have been collected and evaluated by API Research Project 44 and the recent book of selected values (27) covers most of the hydrocarbons containing up to ten carbon atoms. For higher-molecular-weight compounds Egloff (45) reports literature values of the melting points and recommends "best values" whenever possible. For the transitions and heat effects of the C_1 to C_{10} hydrocarbons and for heats of fusions for higher hydrocarbons the data are scattered through the literature. Measurements by Parks, Huffman, Aston, Ubbelohde, and Garner cover most of the available heat data. For the long-chain molecules, transition temperatures have been determined by Müller, Piper, Ubbelohde, and Garner. It is not possible to tabulate here all the available data nor all the publications of these investigators. However, from the literature citations in this chapter, it will be easy to search out individual values which may be of interest.

II. PURITY OF HYDROCARBONS BY MELTING-POINT DETERMINATION

Because it is frequently impossible to analyze hydrocarbon mixtures by chemical methods, the measurement of physical properties is generally used as the means of establishing compositions of such mixtures. For highly purified hydrocarbons which have been prepared by a logical sequence of separation steps, the principal impurities will usually be isomers which have physical properties, i.e., refractive index, density, and boiling point, quite similar in numerical value to those for the major component. In such circumstances, it is necessary to establish the purity of highly purified hydrocarbons by means of a colligative property such as the melting point which is dependent, in ideal systems, only on the molal quantities present and not on the nature of the components. As a result of the character of colligative properties, the rather surprising fact is that, from the determination of the melting point, the purity of a sample can be determined in which not only the identity of the impurities but that of the major component as well is unknown. Therein lies a minor disadvantage of this method, for although the purity can be established, it does not yield any information as to the identity of the impurities. While it is true that the purity of isomeric mixtures of hydrocarbons can be determined by spectrometric methods, it is first necessary to have standard samples of all the components available for the calibration of the spectrometer before such analyses are possible. Further, for highly purified samples, where the impurity is of the order of a tenth of a mole per cent, the precision of spectrometric methods is not sufficient. In contrast, the determination of melting points permits the analysis of new materials for which there are no standards available and is also sufficiently sensitive (0.001 mole %) for use with high-purity materials.

The assumption made in the derivation of the melting-point-depression equation (equation 7) that the minor components are solid-insoluble is an important qualification which must be borne in mind when considering purities established by the melting-point method. It has been found that almost all hydrocarbons which have low heats of fusion tend to form solid solutions with other close-boiling hydrocarbons (46, 47, 48). For hydrocarbons which have normal heats of fusion, solid-solution formation is much less common, particularly among close-boiling low-molecular-weight ones. However, for the long-chain normal paraffins, for which the separation of the homologues is very difficult, solid solutions are formed with the near neighbors (35, 49, 50). Therefore, in using the freezing-point method with hydrocarbons which belong to either of the two types above, the possibility of the formation of solid solutions, which would vitiate the calculated purities, should be borne in mind. The influence of solid-solution formation may be more readily appreciated when it is realized that it is possible in such cases for the melting point to be higher than that for the pure material; calculations, obviously, lead to the ridiculous result of greater than 100% pure material.

1. TECHNIQUES FOR DETERMINATION OF SOLID-LIQUID EQUILIBRIUM TEMPERATURES

Since space does not permit a detailed survey of freezing-point techniques which have already been adequately covered by Skau (51) and since only the most precise methods are of interest here, the discussion will be limited to two techniques. There are, in general, two experimental approaches to the determination of the solid-liquid equilibrium temperature, (1) the dynamic, time-temperature method, and (2) the static, calorimetric method. Theoretically, both methods should yield the same purity results provided that certain conditions are fulfilled in each case.

2. DYNAMIC METHOD—TIME-TEMPERATURE CURVES

The method of Schwab and Wichers (52) which is one of the most precise of the time-temperature techniques has the serious disadvantage that in the course of the measurement the purity of the sample is destroyed. Other procedures of high precision are those of Smittenberg et al. (53) and Skau (54). However, since the technique developed by Rossini et al. (55) at the National Bureau of Standards has been subjected to considerable testing, it will be preferable to discuss it rather than the other methods.

In common with other time-temperature methods, this one of Rossini et al. (55) employés a constant heat-leak, controlled and adjusted in this case by means of an evacuable Dewar, to cool and freeze (or heat and melt) the sample. In addition, the use of a constant-speed stirring mechanism and of large thermal heads between the refrigerant and the sample ensures a constant cooling rate which is essential to the precision of the method. Specially designed basket or spiral-type stirrers are used for ensuring efficient contact between the liquid and the solid phases to promote the attainment of thermodynamic equilibrium. Precise temperature measurements ($\pm 0.001°$C.) are made with platinum resistance thermometers. For materials which have a tendency to supercool it is relatively simple to induce crystallization by appropriate seeding. After the crystallization has begun, the temperature of the sample is recorded at definite time intervals. During the cooling period, just before the crystallization begins, the time is recorded at fixed temperature intervals. While the freezing is going on, the stirring is continued until the crystallization has reached the point where the stirrer begins to labor. At that point, both the stirring and the temperature measurements are stopped. For those samples which do not approach equilibrium readily on freezing, the melting point is determined instead. The apparatus and technique for this method have been carefully described in numerous publications by Rossini to which the reader may refer for further details.

Figure 6 shows a typical set of data which were obtained by the use of this procedure. The lower of the two curves shows the entire time-temperature (resistance) relation for the sample. From this curve, the time at which the freezing begins is determined. Then, using the three points G, H and I on the upper curve, which is a portion of the lower replotted on a more sensitive temperature (resistance) scale, the freezing point of the sample is determined by the geometric construction as developed by Taylor and Rossini (56). This graphical construction is based on a detailed analysis of the dynamics of the crystallization process in this technique. Similarly, the freezing point for zero impurity can be determined from the freezing curve of samples which are at least 99 mole % pure. For a detailed discussion of these methods the reader should consult the paper of Taylor and Rossini (56).

To determine the purity it is necessary to know, in addition to the solid-liquid-equilibrium temperature, the heat of fusion or cryoscopic constant for the sample. Using the time-temperature technique, there are two methods by which the heat of fusion can be determined. The first and most accurate way is to add a known quantity of solid-insoluble impurity to the sample and measure the lowering of the freezing point, thus obtaining the cryoscopic constant directly. However, the obvious disadvantage of this method is that the valuable high-purity sample is lost. If a second sample is available of about 97% purity, the cryoscopic constant can be determined by adding impurity to it, thereby preserving the purest sample. In the absence of such a second sample, it is possible to estimate the heat of fusion and preserve the sample as well. The procedure is to determine the

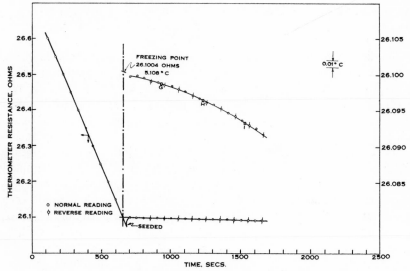

FIG. 6. Time-temperature freezing curve for benzene sample.

time-temperature curve for another hydrocarbon with a known heat of fusion which melts in the same temperature region as the unknown. Then, by comparison of the two time-temperature curves, it is possible to estimate with reasonable accuracy the cryoscopic constant for the unknown material.

The precision of the freezing-point determination by this time-temperature method is a function of the heat of fusion of the hydrocarbons studied. Thus, with samples which have normal heats of fusion, for which the change in cooling rate with the onset of crystallization is quite marked, the maximum precision of the method, of the order of several thousandths of a degree, can be attained. ASTM Standards D940-47T (57), which is based on this method, gives a repeatability of ±0.005°C. and a reproducibility (different operators and apparatus) of ±0.015°C. On the other hand, for hydrocarbons such as cyclopentane with very low heats of fusion, the precision of the freezing point is only of the order of hundredths of a degree.

One of the principal advantages of this time-temperature method is the speed with which a single determination can be made. Normally, a measurement can be completed in 2 hours, which may be further shortened by the use of helium in the evacuable Dewar during the precooling of the samples. Because of the speed of the method and the simplicity of the equipment, this technique is readily adaptable to use as a control method. In fact, it may be used most readily for routine measurements where only relative values are desired. When this method is to be used for absolute values, it is essential to check the lowering obtained by the addition of known quantities of likely impurities to be sure that solid solutions are not formed and/or that the mixtures behave ideally. Although time-consuming, this procedure is a necessary precaution to ensure the validity of the results.

The disadvantages of this technique are apparent from previous discussion. Thus it is necessary to know the freezing point of the pure material or to estimate it by the method of Taylor and Rossini (56) before the purity can be calculated. The accuracy of the method of Taylor and Rossini for the determination of the freezing point for zero impurity will be discussed in a later portion of this chapter. In addition to this solid-liquid-equilibrium temperature, it is also necessary to know the heat of fusion of the sample or it must be determined by a separate measurement. If only one sample is available, which would generally be the case for highly purified synthetic preparations of new materials where the quantity available is small, then, for accuracy in the determination of this heat effect the purity of the sample is destroyed. Indeed, with limited samples of newly prepared synthetic materials it may not always be possible to use the full 50 cc. which is required for the best results by this freezing-point method. Finally, there is no way to determine from the time-temperature curve itself whether or not the impurities form solid solutions with the major component or if the system behaves ideally. To avoid error in the purity determination, it is necessary to know that the likely impurities do not form solid solutions or else to determine the lowering obtained by the addition of known quantities of those compounds.

3. STATIC METHOD—ADIABATIC CALORIMETRY

The second general method for the determination of the melting point is a static, calorimetric technique. In marked contrast with the time-temperature procedure in which the rate of change of the temperature is measured, in the calorimetric procedure great care is taken to measure the temperature at equilibrium conditions. In precision third-law calorimeters (60), the determination of the melting point, or more properly the triple point, and the purity can be made with the maximum precision and accuracy of present day methods.

In addition to the precise determination of the "100% melted" temperature, the calorimetric technique has the advantage that the heat of fusion and the triple point for zero impurity can be determined in the same series of measurements. The determination of the heat of fusion in a calorimeter is the most accurate method of measuring that thermodynamic quantity. When a triple point is determined in a calorimeter, one is also able to measure the heat capacity of the solid below the melting point with very little additional effort. It is possible to calculate the purity of the sample from such solid heat-capacity measurements as well as by the classical melting-point-depression method. From these so-called "premelting" heat capacities, the purity can be determined with a sensitivity of the order of 0.0001 mole % (63), which is greater than that for the more conventional melting-point depression. This method of purity determination, which will be discussed in more detail in later portions of this chapter, serves the purpose of providing a check on the purity as calculated from the melting-point depression and offers a means of detecting the existence of solid solutions. Since measurements in calorimeters are always based on temperature differences, the purity determinations can be made independent of any highly accurate temperature scale. When the thermometric element of the calorimeter has been carefully standardized, the solid-liquid-equilibrium temperature will have accurate absolute value, but it is not essential to the purity determination. In time-temperature methods where the freezing point for zero impurity is usually obtained from data from another laboratory, any difference in temperature scale will, of course, introduce corresponding errors in the purity figures.

To achieve the precision necessary in the heat capacities for the determination of the third-law entropies, for which purpose the calorimeters under discussion were designed, this type of apparatus is rather complex and difficult to use. In fact, for the attainment of highest precision, more than one individual is required for proper operation. As a result of this complexity, even the measurement of a triple point would be very slow and time consuming. The cumbersomeness, slowness, and difficulties preclude determining purities in this type of precision third-law calorimeter except in unusual cases.

Recently, special calorimeters have been designed primarily to determine triple points and purities of hydrocarbons (58, 59). The design of these new calorimeters has been based on that of the precision instruments, but modifications have been introduced which will permit rapid operation by only one individual. Figure 7 is a schematic drawing of such a triple-point calorimeter. One major departure from the precision instruments is the large tube which connects the calorimeter with the vacuum system and through which the sample is introduced. In conventional design, these filling tubes are always as small as possible so as to reduce the heat leak to and from the calorimeter proper. While such narrow tubes necessitate slow distillations for filling and emptying, with large filling tubes it is possible to introduce the sample (some 15 cc.) into the calorimeter by simply

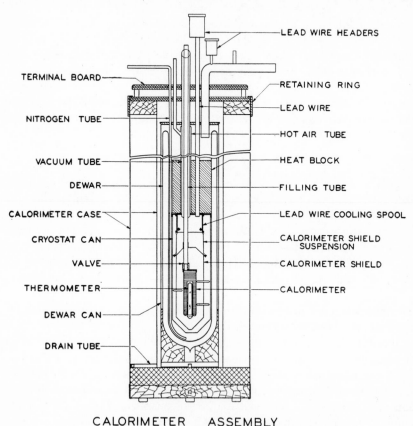

CALORIMETER ASSEMBLY

FIG. 7. Schematic drawing of calorimeter assembly.

pouring it down a funnel inserted into the filling tube. When the measurements are completed and the sample is to be withdrawn, it is a simple matter to slip another tube down inside the large filling tube and remove the sample by siphoning. To increase the strength and ruggedness of the assembly, the calorimeter and shields are spaced apart by means of the wooden pegs shown in Fig. 7. To reduce the heat exchange between the calorimeter and shields along these pegs, the contacts are machined to fine points. Using fewer control points and through the development of semi-automatic controls, the operation of these triple-point calorimeters is simple and straightforward. The use of continuous electronic controls (58) materially increases the precision which can be attained in these units as compared with the earlier manually-operated model (59).

In the determination of the triple point of a substance by means of the calorimetric technique, one of the most important points is to be certain that the sample has been completely crystallized before beginning the measurements. When this has been accomplished, the temperature of the sample is adjusted to the range at which measurements are to be started. In an adiabatic calorimeter, such as the triple-point calorimeters, the procedure is to maintain the temperature difference between the calorimeter (sample container) and its surrounding shields and the filling tube so small that there will be negligible interchange of heat. With the electronic controls set to maintain this temperature difference within the necessary range,

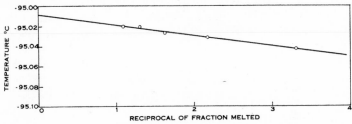

FIG. 8. Fusion curve for ethylbenzene sample.

the temperature of the calorimeter is followed as a function of time by means of the platinum resistance thermometer in the reentrant well. After the fore-drift has been established, a known amount of energy is added to the calorimeter through the electrical heater which is wrapped on the outside of the platinum resistance thermometer. After adding the heat to the calorimeter, the temperature is once again followed to establish the equilibrium after-drift. Such measurements and energy additions are continued into and through the fusion region until all the pertinent data have been obtained. The calculations of the heat capacities and heats of fusion from the data are simple and straightforward. Since space does not permit a discussion of these calculations the reader is referred to the excellent discussion of calorimetry by Sturtevant (60). Since the energy necessary to melt the sample is added in increments, a series of solid-liquid-equilibrium points is established with various fractions of the sample fused. It is then possible to plot these equilibrium temperatures as a function of the reciprocal of the fraction of the sample melted (61). This plot, as illustrated in Fig. 8, generally results in a straight line. Since it is usually impossible to determine experimentally the equilibrium temperature at exactly the "100% melted" point, the straight line plot as shown in Fig. 8 can readily be extrapolated to the 100% melted temperature (reciprocal of fraction melted = 1). Further, since the concentration of the impurity at the 50% melted temperature is twice that at the 100% temperature when the amount of impurity is small, the difference between these two values represents the lowering corresponding to the original amount of impurity present. Therefore by adding the difference between the 50 and 100% melted temperatures to the 100% melted temperature, one obtains directly the triple point for zero impurity. This computation is accomplished simply by extrapolating the straight line in Fig. 8 to zero. Since the interval between the reciprocal values 1 and 2 (100 and 50% melted) is the same as between 0 and 1 and since we are dealing with a straight line, the extrapolation to zero yields the desired temperature. There are no assumptions involved in this calculation of the triple point for zero impurity other than have already been made in the melting-point-depression relation.

The other important piece of information necessary for the calculation of the purity is the heat of fusion. It has already been mentioned that the fusion of the sample is accomplished by the introduction of several known increments of energy. Therefore, to determine the heat of fusion, it is necessary only to sum up these energy increments after suitable deductions have been made for the contribution of each energy addition to the sensible heat of the system. For greatest precision in the determination of the heat of fusion, the sample should be completely melted by one continuous energy addition. Such a procedure involves another and separate determination.

The advantages of this type of calorimeter for determining the purity of hydrocarbons are all those already mentioned for the precision adiabatic calorimeters, namely the determination of the 100% melted temperature, of the triple point for zero impurity, and of the heat of fusion all in one series of measurements; the calculation of the purity by both the melting-point-depression and "premelting" heat capacity methods, and the possibility of recognizing the formation of solid solutions in some cases. In addition, by the modifications incorporated in the triple-point calorimeters, the operation is speeded up so that a complete melting-point determination is possible in 6 to 8 hours, requiring the attention of only one individual. The precision of the determination of the 100% melted temperature is of the order of a few thousandths of a degree. In the electronically controlled units, the heat of fusion, based on the summation of energy increments, can be determined to better than 1% of its value, while heat capacities can be determined to about 0.5%. The greatest value in the use of this type of calorimeter for purity determinations is that a laboratory is rendered independent of any outside sources of information, since, through its use, purities can be determined for new synthetic samples about which the only available information is the molecular weight, providing that the sample is on the right side of the eutectic. The small sample required, about 10–15 cc., is of importance in the analysis of synthetic samples which are usually available in only limited quantities.

Of course, there are some disadvantages in the use of these triple-point calorimeters. For materials which tend to form glasses, and which are therefore difficult to crystallize, there is no simple method to seed the supercooled liquids. It might be possible to use the molecular distillation technique which Aston *et al.* (62) employed to induce crystallization in 1-butene, but this method is very time consuming and may not work for all materials. Because of the complexity of the equipment and because of the length of time required for a purity determination, the calorimetric technique is not readily adaptable to a routine control method. In its present form, the triple-point calorimeter is suitable for use only with substances which are liquid at or below room temperature. For use with normally solid materials, considerable modification of the present design would be necessary.

4. SOLID SOLUTIONS—DETECTION BY CALORIMETRY

The determination of purity of hydrocarbons by means of the melting-point-lowering equation is based on the assumption that the solution will behave ideally and that the impurities are solid-insoluble. If either of these two conditions is not met, then the results of calculations based on the melting-point-lowering equation are not valid. Fortunately, in highly purified hydrocarbon systems, the logical and likely impurities are generally so similar to the major component that ideal solutions are to be expected. Therefore, the greatest source of possible trouble in purity determinations arises from the formation of solid solutions. For that reason, the recognition of the existence of solid solutions between the major component and the impurities is very important. Since it is possible in some cases to recognize solid solutions from calorimetric heat-capacity data, this point will be discussed in some detail.

Figure 9 is a representation of the change in heat capacity of a hydrocarbon as a function of the temperature in the vicinity of the triple point. The full line represents the data for a 100% pure sample. The dashed curve is that for a sample which contains a solid-insoluble impurity forming a eutectic with the major component and which has a composition far-removed from the eutectic. It can be seen that the heat capacity of the impure sample begins to depart from that of the pure material at temperatures considerably below the melting point, increasing rapidly just below the triple point. This dashed line represents the so-called "premelting" heat capacity. If the difference between the heat capacity of the impure sample and the 100% pure sample is the result of melting induced by the impurity, it is then possible to calculate what the contribution to the heat capacity actually is for a given amount of impurity. Conversely, it is possible to calculate the amount of impurity which will produce a given increase in heat capacity as a result of "premelting." According to the method of Johnston and Giauque (63) the purity of a given sample can be calculated from the "premelting" heat capacity quite simply. At any temperature, T, below the triple-point temperature, T_0, the mole fraction. x_1, of the

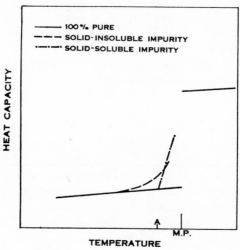

FIG. 9. Effect of impurity on solid heat capacity.

major component of the system in the liquid phase produced by "premelting" can be calculated from the relation:

$$\ln x_1 = -\frac{\Delta H_f}{R}\left(\frac{T_0 - T}{T_0 T}\right), \tag{10}$$

where ΔH_f is the heat of fusion. In heating the sample from temperature T' to T'', the excess heat added will be equal to $\Delta H_f (N'' - N')$ or the heat required to increase the moles of liquid from N' to N''. T' and T'' are two temperatures in the "premelting" region. The excess heat is the difference between the measured input and that calculated by extrapolating the normal heat-capacity curve through the "premelting" region. It is a straightforward calculation to obtain the number of moles of impurity from the mole fractions of the major component in the liquid at temperatures T' and T'' and the change in the number of moles in the liquid phase. Agreement between the purities calculated from the "premelting" heat capacity and from the melting-point-lowering calculations is ample and ufficient evidence of the ideality of the system and the reliability of the results.

It has been pointed out (64) that the shape of the heat capacity vs. temperature curve in the vicinity of the melting point will be quite different for samples with solid-insoluble impurities and with solid-soluble impurities (Fig. 9). For the solid-insoluble samples, eutectics will be formed between the impurities and the major component and normal "premelting" heat capacities will result. For a binary solid solution, melting does not begin until the solidus temperature is attained. Since there will be no melting below the solidus temperature (Point A in Figure 9), there is no "premelting" and, accordingly, purity calculations would show no impurity. Therefore, assuming ideal or sufficiently dilute solutions, when checking purities calculated by the two methods, low values of the impurity from the "premelting" calculations indicate the possibility of solid solution and hence caution is indicated in interpreting the values calculated from the melting-point depression.

Some investigators have questioned whether or not the "premelting" phenomenon is actually the result of melting produced by the impurities present. They suggest that these anomalous observations may instead be the result of a gradual order-disorder transition (33, 65). The evidence in favor of the order-disorder concept is somewhat obscured because the observations have been made on samples which contained undetermined amounts of impurity so that "premelting" as a result of the impurities is not precluded. Thus, in their study of the change in volume of n-tetradecane just below the melting point, Van Hook and Silver (66) observe a rapid increase in the "premelting" range. While the expansion may be the result of gradual transition from order to disorder, they point out that it is not possible to eliminate an explanation based simply on the impurities causing melting and thereby producing the rapid increase in volume. Similarly, the increase in the dielectric constant observed by White and Morgan (67) just below the melting point can also be explained by the presence of impurity. In fact, even the data of Ubbelohde in which he measured the "premelting" heat capacities of n-hexadecane calorimetrically are open to question on the same basis since he has not calculated the purity from the "premelting" and melting point depression data. Gradual order-disorder transitions may be responsible for some "premelting" phenomenon, particularly among the long-chain hydrocarbons, but it would seem that more data on samples of known purity are necessary to establish this hypothesis. The establishing of hybrid structure in crystals of KH_2PO_4 and KH_2AsO_4 by x-ray diffraction studies (68) offers strong evidence in favor of the order-disorder theory and indicates a possible method of resolving this problem in the case of the long-chain hydrocarbons.

5. COMPARISON OF TIME-TEMPERATURE AND ADIABATIC CALORIMETRIC RESULTS

Since Rossini *et al.* at the Bureau of Standards and Huffman *et al.* at th Petroleum Experiment Station of the Bureau of Mines have reported th results of measurements on identical samples of highly purified hydro carbons (API-NBS samples), it is possible to compare the purity results c the time-temperature and the calorimetric techniques. Table III is compilation of data on a variety of hydrocarbons taken from various publi cations of Huffman and Rossini. For comparison, the measured freezin, points and the 100% melted temperatures, the differences between th measured freezing point and the freezing point for zero impurity an between the 100% melted temperature and the triple point, and the im purities calculated by both laboratories have been tabulated. In almos every case, the difference between the two equilibrium temperatures i greatest for the time-temperature method. In the analysis of the disagree ment between these two procedures, it is of prime significance that th difference determined by the calorimetric method is an experimentally determined quantity. It would seem, therefore, that in the method o Taylor and Rossini there is some unevaluated factor which introduces ar error resulting in high values for the freezing point for zero impurity. If it i assumed that the actual freezing point determined from the time-temper ature curve represents the true thermodynamic equilibrium temperature, a much better estimate of the freezing point for the pure material would be to add the difference between the 100% melted temperature and the triple point obtained from the calorimetric methods to the measured time-temper ature freezing point. Obviously since the melting-point depression is greater for the time-temperature measurements, the calculated amount of im purity is also greater for this technique.

In practice, the choice between the static and the dynamic methods of purity determination will be dictated by the use to which the results will be put. If absolute values are unnecessary, as in control analyses, then the time-temperature method is probably to be preferred because of its greater speed. If purities of highly purified, new products are to be established, the calorimetric technique will be more suitable for maximum precision and accuracy.

III. PURIFICATION BY CRYSTALLIZATION

It is well known that purification processes based on equilibria between liquid and crystalline phases are capable of yielding extremely pure products. In general the chemical literature accepts, in itself, a statement that a product has been purified by crystallization as an index of high purity. Reliance on the purity of such a product is warranted since sepa-

TABLE III

Comparison of Time-Temperature and Calorimetric Results

Compound	Measured freezing point T_f, °K [a]	Melting point depression $T_{f_0}-T_f$	Heat of fusion cal./mole	Impurity, mole %	100% Melted temperature T_{100}, °K. [e]	Melting point depression T_0-T_{100}	Heat of fusion cal./mole	Impurity, mole %
n-Hexane	177.818	0.022	3114 [b]	0.11 ± 0.05 [c]	177.8349	0.0015	3126.1	0.0075 [f]
2-Methylpentane	119.475	0.005	1500 [b]	0.03 ± 0.02 [c]	119.546	0.006	1497.6	0.029 [f]
2,2-Dimethylbutane	173.19	0.24	138.5 [b]	0.05 ± 0.03 [c]	174.212	0.067	138.4	0.015 [f]
2,3-Dimethylbutane	144.59	0.16	194 [b]	0.07 ± 0.03 [c]	145.154	0.032	191.4	0.015 [f]
Cyclopentane	179.26	0.10	145.0 [b]	0.023 ± 0.01 [c]	179.692	0.021	145.54	0.005 ± 0.002 [g]
Methylcyclopentane	130.686	0.029	1656 [b]	0.16 ± 0.06 [c]	130.707	0.019	1656.0	0.093 ± 0.003 [g]
Methylcyclohexane	146.564	—	1613 [b]	0.10 ± 0.08 [c]	146.573	0.003	1613.4	0.011 ± 0.002 [g]
Cis-2-pentene	121.757	0.033	1826	0.20 ± 0.15 [d]	121.785	0.012	1699.7	0.071 ± 0.005 [h]
Trans-2-pentene	132.912	0.013	1861	0.07 ± 0.05 [d]	132.947	0.004	1996	0.022 ± 0.005 [h]
2-Methyl-1-butene	135.578	0.022	1887	0.11 ± 0.08 [d]	135.506	0.112	1890.6	0.58 ± 0.05 [h]
3-Methyl-1-butene	104.622	0.038	1260	0.22 ± 0.12 [d]	104.7074	0.0096	1280.6	0.056 ± 0.005 [h]
2-Methyl-2-butene	139.368	0.012	1783	0.055 ± 0.046 [d]	139.397	0.024	1815.8	0.11 ± 0.05 [h]

[a] Ice point 273.160°K. Measurements made in air at 1 atmos. pressure.
[b] Obtained from Z Tables "Selected Values of Properties of Hydrocarbons." Natl. Bur. Standards U.S. Civ. C461 Nov. 1947.
[c] Glasgow, Murphy, Willingham, and Rossini, J. Research Natl. Bur. Standards 37, 141 (1946).
[d] Streiff, Murphy, Sedlak and Rossini, J. Research Natl. Bur. Standards 37, 331 (1946).
[e] Measurements made at saturation pressure.
[f] Douslin and Huffman, J. Am. Chem. Soc. 68, 1704 (1946).
[g] Douslin and Huffman, J. Am. Chem. Soc. 68, 175 (1946).
[h] Todd, Oliver and Huffman, J. Am. Chem. Soc. 69, 1519 (1947).

ration processes based on solid-liquid equilibria are the only ones which ca
offer promise, at least theoretically, of a 100% pure product in a one-ste
operation. While the transition from theory to practice is a big one and whi
often the results fall short of the theoretical, the potentialities of thes
purification methods are so great that consideration should always be give
to them whenever the highest purity products are desired.

1. PHASE RULE

In any separation process involving more than one phase, it is of obviou
importance to be able to predict the behavior of the phases in the syster
under all possible conditions. The phase rule, which was first developed b
Willard Gibbs, is the means of predicting such relations. If the degrees c
freedom (the number of independent variables) of the system is F, th
number of phases present is P, and the number of components in th
system is C, then according to the phase rule $F = C + 2 - P$. The deriva
tion of this equation from fundamental thermodynamic relations is give
in almost any of the texts on thermodynamics to which the reader ma
refer if interested in the details of the development. Thus, for a two-com
ponent system, when three phases (vapor, liquid, and solid) are present
there is one degree of freedom remaining. To completely define the state o
the system, it is necessary to fix either its temperature, pressure, or the con
centration of one component of one phase (the composition of a phas
which is a pure substance is obviously not a variable). However, when ther
are four phases (vapor, liquid, and two solid phases) present, then there ar
no degrees of freedom remaining and the temperature, pressure, and th
composition of the phases are fixed. In other words in a two componen
system the presence of four phases completely defines the system. For
three-component system, five phases are required before all the degrees o
freedom are removed. If only four phases are present, either the temper
ature, the pressure or the concentration of one component of one phase ha
to be fixed before the state of the system is completely defined. When onl
three phases are present, it is necessary to fix two phase-rule variables.

When a single solid phase separates from a two-component liquid phase
that solid must be either a pure crystal or a solid solution. Unfortunately
the phase rule does not predict which of the two possibilities will be realized
so that it is necessary to have actual experimental determinations to know
the distribution of the components among the various phases. The solid-
liquid-phase behavior of binary systems can be divided into two majo
groups, the eutectic systems in which pure crystals separate and the solid-
solution systems in which solid solutions are formed between the components.

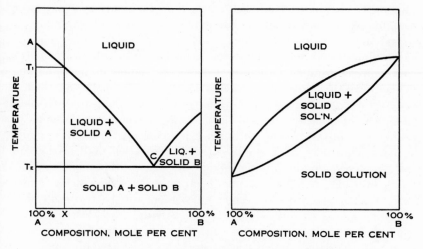

FIG. 10   FIG. 11

FIG. 10. Solid-insoluble eutectic phase diagram.
FIG. 11. Continuous solid-solution phase diagram.

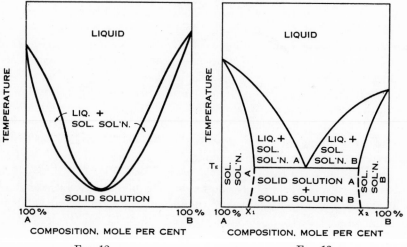

FIG. 12   FIG. 13

FIG. 12. Minimum liquidus solid-solution phase diagram.
FIG. 13. Solid-soluble eutectic phase diagram.

2. LIQUID-SOLID-PHASE DIAGRAMS

It is conventional and convenient to present binary and ternary phase-equilibrium data in the form of diagrams. For binary systems these diagrams are simple to construct and understand. Some idealized diagrams for binary solid-liquid equilibria are presented in Figs. 10 to 13.

Figure 10 is an illustration of the behavior of a binary system in which the liquid phase shows complete miscibility while the solid phases are completely immiscible. To appreciate the behavior of this type of system, consider a liquid mixture of composition x, in Fig. 10, which is originally at some temperature higher than T_1. Cooling this liquid produces no phase changes until the temperature reaches T_1, the liquidus point, at which the first crystal of pure component A will separate. Since there are three phases present at this temperature and since it is a two-component system, it is possible to cool the system still further and continue to separate pure A. As more component A crystallizes, the concentration of B in the liquid increases; the composition of the liquid will change with temperature along the liquidus line AC. When the temperature reaches the eutectic temperature, T_E, the phase diagram shows that there will be two solid phases separating out as an intimate mechanical mixture (the eutectic). At this point, the phase rule shows that with four phases present there are no independent variables so that neither the temperature, the pressure nor the composition can be changed until one or more of the phases disappears. Finally, the diagram shows that cooling the mixture to lower temperatures will produce no further phase changes.

When the two components are miscible in the solid state, the number of possible solid-liquid-phase diagrams which can be obtained increases considerably. For those combinations in which the two components are solid-soluble over the entire range of compositions, there are three principal types of diagrams which could be found. The simplest of these is illustrated in Fig. 11. In this system, the liquidus temperatures for all mixtures are between the values for the two pure components. On cooling any liquid solution of this type of system, crystals will appear when the temperature reaches the liquidus curve (the upper curve, Fig. 11). The solid phase which separates will have a composition indicated by a horizontal line drawn from the liquidus curve to the solidus (the lower curve, Fig. 11). It should be noted that, with this type of phase behavior, the solid phase which separates from a liquid mixture is not a pure component and is richer in the higher melting component than the liquid phase. Figure 12 illustrates a second possibility in systems with complete solid-phase miscibility. In this case there is a mixture which has a liquidus temperature which is lower than the melting points of either pure constituent and represents a minimum for the system. At that minimum point, the composition of the solid and liquid phases which are in equilibrium are the same. For this type of system, once again, the solid phases which separate from liquid solutions are solutions and not pure components. However, in this case, crystals which separate from liquids with a concentration of A greater than that of the minimum will be richer in A than the liquids. Similarly, liquids whose compositions contain more B than the minimum will yield crystals enriched in B. The third possibility for total solid-phase miscibility is one in which there is a liquid mixture with a liquidus temperature which is a maximum for the binary system. Since this type of phase behavior is uncommon, it will not be given further attention.

In addition to the systems in which there is complete solid-phase miscibility, there are those in which there is only limited solubility. Thus, if both components are soluble to only a limited extent in the crystalline phase of the other, then the phase behavior is a combination of the simple eutectic and the continuous solid solution. Thus, Fig. 13 is an illustration of this type of behavior; the solid phases which separate are always mixed crystals.

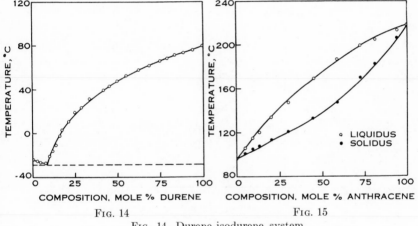

COMPOSITION, MOLE % DURENE COMPOSITION, MOLE % ANTHRACENE

FIG. 14   FIG. 15

FIG. 14. Durene-isodurene system.
FIG. 15. Anthracene-phenanthrene system.

However, when the composition of the liquid phase lies between x_1 and x_2, cooling the system to temperature T_E results in the formation of a eutectic, but in this case the two solid phases are solid solutions of composition x_1 and x_2, respectively. Similarly, if only one component is partially miscible with the solid phase of the other, the resulting diagram is a combination of that shown in Fig. 13 on one side of the eutectic, while, on the other, the behavior is the usual immiscible type shown in Fig. 10.

For binary hydrocarbon systems, the most frequently observed solid-liquid-phase behavior is the solid-insoluble eutectic-type diagram, particularly among the lower-molecular-weight compounds (53, 69, 71). Typical of this group is the durene-isodurene system (70) shown in Fig. 14. For this system, the liquidus points were determined from freezing-point measurements. The eutectic composition is 9% durene, 91% isodurene, and melts at approximately −28°C. Figure 15, the phase diagram for the anthracene-phenanthrene system (72) is typical for the continuous solid-solution systems. Some of the hydrocarbon mixtures which are found to exhibit this behavior are 2,2,3,3-tetramethylbutane-2,2,3-trimethylbutane (53), *n*-hexadecane-*n*-1-hexadecene (73), and some combinations of the long-chain paraffins (35). For further systems, the reader should consult the literature (71). Phase behavior similar to that of the *n*-hexadecane-*n*-heptadecane system (50), Fig. 16, has been observed with some of the long-chain paraffins (33, 49, 50). It would appear that this behavior shows the minimum in a continuous series of solid solutions, but these diagrams for long-chain molecules are complicated by solid-phase transitions which were previously discussed. The minima may therefore be the result of two different crystal forms and hence not be truly representative of the phase behavior illus-

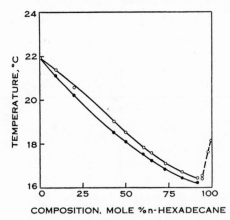

COMPOSITION, MOLE % n-HEXADECANE

FIG. 16. *n*-Hexadecane-*n*-heptadecane system.

trated in Fig. 12. It is of interest to note that two binary hydrocarbon systems, 2,2-dimethylbutane-2,3-dimethylbutane and 2,3-dimethylbutane-cyclopentane, have been found (74) to form complexes in the solid phase. In these systems solid solutions are formed between the complexes and each of the individual components which further increases the complexity of the phase diagrams.

The behavior of ternary, quaternary, and other multicomponent systems is also predicted by the phase rule. However, the problem of the distribution of the components among the various phases becomes more complex by virtue of the number of constituents and the increased number of combinations of phase behavior. For the general characteristics of multicomponent systems, the reader should consult some of the texts which deal exclusively with the phase rule and phase behavior. For those systems in which there is no solid-solution formation, even though the liquid phase is made up of several constituents, it is still possible to adjust the conditions of the system so that the liquid is in equilibrium with only one pure solid phase, just as in the case of the binary eutectic system. It is therefore possible to effect purifications from multicomponent as well as binary mixtures.

3. PURIFICATION BY FREEZING: SOLID-INSOLUBLE COMPONENTS

Now, in the light of what has been discussed above, we will consider the purifications which can be achieved through a process involving solid-liquid equilibria. First, let us restrict our attention to a simple binary eutectic system in which there is no solid-phase miscibility. It has already been mentioned that, when a binary liquid is cooled to the freezing point, the solid which separates out is either a pure substance or a solid solution. Since we have, for the present, restricted our attention to those systems in which the separated solid is a pure substance, the purification which is achieved is immediately obvious. In carrying out a purification in such a system it is also equally obvious that it would be very undesirable to lower the temperature to that of the eutectic, for two solid phases would then separate and the purity of the product would be reduced. Although it would appear to be simple to prepare 100% pure material by such a method, there are certain practical difficulties which must be overcome in order to realize this extreme purity. During the crystallization process it is essential that the crystals are formed as nearly perfectly as possible and are produced slowly enough to prevent interlocking and intergrowth with the accompanying occlusion of the liquid. Clearly, any such liquid entrapped with or in the crystals will proportionately reduce the purity of the final product. After the crystals have been formed and the crystallization stopped, it is then necessary to separate the solid and liquid phases. It is important that this separation be as complete as possible since any mother liquor which remains associated with the solid is a source of impurity and hence very undesirable. It is equally important in obtaining maximum yield of pure product to approach the eutectic temperature as closely as possible and yet avoid any localized supercooling which will solidify eutectic. Because of the large thermal heads necessary in carrying out these crystallizations, the final temperature of the system is always considerably above the theoretical minimum in order to avoid such localized freezing of the eutectic liquid. Thus, the yield of the pure product is reduced. Of course the theoretical yield of pure product from any given mixture is dictated by the difference in composition between it and the eutectic. Only enough pure component may be removed from the liquid which will leave the composition just at the eutectic. Any attempt to carry beyond that point will result in the separation of the second solid phase. In some cases it is possible to effect a separation of two components beyond the eutectic composition through the use of a third component. The ratio of the original two components at the point of separation of two solid phases may be shifted from the binary eutectic value by the addition of the third component (75, 76). Although numerous patents have been issued covering purification processes involving solid-liquid equilibria, because of the difficulties, the use of crystallization from melts as a commercial separation process has been rather restricted, particularly in the case of normally liquid hydrocarbons. However, very pure benzene has been prepared commercially by a process involving crystallization at sub-atmospheric temperatures. On a small scale, the great success which can be achieved by the freezing technique is exemplified by the 99.998 mole % pure benzoic acid prepared by Schwab and Wichers (77).

4. PURIFICATION BY FREEZING: SOLID-SOLUBLE COMPONENTS

While it has been shown that, at least theoretically, it is possible to prepare a 100% pure material in one crystallization from the liquid phase, when the solid phase is a mixed crystal rather than a pure one, such separations cannot be achieved in one step. With solid solutions, the purification must be carried out by a stepwise procedure very much as the rectification of a binary liquid. If, for example, one component of a binary mixture, whose solid-liquid-phase diagram is that shown in Fig. 17 is to be recovered by a crystallization process, a series of crystallizations and meltings will be necessary. When the original mixture has the composition indicated by x_1 in Fig. 17, then on cooling the liquid to temperature T_1, being careful to ensure that equilibrium is established between the phases, the liquid phase will have the composition x_2 and the solid the composition y_1. If the solid and liquid phases are then separated, and the liquid phase is cooled still further to temperature T_2, the composition of the liquid will be x_3 and that of the solid y_2. Clearly, the purity of the liquid phase has been increased by this fractional crystallization process, but it is equally clear that only an infinitesimal amount of pure A will be recovered. However, if we not only freeze the liquid, but melt the solid as well, then by a series of solidifications and fusions we will be able, eventually, to completely separate the two pure components. Thus, if the solid from the first crystallization is heated from temperature T_1 to T_3, the solid phase, y_3, will have been enriched in component B, while a liquid of composition x_4 will have been formed. If the crystallization were to be carried out as a countercurrent operation, the separation would be effected much like that for the distillation of a binary liquid in a column. When, instead of the phase diagram being the simple continuous series shown in Fig. 17, we have to deal with either a minimum melting point, or even with the formation of complexes in the solid phase (74), it will be impossible to separate both components as pure materials.

In fact, when complexes are formed between the two pure components, it may be impossible to separate even one of the constituents as a pure substance. It will be seen from the above statements that the limitations on the separations in these solid-solution systems are in many respects analogous to those in liquid systems in which azeotropes are formed.

The difficulties of carrying out the crystallization procedure are the same for both solid solutions and simple eutectic systems. Since, as yet, a method has not been developed for carrying out the crystallization of a solid solution in a continuous countercurrent apparatus, separation of a constituent of a

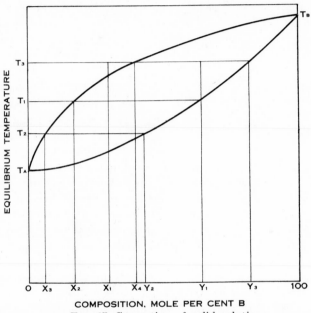

COMPOSITION, MOLE PER CENT B

FIG. 17. Separation of solid solution.

solid solution must be accomplished by a series of batch operations. Each additional step serves to increase the difficulty of the separation. Therefore, the use of this technique to recover a pure hydrocarbon should be used only as a last resort after all other simpler and more conventional methods have failed to produce the desired purity of product.

5. PURIFICATION BY FREEZING: USE OF SOLVENTS

In actual practice, it is much more common to carry out a crystallization from some inert solvent rather than directly from a melt. Even so, the preceding discussion applies equally well to techniques employing solvents. The introduction of the word solvent does not change the physicochemical principles which determine the phase equilibria; the phase rule remains un-changed even though one constituent of the system is called solvent. There will be no difficulty in understanding procedures which make use of solvents if it is borne in mind that the solvent behaves as any other single component and that exactly the same relations apply to these systems as to any other. The same precautions and restrictions apply to purification by crystalliza-tion from solvents as from melts. There is, however, the added difficulty that the desired constituent will generally be a minor component and there-fore any occluded liquor will affect the purity more in this case than where the desired product is a major component of the mother liquor, i.e., a melt.

On the other hand, definite advantages may be attained through the use of an inert solvent. Quite frequently the material to be purified may de-compose at or below its melting point, so that it is obviously impossible to use a technique based on partial freezing of the molten sample. In such cases, crystallization from an inert solvent would be the only procedure. Even though stable at the melting point, a melt may be so viscous as to interfere with the formation of crystals. The dilution achieved by the use of a solvent reduces the viscosity, thereby assisting the production and growth of crystals. In addition to impeding crystallization, a viscous melt will make the separation of the liquid and solid phases much more difficult; here again the increased fluidity obtained through the use of the inert solvent materially assists in the purification process. An ingenious low-temperature adaption of the use of solvents was developed by Leslie (78) for the crystallization of hydrocarbon mixtures which could not otherwise be crystallized. The mixture was dissolved in either propane or ethane, at the boiling point, and then cooled down to the boiling point of methane. Then, by adding the propane (or ethane) solution to liquid methane, a crystalline product was obtained from the constituents of the original hydrocarbon mixture. The liquid and crystals were then separated by a low-temperature centrifuge.

In the work of Schwab and Wichers (77) on the purification of benzoic acid it is possible to obtain a good comparison of the efficiency of purifica-tion from a melt and from solution in an inert solvent. By slowly freezing a benzoic acid melt at a constant rate, they were able to obtain, as the final product of a two-step operation, material that was 99.998 mole % pure. They estimate that the average efficiency for a single step was 85%. On the other hand, when the crystallizations were carried out from either a water or a benzene solution, the efficiencies were much lower, 14 and 29%, respec-tively. Thus, to achieve the same purity by the solvent route as had been attained from the melt, it would require 25 recrystallizations from water or 11 from benzene. On this basis then, wherever possible, greatest efficiency will be obtained by the elimination of the use of solvents.

6. PURIFICATION BY MELTING: SOLID-INSOLUBLE COMPONENTS

Although the previous discussion has been limited to purifications based on the formation of crystals from the liquid phase, either by freezing a melt or by precipitation from a solvent, it is equally possible to achieve the desired purification by approaching the solid-liquid equilibria from the opposite direction, that is, the melting of a completely solid sample. When such a solid sample is heated into the fusion region, and when the solid phases are immiscible, the first liquid is formed from the eutectic. If the melting is stopped after all the eutectic has been fused, and then, if the solid and liquid are completely separated, the solid product would then be a pure material.

Some use of this procedure at low temperatures has been made by Hicks (79) and Hicks-Bruun and Bruun (80), in the separation of hydrocarbon mixtures. In the former work, the sample was entirely solidified and then fractionally melted in a vacuum-jacketed funnel so that the liquid could be drawn off after each melting. Hicks-Bruun and Bruun combined fractional crystallization and fractional melting. They partially froze a mixture, transferred the solid to a centrifuge, and then fractionally melted. With this procedure, they were able to prepare a sample of n-heptane which had a melting point of $-90.66°C.$, recovering only 50 cc. of the original 225 cc. of n-heptane (melting point $-90.96°C.$) charged.

Recently, a new technique based on fractional melting has been developed by J. G. Aston and his coworkers (81). This new method, which has been remarkably effective in purifying mixtures which had resisted purification by fractional crystallization, is based on the procedure used in low-temperature adiabatic calorimetry in determining triple points. One of the apparatus used is shown in Fig. 18. The sample which has been suitably prepared is introduced into the sample container (calorimeter) through the tubes provided. It is then carefully crystallized and slowly heated into the fusion region. By means of the heater in the reentrant well, the calculated amount of energy is added to the sample to melt that fraction which will contain all the impurity (assumed to be solid-insoluble). The heat input to the adiabatic shield is maintained at the level necessary to prevent any heat interchange between the sample container and its surroundings. Then, when the calorimeter has reached thermal and presumably state equilibrium, the liquid is withdrawn from the system through the siphon provided. The energy additions are continued until the sample remaining has reached the desired purity. The close temperature control which is possible in these units makes for high efficiency and high recovery of purified product. Units as small as 100 cc. and as large as 500 cc. capacity have been used. The principal difference between various units is the means of attaining equilibrium. Some have been provided with screw-type stirrers. Others have replaced the radial vanes with copper screens or horizontal vanes. In the apparatus utilizing horizontal vanes, the addition of springs between the vanes permits their compression which aids in the separation of the phases after equilibrium has been attained. The high purity which is achieved by this

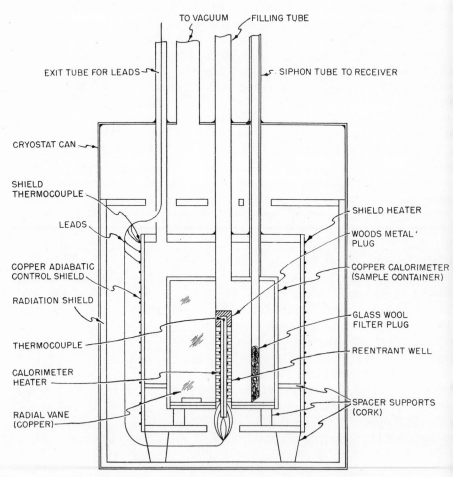

FIG. 18. Schematic diagram of a fractional melting apparatus.

fractional melting process can be illustrated by the results of the separation of cis- and trans-2-butene. To appreciate the power of this separation method, it must be realized that the calculated composition of the eutectic between these two hydrocarbons is 85 mole % cis-2-butene with the corresponding eutectic temperature of 131°K. This temperature is only 3° below the melting point for pure cis-2-butene. In spite of these serious limitations, starting with a mixture containing 96 mole % cis-2-butene, a 50% yield of 99.99 mole % pure cis-2-butene was obtained. This yield is 70% of the theoretical maximum. Numerous previous attempts to purify this 96% pure sample by fractional crystallization had failed. Similarly, a 99.99% pure n-heptane sample was prepared by this new technique with a 60% yield.

7. PURIFICATION BY MELTING: SOLID-SOLUBLE COMPONENTS

There has been commercial use of fractional or partial fusion ("sweating") for the purification of commercial waxes. However, since the long-chain paraffins are known to form solid solutions with each other, this "sweating" process cannot achieve the same degree of purification possible in the eutectic systems. It is probable that the major function of the "sweating" of waxes is to provide a means of washing out the undesirable oils (82).

It was pointed out previously in the discussion of the purification of solid solutions, that fractional crystallization is not a very efficient process and should be utilized only as a last resort. If it is necessary to use solid-liquid-phase equilibria as the means to achieve the separation of a mixture which forms solid solutions, it is possible to increase the efficiency of the technique by resorting to fusion rather than crystallization. The similarity between the solid-liquid equilibrium in mixed crystal systems and vapor-liquid equilibria for miscible liquids has been pointed out. If a solid solution is to be enriched in one component by a batch nonrefluxing operation, then by analogy with the liquid-vapor system, the most efficient and effective method of achieving the enrichment is by a differential fusion process. Therefore, to purify a solid solution by a batch process in the absence of reflux, the closest approach to a continuous removal of liquid will be the best way to carry out the separation (83).

The difficulties of crystallization processes have impeded their use on a large scale, particularly for separations which require refrigeration. To the difficulties of separating the solid and liquid phases and of preventing the freezing of the eutectic, low-temperature processes such as would be necessary for low-molecular-weight hydrocarbons have the added problem of the recovery of the refrigeration from the products. However, as the demand for high-purity hydrocarbons increases and as the purity level is raised, the inherent efficiency of solid-liquid equilibria will be sufficiently attractive that someone will surmount the difficulties of commercial operation.

There are, of course, some systems that cannot be readily handled by the crystal route. Thus, hydrocarbons which have a pronounced tendency to form glasses would be very difficult to handle. If, by marked supercooling, crystallization can then be effected, such a hydrocarbon could be handled by the fractional melting procedure. However, only after a mixture has been raised to reasonable purity levels by other methods should solid-liquid equilibria be used. If the mixture is too impure, the number of components may impede the formation of crystals. Then, too, if the purity level is on the wrong side of the eutectic, obviously the wrong crystals will separate on freezing.

In general, the highest purities can be achieved by the use of separation methods based on solid-liquid equilibria for mixtures which do not form mixed crystals. However, the difficulties, particularly at low temperatures, have restricted the use of these techniques to all but the most exacting cases. The development of the new technique by Aston *et al.* will, because of its simplicity and efficiency, undoubtedly increase the use of fractional melting and make the preparation of very-high-purity samples possible for all laboratories.

REFERENCES

1. Rozental, D. *Bull. soc. chim. Belg.*, **45**, 585 (1936).
2. Corbin, N., Alexander, M. and Egloff, G. *J. Phys. Colloid Chem.*, **52**, 387 (1948).
3. Schmidt, A. W. *Ber.*, **75B**, 1399 (1942).
4. Francis, A. W. *Chem. Revs.*, **42**, 107 (1948).
5. Garner, W. E. and King, A. M. *J. Chem. Soc.*, **1929**, 1849.
6. Timmermans, J. *Inst. intern. chim. Solvay, Conseil Chim.*, 4th Conseil, Brussels **1931**, 191.
7. Garner, W. E., VanBibber, K., and King, A. M. *J. Chem. Soc.*, **1931**, 1533.
8. Powell, R. E., Clark, C. R., and Eyring, H. *J. Chem. Phys.*, **9**, 268 (1941).
9. Oldham, J. W. H. and Ubbelohde, A. R. *Trans. Faraday Soc.*, **35**, 328 (1939).
10. Tsakalotos, D. E. *Compt. rend.*, **143**, 1235 (1906).
11. Merckel, J. H. C. and Holleman, A. F. *Proc. Acad. Sci. Amsterdam*, **40**, 164 (1937).
12. Moullin, E. B. *Proc. Cambridge Phil. Soc.*, **34**, 459 (1938).
13. Levene, P. A., West, C. J., and van der Scheer, J. *J. Biol. Chem.*, **20**, 521 (1915).
14. Hildebrand, J. H. and Wachter, A. *J. Am. Chem. Soc.*, **51**, 2487 (1929).
15. Etessam, A. H. and Sawyer, M. F. *J. Inst. Petroleum*, **25**, 253 (1939).
16. Baeyer, A. *Ber.*, **10**, 1286 (1877).
17. Verkade, P. E., Coops, J., and Hartman, H. *Rec. trav. chim.*, **45**, 373, 503 (1926).
18. Hinrich, G. D. *Compt. rend.*, **112**, 998, 1127, **113**, 313 (1891).
19. Biach, O. *Z. physik. Chem.*, **50**, 43 (1905).
20. Cuy, E. J. *Z. anorg. allgem. Chem.*, **115**, 273 (1921).
21. Pauly, H. *Z. anorg. allgem. Chem.*, **119**, 271 (1922).
22. Nikrassov, B. *Z. physik. Chem.*, **128**, 208 (1927).
23. Müller, A. *Proc. Roy. Soc. London*, **A124**, 318 (1929).
24. Malkin, T. *J. Chem. Soc.*, **1931**, 2796.
25. Müller, A. *Proc. Roy. Soc. London*, **A127**, 417 (1932).
26. Gorin, E., Walter, J., and Eyring, H. *J. Am. Chem. Soc.*, **61**, 1876 (1939).
27. Selected Values of Physical Properties of Hydrocarbons, API Research Project 44 Circular of National Bureau Standards C461, November, 1947.
28. Schiessler, R. W., Herr, C. H., Rytina, A. W., Weisel, C. A., Fischl, F., McLaughlin, R. L., and Kuehner, H. H. Presented at 12th Mid-Year Meeting API St. Louis, June 2, 1947.
29. Ruzicka, L., Hürbin, M., and Furter, M. *Helv. Chim. Acta*, **17**, 78 (1934); Ruzicka, L., Plattner, Pl. A., and Wild, A. *Helv. Chim. Acta*, **29**, 1611 (1946).

30. Clar, E. and Guzzi, A. *Ber.*, **65B**, 1521 (1932).
31. Aston, J. G. and Messerly, G. H. *J. Am. Chem. Soc.*, **62**, 1917 (1940).
32. Parks, G. S., Huffman, H. M. and Todd, S. S. *J. Am. Chem. Soc.*, **52**, 2881 (1930).
33. Ubbelohde, A. R. *Trans. Faraday Soc.*, **34**, 282 (1938).
34. Müller, A. *Proc. Roy. Soc. London*, **A136**, 515 (1932).
35. Piper, S. H., Chibnall, A. C., Hopkins, S. J., Pollard, A., Smith. J. A. B., and William, E. F. *Biochem. J.*, **25**, 2072 (1931).
36. Müller, A. *Proc. Roy. Soc. London*, **A138**, 515 (1932).
37. Seyer, W. F., Patterson, R. F., and Keays, J. L. *J. Am. Chem. Soc.*, **66**, 179 (1944).
38. Turkevich, A. and Smyth, C. P. *J. Am. Chem. Soc.*, **62**, 2468 (1940).
39. King, A. M. and Garner, W. E. *J. Chem. Soc.*, **1936**, 1368.
40. Parks, G. S. and Huffman, H. M. *Ind. Eng. Chem.*, **23**, 1138 (1931).
41. Pauling, L. *Phys. Rev.*, **36**, 430 (1930).
42. White, A. H. and Morgan, S. D. *J. Chem. Phys.*, **5**, 655 (1937).
43. Smyth, C. P. and Baker, W. O. *J. Am. Chem. Soc.*, **61**, 1695 (1939); Smyth, C. P. and Lewis, G. L. *J. Am. Chem. Soc.*, **62**, 949 (1940).
44. Hirshfelder, J. D., Stevenson, D., and Eyring, H. *J. Chem. Phys.* **5**, 896 (1937).
45. Egloff, G. Physical Constants of Hydrocarbons. Reinhold, New York, Vol. I, II, III and IV. (1939, 1940, 1946, 1947).
46. Tooke, J. W. and Aston, J. G. *J. Am. Chem. Soc.*, **67**, 2275 (1945).
47. Timmermans, J. *Inst. intern. chim. Solvay, Conseil Chim.*, 4th Conseil, Brussels **1931**, 191.
48. Landolt-Börnstein, Physikalisch-chemische Tabellen. Julius Springer, Berlin 1935.
49. Smith, J. C. *J. Chem. Soc.*, **1932**, 737.
50. Carey, P. C. and Smith, J. C. *J. Chem. Soc.*, **1933**, 1348.
51. Skau, E. L. and Wakeham, H., in A. Weissberger's Physical Methods of Organic Chemistry. Interscience, New York, 1945, Vol. I, Chapter I.
52. Schwab, F. W. and Wichers, E. in Temperature, Its Measurement and Control in Science and Industry. Reinhold, New York, 1941, p. 256.
53. Smittenberg, J., Hoog, H., and Henkes, R. A. *J. Am. Chem. Soc.*, **60**, 17 (1938).
54. Skau, E. L. *Proc. Am. Acad. Arts Sci.*, **67**, 551 (1933).
55. Glasgow, A. R., Jr., Streiff, A. J., and Rossini, F. D. *J. Research Natl. Bur. Standards*, **35**, 355 (1945).
56. Taylor, W. J. and Rossini, F. D. *J. Research Natl. Bur. Standards*, **32**, 197 (1944)
57. ASTM Standards D940-47T, 1947 Supplement to Book of ASTM Standards, Part IIIA, p. 222.
58. Aston, J. G., Fink, H. L., Hardwick, C. T., and Salzman, C. F. Presented at Chicago Meeting, Am. Chem. Soc., April, 1946.
59. Aston, J. G., Fink, H. L., Tooke, J. W., and Cines, M. R. *Ind. Eng. Chem., Anal. Ed.*, **19**, 218 (1947).
60. Sturtevant, J. M. in A. Weissberger's Physical Methods of Organic Chemistry, Interscience, 1945, Vol. I, Chapter X.
61. Aston, J. G. and Messerley, G. H. *J. Am. Chem. Soc.*, **58**, 2354 (1936).
62. Aston, J. G., Fink, H. L. Bestul, A. B., Pace, E. L., and Szasz, G. J. *J. Am. Chem. Soc.*, **68**, 52 (1946).
63. Johnston, H. L. and Giauque, W. F. *J. Am. Chem. Soc.*, **51**, 3194 (1929).
64. Aston, J. G., Fink, H. L., and Cines, M. R. *J. Am. Chem. Soc.*, **69**, 1532 (1947).
65. Ubbelohde, A. R. and Oldham, J. W. H. *Proc. Roy. Soc., London*, **A176**, 50 (1940).

66. Van Hook, A. and Silver, L.   *J. Chem. Phys.*, **10**, 686 (1940).
67. White, A. W. and Morgan, S. A.   *J. Chem. Phys.*, **5**, 655 (1937).
68. Ubbelohde, A. R. and Woodward, I.   *Proc. Roy. Soc. London*, **A188**, 358 (1947).
69. Timmermans, J.   *Bull soc. chim. Belg.*, **37**, 409 (1928); **39**, 239 (1930).
70. Smith, L. I. and MacDougall, F. H.   *J. Am. Chem. Soc.*, **51**, 3006 (1929).
71. Landolt-Börnstein, Physikalisch-chemische Tabellen.   Julius Springer, Berlin, 1935, 3rd Supplement, Part I, p. 564.
72. Bradley, G. and Marsh, J. K.   *J. Chem. Soc.*, **1933**, 650.
73. Langedijk, S. L. and Brezesinska Smithuysen, W. C.   *Rec. trav. chim.*, **57**, 1050 (1938).
74. Fink, H. L., Cines, M. R., Frey, F. E. and Aston, J. G.   *J. Am. Chem. Soc.*, **69**, 1501 (1947).
75. Swietoslawski, W.   U. S. Patent 2,428,102, September 30, 1947.
76. Arnold, J. C.   British Patent 585,076, January 29, 1947.
77. Schwab, F. W. and Wichers, E.   *J. Research Natl. Bur. Standards*, **32**, 253 (1944); **25**, 747 (1940).
78. Leslie, R. T.   *J. Research Natl. Bur. Standards*, **10**, 609 (1933).
79. Hicks, M. M.   *J. Research Natl. Bur. Standards*, **2**, 483 (1929).
80. Hicks-Bruun, M. M. and Bruun, J. H.   *J. Research Natl. Bur. Standards*, **8**, 525 (1932).
81. Mastrangelo, S. V. and Aston, J. G.   In press.
82. Sawyer, M. F., Hunter, T. G., and Nash, A. W.   *J. Inst. Petroleum* **26**, 390, 430 (1940); **27**, 1, 143 (1941).
83. Sailors, H. R.   Private communication.

CHAPTER 9

CHEMICAL THERMODYNAMIC EQUILIBRIA AMONG HYDROCARBONS

By

FREDERICK D. ROSSINI

National Bureau of Standards, Washington, D. C.

CONTENTS

I. Elements of Chemical Thermodynamics

1. fundamental properties

One may take as the fundamental thermodynamic properties of a system the following: the pressure, P; the volume, V; the temperature, T; the internal or intrinsic energy, E; and the entropy, S.

2. first law of thermodynamics

The first law of thermodynamics states the change in energy of a system participating in any process is

$$dE = \delta Q - \delta W, \tag{1}$$

where δQ is the algebraic net heat absorbed by the system from its surroundings, δW is the algebraic net work done by the system on the surroundings, and dE is the algebraic net increase in the energy of the system.

3. heat content (or enthalpy)

When the process takes place at constant pressure, with only work of the "PV" kind, then

$$\delta W = PdV = d(PV) \tag{2}$$

and, in this special case, equation 1 becomes

$$dE = \delta Q = d(PV) \tag{3}$$

or

$$d(E + PV) = \delta Q \tag{4}$$

Because this combination of properties, $E + PV$, is encountered frequently in thermodynamic problems, it is convenient to let

$$H = E + PV, \tag{5}$$

where H is the heat content (or enthalpy). In terms of the heat content, equation 4 becomes

$$dH = \delta Q \tag{6}$$

4. second law of thermodynamics

The second law of thermodynamics treats of the decrease in the availability of energy for doing useful work, which is the result of the tendency of every system to approach a state of final equilibrium or maximum probability. The second law of thermodynamics states that the change in entropy of a system participating in a reversible process (that is, a process in which the resisting force or pressure differs from the applied force or pressure by only an infinitesimal amount) is

$$dS = \delta Q/T, \tag{7}$$

where δQ is the algebraic net heat absorbed by the system, T is the absolute temperature, and dS is the algebraic net increase in entropy of the system. Equation 7 may also be written as

$$\delta Q = TdS \tag{8}$$

5. CRITERION OF EQUILIBRIUM

For any system taking part in a reversible process, combination of the first and second laws (as expressed by equations 1 and 8) yields

$$dE = TdS - \delta W \tag{9}$$

The work term δW may be separated into two parts.

$$\delta W = PdV + \delta W' \tag{10}$$

where PdV represents the "PV" work against the boundaries confining the system and $\delta W'$ represents all other work done by the system.

Combining equations 9 and 10, one obtains

$$\delta W' = -(dE + PdV - TdS) \tag{11}$$

If the value of $\delta W'$ is positive, the given system is capable of performing work (over and above the "PV" work) that can be put to useful purposes, and the system can be thermodynamically harnessed to do this useful work. In such circumstances, the system being some distance removed from its state of equilibrium, it will tend to proceed toward that state of equilibrium naturally and of its own accord, and, during this spontaneous passage from its initial state to the state of equilibrium, the system may be harnessed to perform useful work. When $\delta W'$ is negative, useful work must be supplied to the system to produce the prescribed change, and the change is, therefore, away from the state of equilibrium in an unnatural direction.

When $\delta W'$ is zero for a given process, the system can neither yield nor absorb useful work and it must therefore already be at the state of equilibrium.

The foregoing may be used as the general criterion of equilibrium for any system with respect to any prescribed process. That is, the system is at equilibrium with respect to any process whenever

$$\delta W' = -(dE + PdV - TdS) = 0 \tag{12}$$

Many processes occur at constant temperature and constant pressure, and, under such circumstances,

$$TdS = d(TS) \tag{13}$$

and

$$PdV = d(PV). \tag{14}$$

Combination of equations 12, 13, and 14, yields

$$\delta W' = -d(E + PV - TS) = 0 \tag{15}$$

which becomes the criterion for equilibrium for processes occuring at constant temperature and constant pressure.

6. FREE ENERGY

The combination of properties, $E + PV - TS$, occurs frequently in chemical thermodynamic problems and it is convenient to define a function called the free energy, as

$$F = E + PV - TS. \tag{16}$$

With this notation, equation 15 may be written as

$$\delta W' = -dF = 0. \tag{17}$$

That is to say, a system is at equilibrium with respect to a given process at constant temperature and pressure whenever the change in free energy is zero.

If for a given process at constant temperature and pressure, the value of $\delta W'$ is positive (or if dF is negative), the energy liberated by the system is free to be put to useful purposes.

It should be noted that the definition of the two functions, H and F, as given in equations 5 and 16, has been such as to produce the relation:

$$F = H - TS. \tag{18}$$

7. CHANGE OF FREE ENERGY WITH PRESSURE AND TEMPERATURE

When a substance is subjected to a reversible process involving only changes of temperature, pressure, and volume, with work only of the "PV" kind, the term δW in equation 9 becomes

$$\delta W = PdV \tag{19}$$

and equation 9 may be written for this special case as

$$dE = TdS - PdV. \tag{20}$$

From the definition of F in equation 16, one may obtain by differentiation

$$dF = dE + PdV + VdP - TdS - SdT. \tag{21}$$

Combination of equations 20 and 21 yields

$$dF = VdP - SdT. \tag{22}$$

At constant temperature, equation 22 reduces to

$$dF = VdP, \tag{23}$$

which gives the change of free energy with pressure at constant temperature. Similarly, at constant pressure, equation 22 reduces to

$$dF = -SdT, \tag{24}$$

which gives the change of free energy with temperature at constant pressure.

8. FREE ENERGY OF AN IDEAL GAS

If one has an ideal gas participating in a reversible process at constant temperature, with no work other than that of the "PV" kind, then since

$$V = RT/P \tag{25}$$

equation 23 becomes

$$dF = VdP = (RT/P)dP = RTd \ln P, \tag{26}$$

which gives the change in free energy of an ideal gas with pressure at constant temperature.

9. HEAT CAPACITY

The heat capacity of a system is defined so that, at constant pressure,

$$C_p = dH/dT. \tag{27}$$

For a specified range of temperature, T_1 to T_2, heat capacity may be expressed as a relatively simple function of temperature, as

$$C_p = a + bT + cT^2; \ (T_1 \text{ to } T_2). \tag{28}$$

All such equations, and all other derived equations involving these same constants, are valid only within the specified range of temperature.

10. HEAT OF REACTION AND ITS CHANGE WITH TEMPERATURE

For any given process or reaction, proceeding from an initial state A to a final state B, the increment in heat content (or the heat of reaction) is

$$\Delta H = H_B - H_A. \tag{29}$$

For the same reaction, the increment in heat capacity may be written as

$$\Delta C_p = C_{p_B} - C_{p_A}. \tag{30}$$

Combination of equations 27, 28, 29, and 30 yields

$$d(\Delta H)/dT = \Delta C_p = (a_B - a_A) + (b_B - b_A)T + (c_B - c_A)T^2$$
$$= \Delta a + (\Delta b)T + (\Delta c)T^2. \tag{31}$$

Integration of this expression yields

$$\Delta H = \Delta H_* + (\Delta a)T + \tfrac{1}{2}(\Delta b)T^2 + \tfrac{1}{3}(\Delta c)T^3; \; (T_1 \text{ to } T_2). \tag{32}$$

It is important to note that the constant in equation 32, namely ΔH_*, must be evaluated from the values of the constants of the heat capacity equations and the value of ΔH for a given temperature within the range T_1 to T_2. Furthermore, equation 32 is applicable only within the range of temperature T_1 to T_2.

11. EQUILIBRIUM CONSTANT FOR IDEAL GAS REACTION

Consider a simple reaction occurring in the ideal gaseous state at a given temperature:

$$nN(\text{gas}) = mM(\text{gas}). \tag{33}$$

For the substances M and N in certain states s, one may write the change in free energy for this reaction as

$$\Delta F^s = mF_M^s - nF_N^s. \tag{34}$$

Likewise, for the substances M and N in certain states e, one may write

$$\Delta F^e = mF_M^e - nF_N^e. \tag{35}$$

Subtraction of equation 35 from equation 34 yields

$$\Delta F^s - \Delta F^e = m(F^s - F^e)_M - n(F^s - F^e)_N, \tag{36}$$

which represents the difference in the change in free energy for the two sets of conditions.

Integration of equation 26, between the pressures corresponding to the states s and e, respectively, yields for the difference in free energy of one mole of the ideal gas M between the states s and e,

$$(F^s - F^e)_M = RT \ln (P^s/P^e)_M \tag{37}$$

and similarly for the ideal gas N,

$$(F^s - F^e)_N = RT \ln (P^s/P^e)_N. \tag{38}$$

Combination of equations 36, 37, and 38 yields

$$\Delta F^s - \Delta F^e = mRT \ln (P^s/P^e)_M - nRT \ln (P^s/P^e)_N, \qquad (39)$$

which on rearrangement yields

$$\Delta F^s - \Delta F^e = RT \ln (P_M^m/P_N^n)^s - RT \ln (P_M^m/P_N^n)^e. \qquad (40)$$

Letting

$$Q = P_M^m/P_N^n \qquad (41)$$

be the "proper quotient of pressures" for the reaction given in equation 33, one may write equation 40 as

$$\Delta F^s - \Delta F^e = RT \ln Q^s - RT \ln Q^e. \qquad (42)$$

Let the states s be identified as standard states, with

$$P_M = P_N = 1. \qquad (43)$$

Then

$$RT \ln Q^s = 0 \qquad (44)$$

and, following the Lewis and Randall (2) nomenclature for designating standard states, one may write

$$\Delta F^s = \Delta F^0. \qquad (45)$$

Likewise, let the states e be identified as equilibrium states. Then for these states the "proper quotient of pressures" will be the equilibrium constant and the change in free energy will be zero, so that one may write

$$Q^e = K \qquad (46)$$

and

$$\Delta F^e = 0. \qquad (47)$$

On appropriate substitution equation 42 reduces to the familiar relation between the equilibrium constant and the standard change in free energy:

$$\Delta F^0 = -RT \ln K. \qquad (48)$$

From equation 18, one may write for any reaction,

$$\Delta F = \Delta(H - TS). \qquad (49)$$

At constant temperature, this equation becomes

$$\Delta F = \Delta H_s - T\Delta S. \qquad (50)$$

If each reactant and product is in its thermodynamic standard state, then, further,

$$\Delta F^0 = \Delta H^0 - T\Delta S^0 = -RT \ln K. \tag{51}$$

From equation 51, one may write the equilibrium constant explicitly as

$$K = (e^{\Delta S^0/R})(e^{-\Delta H^0/RT}). \tag{52}$$

For a reaction involving a given number and kind of atoms, equation 52 shows that the atoms will tend to go into those molecular configurations in which the entropy is greatest, corresponding to the largest number of states of existence, and, at the same time, into those molecular configurations having the lowest energy, that is, those molecules in which the energy of binding of the atoms, one to another, is greatest.

In the production of a given material by means of a proposed reaction, one of the practical things to know is the value of the equilibrium constant for the given reaction. For most reactions involving hydrocarbons, it is usually not possible to determine the equilibrium constant directly, and it becomes necessary to evaluate it by way of the standard change in entropy, ΔS^0, and heat content, ΔH^0, for the reaction.

In general, the values of the change in entropy, ΔS^0, may be obtained from the values of the entropies of the reactants and products, determined in each case by (a) application of the third law of thermodynamics to measurements of heats of transition, fusion, and vaporization, and heat capacities, down to low temperatures, or (b) statistical calculations utilizing spectroscopic and other molecular data.

Likewise, the values of the change in heat content, ΔH^0, may be obtained, in general, from calorimetric measurements of the heats of appropriate reactions.

12. FUGACITY AND ACTIVITY

Since actual gases are not ideal, Lewis (1) found it desirable to invent a new thermodynamic function, f, called the fugacity, which permits the retention, in thermodynamic calculations, of the simple form of equations 26 and 37, with the pressure being replaced by the fugacity. The fugacity may therefore be looked upon as the actual pressure corrected to fit the requirements of equations 26 and 37. The fugacity is defined by the relation

$$RT \ln (f/P) = - \int_0^P \alpha \, dP \tag{53}$$

where

$$\alpha = RT/P - V, \tag{54}$$

he difference between the molal volume of the ideal gas and that of the
actual gas at the same temperature and pressure.

In order to simplify thermodynamic calculations involving condensed
phases, under conditions where the vapor pressures, and hence the fugacities,
are very small, it is convenient and desirable to follow Lewis and Randall (2)
in the use of still another thermodynamic function called the activity.
The activity of a given substance is defined as the ratio of its fugacity, f_i,
in the given state to its fugacity, f_i^0, in an appropriately selected standard
reference state, as

$$a_i = f_i/f_i^0. \tag{55}$$

By this definition, the activity of any substance in its standard reference
state is unity.

Furthermore, the definitions of fugacity and activity are such that the
following relations hold:

$$F_i - F_i^0 = RT \ln f_i/f_i^0 \tag{56}$$

$$F_i - F_i^0 = RT \ln a_i \tag{57}$$

and the equilibrium constant for equation 33 becomes

$$K = a_M^m/a_N^n. \tag{58}$$

For details concerning fugacity and activity as thermodynamic functions, the reader is referred to Lewis and Randall (2). Values of the fugacity
as a function of pressure are discussed by Newton (3), Edmister (4),
Hougen and Watson (5), and Watson (6).

II. Evaluation of Entropies

1. entropies from the third law of thermodynamics

In evaluating entropies by means of the third law, use is made of the
relation given by the second law, namely,

$$dS = dQ/T. \tag{59}$$

On integration, one obtains the relation

$$S_T - S_0 = \int_0^T dQ/T \tag{60}$$

where S_0 is the entropy of the substances at the absolute zero. Actually,
of course, measurements can never be carried to the absolute zero and the

investigator starts at T_*, with the values of the integral below T_* being obtained by extrapolation. Indicating this fact, one may write

$$S_T = S_0 + \int_0^{T_*} dQ/T + \int_{T_*}^{T} dQ/T. \tag{61}$$

Here the last term is derived completely from the experimental observations of heat capacity, and heats of transition, fusion and vaporization, and the value of the second term on the right side of equation 61 is obtained by extrapolating from T_* to the absolute zero the measurements of heat capacity made above T_*, in conjunction with an appropriate theoretical equation (usually the Debye equation for the heat capacity of solids). The extrapolation from T_* to 0°K. in this way accounts for the entropy associated with the ordinary thermal energy resident in the substance at T_*, the lowest temperature of measurement. The term S_0 represents, therefore, the entropy of the substance at absolute zero as determined essentially by its quantum condition at T_*.

A simple statement of the third law is the following: If at the lowest temperature of measurement, T_*, the substance is in a single pure quantum state (except for the ordinary thermal energy that is accounted for by the extrapolation from T_* to 0°K.), then S_0 may be placed equal to zero. When this condition holds, then equation 61 becomes

$$S_T = \int_0^{T_*} dQ/T + \int_{T_*}^{T} dQ/T \tag{62}$$

and the entropy at the temperature T becomes determined substantially completely from the calorimetric observations. (It is obvious that T_* should be made as low as possible in order that the extrapolation shall introduce as small an error as possible. For most hydrocarbons, T_* should preferably be as low as the temperatures attainable with liquid hydrogen, 10 to 20°K.).

For a substance that conforms to the third law, that is a gas at the temperature T, and that has two stable crystalline forms, the entropy of the gas at the temperature T would be given as follows:

$$
\begin{aligned}
S_T(\text{gas}) = {} & \int_0^{T_*} dQ/T + \int_{T_*}^{T_{tr}} C_p(c,\text{II})\, d\ln T + \left(\frac{\Delta H}{T}\right)_{tr} \\
& + \int_{T_{tr}}^{T_f} C_p(c,\text{I})\, d\ln T + \left(\frac{\Delta H}{T}\right)_f + \int_{T_f}^{T_v} C_p(\text{liq})\, d\ln T \qquad (63) \\
& + \left(\frac{\Delta H}{T}\right)_v + \int_{T_v}^{T} C_p(g)\, d\ln T.
\end{aligned}
$$

The terms on the right in equation 63 represent, respectively, the extrapolated entropy from 0 to T_*, the increase in entropy of crystalline form II from T_* to the temperature of transition, the entropy of transition of crystalline form II, to crystalline form I, the increase in entropy of crystalline form I from the temperature of transition to the temperature of fusion, the entropy of fusion of crystalline form I, the increase in entropy of the liquid from the temperature of fusion to the temperature of vaporization, the entropy of vaporization and the increase in entropy of the gas from the temperature of vaporization to the given temperature T.

From the data that are now available, it appears that all the hydrocarbons so far investigated conform to the requirements of the third law as stated above. The following substances have been measured calorimetrically down to the temperature of liquid hydrogen and have, for the reasons indicated, been found to possess at the lowest temperature of measurement entropy in excess of that associated with the ordinary thermal energy of the crystal at that temperature: H_2 and D_2, entropy of mixing of ortho- and para-forms in nonequilibrium amounts (7); H_2O and D_2O, entropy associated with the randomness of arrangement of the hydrogen bonds in the crystal (8); CO, NO, and N_2O, entropy associated with a random or partially random "end-for-end" arrangement of the molecules in the crystal (9, 10, 11, 12).

For further discussion regarding the third law, the reader is referred to Lewis and Randall (2), Eastman (13), and Pauling and Eastman (14).

2. ENTROPIES FROM STATISTICAL CALCULATIONS

In evaluating the energy and entropy of gaseous molecules by means of statistical calculations utilizing spectroscopic and other molecular data, the procedure is to consider the energy (referred to the absolute zero) of a given gaseous molecule in the ideal state as being made up of translational, rotational, vibrational, and electronic parts:

$$E = E_0 + E(\text{trans}) + E(\text{rot}) + E(\text{vib}) + E(\text{electronic}). \quad (64)$$

Once the energy is known as a function of the temperature, the heat capacity and entropy are determined by the usual equations:

$$C_v = (\delta E/\delta T)_v \quad (65)$$

$$S = \int C_v d \ln T = \int (\delta E/\delta T)_v d \ln T. \quad (66)$$

If a molecule is capable of existing in any one of a set of definite states of energy, and if its distribution among the given states of energy is governed by a known law, the energy (referred to the ground level) resident in one mole of such molecules at any given temperature can easily be calculated. Let the horizontal lines of the following energy level diagram represent the possible states of energy for a given molecule.

No. of given level	Energy levels	Energy of given level	No. of states at given level
i	——————	ϵ_i	g_i
3	——————	ϵ_3	g_3
2	——————	ϵ_2	g_2
1	——————	ϵ_1	g_1
0	——————	ϵ_0	g_0

The levels of energy are numbered as indicated, beginning with zero at the bottom or ground level. The multiplicity, or number of individual states existing at each level of energy, is given by g_0, g_1, g_2, etc., and the energy of each level is represented by ϵ_0, ϵ_1, ϵ_2, ϵ_3, etc.

Let n_i be the number of molecules in one state at the energy level ϵ_i, n_0 the number in one state at the ground level ϵ_0, etc. Then, according to the Boltzmann distribution law,

$$n_i = n_0 e^{-(\epsilon_i - \epsilon_0)/kT}. \tag{67}$$

The number of molecules having an energy ϵ_i will be $n_i g_i$, where g_i is the multiplicity or number of states at the level ϵ_i. The total number of molecules is

$$1 \text{ mole} = N = \sum n_i g_i = n_0 \sum g_i e^{-(\epsilon_i - \epsilon_0)/kT}. \tag{68}$$

From equations 67 and 68, there is obtained for the number of molecules in the ground level

$$n_0 = N / \sum g_i e^{-(\epsilon_i - \epsilon_0)/kT} \tag{69}$$

and for the number in one state at the level ϵ_i,

$$n_i = N e^{-(\epsilon_i - \epsilon_0)/kT} / \sum g_i e^{-(\epsilon_i - \epsilon_0)/kT}. \tag{70}$$

The total energy, referred to the ground level, becomes

$$E - E_0 = \sum n_i g_i (\epsilon_i - \epsilon_0)$$
$$= N \sum g_i (\epsilon_i - \epsilon_0) e^{-(\epsilon_i - \epsilon_0)/kT} / \sum g_i e^{-(\epsilon_i - \epsilon_0)/kT}. \tag{71}$$

For convenience, the following abbreviations are used (15):

$$A_i = g_i e^{-(\epsilon_i - \epsilon_0)/kT} \tag{72}$$

$$B_i = g_i (\epsilon_i - \epsilon_0) e^{-(\epsilon_i - \epsilon_0)/kT} \tag{73}$$

$$D_i = g_i (\epsilon_i - \epsilon_0)^2 e^{-(\epsilon_i - \epsilon_0)/kT} \tag{74}$$

It will be noted that

$$dA_i/dT = B_i/kT^2 \tag{75}$$

and

$$dB_i/dT = D_i/kT^2. \tag{76}$$

Substituting the above abbreviations into equation 71, there is obtained for the energy of one mole of molecules referred to the ground level

$$E - E_0 = N\sum B_i/\sum A_i. \tag{77}$$

From equations 65 and 77, there is obtained

$$C_v = (N/kT^2)[(\sum D_i/\sum A_i) - (\sum B_i/\sum A_i)^2]. \tag{78}$$

From equations 66 and 77, there is obtained

$$S = R \ln \sum A_i + (E - E_0)/T. \tag{79}$$

From equations 16 and 79, and the ideal gas relation, $PV = RT$, there is obtained for the free energy function:

$$(F - E_0)/T = R(1 - \ln \sum A_i). \tag{80}$$

When the actual energy levels of a given molecule are known, the foregoing equations make it possible to calculate the given thermodynamic properties with an accuracy commensurate with the accuracy of the energy level diagram. In making such calculations, it is convenient to consider separately the contributions from translation, rotation, vibration, and electronic excitation.

In the case of the translational contribution, the energy levels for a gaseous particle of mass m, in a box of volume V, with the concentration of the particles being low enough to produce negligible interaction between them, are given by the following expression (16, 17):

$$(\epsilon_i - \epsilon_0)(\text{trans}) = (n_x^2 + n_y^2 + n_z^2)(h^2/8mV^{2/3}) \tag{81}$$

where n_x, n_y, and n_z are the quantum numbers associated with the three coordinates of the system and have values running from 0 to ∞. The proper value for the partition function for translation is

$$\sum A_i(\text{trans}) = (2\pi mkT)^{3/2}Veg_0/Nh^3 \tag{82}$$

where g_0 is the multiplicity of the ground state of the particle and e is the base of the natural logarithm. Substitution into equations 77, 78, and 79 yields

$$(E - E_0)(\text{trans}) = 3/2RT \tag{83}$$

$$C_v(\text{trans}) = 3/2R \tag{84}$$

$$S(\text{trans}) = R \ln [(2\pi mkT)^{3/2}Veg_0/Nh^3] + 3/2R \tag{85}$$

where R is the gas constant per mole in cal./deg. The foregoing equations for the translational contribution are applicable to all except those extremely low temperatures that are of little practical interest at the present time.

In the case of the rotational contribution, the most accurate procedure utilizes the actual rotational energy levels of the molecule as determined from the analyses of appropriate spectrograms. The value of $\sum A_i$, as defined by equation 72, may be obtained by summation over these actual levels of energy, term by term, or the levels of energy may be expressed in terms of an appropriate series and the value of $\sum A_i$ obtained by an analytical summation.

Whenever the actual diagram of energy levels for rotation is not known, a very good approximation for ordinary temperatures may be obtained by using the levels of energy deduced theoretically for a rigid rotator, which requires a knowledge of the moment of inertia of the molecule. For a linear molecule, which effectively has only two degrees of rotational freedom, the energy levels are given by the relation (16, 17):

$$(\epsilon_i - \epsilon_0)(\text{rot}) = j(j + 1)h^2/8\pi^2 I \tag{86}$$

where I is the moment of inertia of the molecule and j is the rotational quantum number. For the rotational levels, the multiplicity, g_i, is equal to $2j + 1$, and the proper value of the partition function for rotation for a linear molecule is

$$\sum A_i \,(\text{rot}) = \frac{1}{\sigma} \sum (2j + 1)e^{-j(j+1)h^2/8\pi^2 IkT} \tag{87}$$

where σ is the symmetry number,* being either 1 or 2 for a linear molecule. Whenever $h^2/8\pi^2 IkT$ is very much less than unity, as it is for most molecules at ordinary and high temperatures, the above partition function for rotation, on replacing the summation by an integration, simplifies to

$$\sum A_i(\text{rot}) = 8\pi^2 IkT/h^2\sigma. \tag{88}$$

Substitution into equations 77, 78, and 79 yields for any linear molecule

$$(E - E_0)(\text{rot}) = RT \tag{89}$$

$$C(\text{rot}) = R \tag{90}$$

$$S(\text{rot}) = R \ln (8\pi^2 IkT/h^2\sigma) + R \tag{91}$$

$$= R \ln (IT/\sigma) + 177.67 \text{ cal./deg. mole} \tag{92}$$

when R is in cal./deg. mole and I is in g.cm.²

---

* The symmetry number is the number of ways the molecule may be superimposed upon itself by rotation of the entire molecule. Examples of the value of the symmetry number for several polyatomic molecules are: CO_2, 2: CH_4, 12: NH_3, 3: N_2O, 1: C_2H_2 (acetylene), 2: C_2H_4 (ethylene), 4.

For any nonlinear polyatomic molecule, which has three degrees of rotational freedom, the partition function for rotation is, for small values of $h^2/8\pi^2IkT$,

$$\sum A_i(\text{rot}) = (8\pi^2kT/h^2)^{3/2}(\pi I_A I_B I_C)^{1/2}/\sigma \tag{93}$$

where I_A, I_B and I_C are the three moments of inertia of the molecule. Substitution into equations 77, 78, and 79 yields for any nonlinear molecule

$$(E - E_0)(\text{rot}) = 3/2RT \tag{94}$$

$$C(\text{rot}) = 3/2R \tag{95}$$

$$S(\text{rot}) = R \ln [(8\pi^2kT/h^2)^{3/2}(\pi I_A I_B I_C)^{1/2}/\sigma] + 3/2R \tag{96}$$

$$= R \ln [(I_A I_B I_C)^{1/2}T^{3/2}/\sigma] + 267.65 \text{ cal./deg. mole.} \tag{97}$$

Corrections to the foregoing approximation equations for the "stretching" of the molecule in the higher rotational states have been derived, and may be applied whenever the population of molecules in such states is large enough (49, 50).

In the case of the vibrational contribution, the most accurate procedure utilizes the actual vibrational energy levels of the molecule. As in the case of the rotational part, the value of $\sum A_i$ (equation 72) for vibration may be obtained by a summation over the actual energy levels, term by term, or by analytical summation of an appropriate series expressing the vibrational energy levels as a function of their quantum number.

Whenever the actual energy level diagram for vibration is not known, a very good approximation may be obtained by utilizing the energy levels deduced theoretically for a harmonic oscillator. This requires a knowledge of the value of each of the fundamental frequencies of vibration in the molecule, which, for a molecule of a atoms are $3a - 5$ in number for a linear molecule and $3a - 6$ in number for a nonlinear molecule. For this procedure, the energy levels for each degree of vibrational freedom are given by the relation (16, 17)

$$(\epsilon_i - \epsilon_0)(\text{vib}) = n_i h\nu \tag{98}$$

where ν is the fundamental frequency of vibration for the given degree of vibrational freedom, and n_i has values from 0 to ∞. The proper value of the partition function for each degree of vibrational freedom is

$$\sum A_i(\text{vib}) = \sum e^{-n_i h\nu/kT} = (1 - e^{-h\nu/kT})^{-1}. \tag{99}$$

Letting

$$x = h\nu/kT = (hc/k)(\omega/T) \tag{100}$$

where c is the velocity of light and ω is the wave number or the reciprocal of the wave length, and substituting into equations 77, 78, and 79 yields for each degree of vibrational freedom,

$$(E - E_0)(\text{vib}) = RTx/(e^x - 1) \tag{101}$$

$$C(\text{vib}) = R(x^2 e^x)/(e^x - 1)^2 \tag{102}$$

$$S(\text{vib}) = R \ln (1 - e^{-x})^{-1} + Rx/(e^x - 1) \tag{103}$$

$$= R[x/(e^x - 1) - \ln (1 - e^{-x})]. \tag{104}$$

When x is small, as for large values of T, $C(\text{vib})$ approaches the value R.

The total vibrational contribution to each of these properties is obtained by summing over all the fundamental frequencies of vibration. The labor of such calculation is greatly lessened by making use of the several published tables which give the values of the above functions for various values of x, as defined above, or of ω/T, where ω is the wave number (reciprocal of the wavelength) in cm.$^{-1}$ (20, 51).

Because for most molecules the first electronic energy level is so high in energy above the ground level, its population is usually negligible, and the contribution to the several thermodynamic properties arising from the electronic energy does not enter even into the most accurate calculations. Whenever the population of such levels does become significant, as for extremely high temperatures or in the case of certain molecules having electronic states of relatively low energy, their contribution must, of course, be included in the total value of the given property.

Table I gives the equations for calculating the exact translational contributions (from equations 83, 84, and 85) to the thermodynamic functions and the equations for calculating the approximate rotational contributions (from equations 89, 90, 92, 94, and 95) to the thermodynamic functions.

By adding to the equations given in Table I the appropriate contributions for vibration (as given by equations 101, 102, 103, and 104, with the summations taken over all of the vibrational degrees of freedom), one may obtain the total value of the given thermodynamic function for the given molecule.

For further details regarding the statistical calculation of thermodynamic functions, the reader is referred to Tolman (16) and Mayer and Mayer (17).

3. RESTRICTED INTERNAL ROTATION

In the case of hydrocarbon and other molecules having a group which can oscillate with rather large amplitude, or even rotate completely, about a given bond in a plane perpendicular to it, the foregoing method becomes

omplicated by the difficulty of ascertaining the proper diagram of energy
levels to be associated with such a degree of freedom. When the restric-
ion to rotation is extremely large, the energy levels may be taken to be
hose of a simple harmonic oscillator, while, when the restriction to rotation

TABLE I

USEFUL EQUATIONS WITH NUMERICAL CONSTANTS, FOR CALCULATING THE THERMO-
DYNAMIC FUNCTIONS FOR TRANSLATION (OF ALL MOLECULES) AND
ROTATION (OF RIGID MOLECULES)

The equations in this table may be used to calculate the translational and rota-
ional contributions (in cal./deg.mole) to the heat content function, $(H^\circ - H_0^\circ)/T$,
he free energy function, $(F^\circ - H_0^\circ)/T$, and the entropy, S°, the translational heat
apacity at constant pressure, $C_p{}^\circ$, and the rotational heat capacity, 0°; all for a
gas in the thermodynamic standard gaseous state of unit fugacity (1 atmosphere),
at the given absolute temperature T (in $°K$.). M is the molecular weight (g./mole).
I (g.cm.²) is the value of the two equal moments of inertia of a linear molecule about
axes perpendicular to the axis of the molecule; and I_1, I_2, and I_3 (g. cm.²) are the
three principal moments of inertia of a nonlinear molecule.

TRANSLATION
(of all molecules)

$$(H^\circ - H_0^\circ)/T = C_p{}^\circ = 4.9680$$
$$(F^\circ - H_0^\circ)/T = -6.8635 \log M + 7.2820 - 11.4392 \log T$$
$$S^\circ = 6.8635 \log M - 2.3141 + 11.4392 \log T$$

ROTATION
(of rigid molecules)

I. Diatomic or Linear Polyatomic Molecules

$$(H^\circ - H_0^\circ)/T = C^\circ = 1.9872$$

(a) σ (symmetry number) = 1:

$$(F^\circ - H_0^\circ)/T = -4.5757 \log (I \times 10^{39}) + 2.7676 - 4.5757 \log T$$
$$S^\circ = 4.5757 \log (I \times 10^{39}) - 0.7804 + 4.5757 \log T$$

(b) σ (symmetry number) = 2:

$$(F^\circ - H_0^\circ)/T = -4.5757 \log (I \times 10^{39}) + 4.1450 - 4.5757 \log T$$
$$S^\circ = 4.5757 \log (I \times 10^{39}) - 2.1578 + 4.5757 \log T$$

II. Nonlinear Polyatomic Molecules

$$(H^\circ - H_0^\circ)/T = C^\circ = 2.9808$$
$$(F^\circ - H_0^\circ)/T = -2.2878 \log (I_1 I_2 I_3 \times 10^{117}) + 4.5757 \log \sigma + 3.0140 - 6.8635 \log T$$
$$S^\circ = 2.2878 \log (I_1 I_2 I_3 \times 10^{117}) - 4.5757 \log \sigma - 0.0332 + 6.8635 \log T$$

is extremely small, the energy levels may be taken to be those of a simple
rotator.

It is generally assumed (17, 19, 20, 21), that the potential restricting
such rotation of a given group follows the relation

$$U = 1/2V(1 - \cos n\alpha) \tag{105}$$

where V is the height of the potential barrier, n is the number of maxima for a complete rotation of the group, and α is the angle of rotation. Theo retical calculations of the resulting levels of energy have been made and discussed by several authors (20, 21, 22, 23).

Pitzer (21) and Pitzer and Gwinn (24) prepared tables for determining the contribution made by the degree of freedom associated with the restricted rotation of a given group to the thermodynamic properties of energy, heat capacity, entropy, and free energy function.

The manner of determining the value of the potential barrier restricting internal rotation in a given molecule may be illustrated by considering the case of ethane, which has a total of twenty-four degrees of freedom. Of these, three are of translation, three of rotation, seventeen of ordinary vibration, and the remaining one is that of the restricted rotation. By appropriate analysis and calculation, the contribution to the energy (referred to 0°K.), heat capacity, and entropy arising from the $3 + 3 + 17$ or 23 "known" degrees of freedom may be calculated. The given property (most conveniently the heat capacity or entropy) is then measured experimentally. The difference between the measured value and the value calculated for the twenty-three degrees of freedom serves to yield, for the given temperature or temperatures, the contribution arising from the restricted rotation, within the limits of uncertainty of the experimental measurements and the calculations. For ethane, the magnitude of the potential barrier restricting internal rotation has been evaluated from measurements both of the entropy and the heat capacity, and the results of both methods are in good accord (19, 25). Propane has similarly been investigated, with equally good results (26, 27).

III. Evaluation of Heats of Formation

1. the thermochemical table (28)

The ideal thermochemical table is one which will permit calculation of the heat of every chemical reaction. Obviously it would be impractical to list in a table the heat of every reaction, but the same end is accomplished by listing for each chemical substance its heat of formation from the elements in selected standard states. It is evident that, by proper selection, the number of chemical reactions whose heats must be measured will be about the same as the number of substances listed in the table. Some saving in the number of reactions to be measured will occur among the organic compounds because of certain correlations which permit the evaluation of the heat of formation of higher members of homologous series, similar isomeric structures, etc.

The value of the heat of formation of a given substance may be the result of the determination of the heat of one reaction, as in the formation of liquid water from gaseous oxygen and hydrogen. For many other substances, however, the value will result from the measurement of the heats of several reactions. For example, the value of the heat of formation of methane, from its elements carbon and hydrogen, depends upon measurements of the heats of the following three reactions: the heat of combustion of gaseous methane in gaseous oxygen to form liquid water and gaseous carbon dioxide; the heat of combustion of solid carbon in gaseous oxygen to form gaseous carbon dioxide; and the heat of combustion of gaseous hydrogen in gaseous oxygen to form liquid water.

There will be certain basic values in the table which will be used very frequently in the derivation of other values. These basic values, which should be known with considerable accuracy, include the heats of formation of water, carbon dioxide, nitric acid, sulfuric acid, hydrogen chloride, hydrogen sulfide, and others. Because of this interdependence of many of the values of heats of formation, it is extremely desirable that values for the important thermochemical constants be carefully selected, and when any change is made in any one of the basic values, corresponding changes should be made in all the values which depend upon it. It is for this same reason that the addition or subtraction of values of heats of formation from different tables is a precarious undertaking.

2. GENERAL METHOD (28)

In order to determine the value of the heat of formation of a substance, one selects for measurement reactions in which all the reactants and products, except the given substance, are either elements in their standard reference states or are substances whose heats of formation are known.

The chemical reactions whose heats are to be measured must be ones which proceed to completion (except in so far as a small amount of side reaction is known and can be corrected for) and for which the amount of reaction can be accurately measured.

The principle of the modern experimental method in thermochemistry is to carry out the reaction to be studied in the calorimeter in such a manner that it will be possible to compare the heat evolved by the chemical reaction with the heat evolved by electrical energy or with the heat evolved by a measured amount of a standard chemical reaction, the heat of which has already been compared with electrical energy.

3. HOMOLOGOUS SERIES

For any homologous series of molecules, $Y - R$, consisting of any group Y attached to the end of a normal alkyl radical, R, the heat of formation of the molecule in the gaseous state at a given temperature, from the elements in their standard states, may be represented by a relation of the form

$$\Delta Hf = A + Bm + \delta \qquad (106)$$

Where A is a constant for the given homologous series characterized by the end group Y, B is a constant for all series independent of the end group Y, m is the number of carbon atoms in the normal alkyl radical, and δ is a deviation term which has a decreasingly significant value for the first, second, and third members of the series, becomes zero at about the fourth and fifth members, and is zero for all the higher members. After the value

TABLE II

RELATION BETWEEN THE VALUE OF THE DEVIATION FROM LINEARITY IN THE HEAT OF FORMATION FOR $m = 0$ AND THE NUMBER AND KIND OF BONDS ASSOCIATED WITH THE MAIN OR ATTACHING CARBON ATOM OF THE END GROUP

(From Prosen, Johnson, and Rossini 29)

End group	Value of δ for $m = 0$	Bonds associated with the main or attaching carbon atom of the given end group (not including the attaching bond)				
		C—H	C—C (paraffin)	C=C (phenyl)	C=C (olefin)	C≡C (acetylene)
	kcal./mole					
Methyl	-2.55 ± 0.37	3	..	..	..	..
Ethyl	0.02 ± 0.33	2	1	..	..	..
Cyclohexyl	1.82 ± 0.41	1	2	..	..	..
Cyclopentyl	2.05 ± 0.40	1	2	..	..	..
Isopropyl	2.05 ± 0.50	1	2	..	..	..
tert-Butyl	2.55 ± 0.50	..	3	..	..	..
Vinyl	2.76 ± 0.37	1	..	..	1	..
Phenyl	3.42 ± 0.38	..	..	2	..	..
Isopropenyl	3.68 ± 0.40	..	1	..	1	..
Ethynyl	4.94 ± 0.55	..	..	..	..	1

of the constant B has been accurately determined from measurements on a sufficient number of compounds of one series, this value may then be used for all other series. Then the evaluation of the heats of formation of all the members of any other homologous series of compounds will require measurements only on the first three or four members of the series. For several such homologous series, the value of the deviation term δ, for $m = 0$, is illustrated in Table II, which gives the deviations from linearity in the heats of formation of the members of several homologous series of hydrocarbons (29).

The values of the deviations from constancy in the increment per CH_2 group, for $m = 0$, are characteristic of the end group in each series, and can be seen to vary regularly with changes in the number of hydrogen atoms and number and kind of carbon atoms bonded to the main or attaching carbon atom of the end group. The values of δ for $m = 0$ for several end groups are shown in Table II in relation to the number of carbon-hydrogen bonds and the number and kind of carbon-carbon bonds associated with the main or attaching carbon atom of the end group.

TABLE III

HEATS OF ISOMERIZATION* OF SOME PARAFFIN HYDROCARBONS IN THE GASEOUS STATE AT 0°K.

Compound	$H(n\text{-paraffin}) - H(\text{isoparaffin})$
	kcal./mole
n-Pentane	0.00
2-Methylbutane (isopentane)	1.39
2,2-Dimethylpropane (neopentane)	4.03
n-Hexane	0.00
2-Methylhexane	1.10
3-Methylhexane	0.51
2,2-Dimethylbutane	3.63
2,3-Dimethylbutane	1.90
n-Heptane	0.00
2-Methylhexane	1.12
3-Methylhexane	0.31
3-Ethylpentane	− .55
2,2-Dimethylpentane	3.35
2,3-Dimethylpentane	1.64
2,4-Dimethylpentane	2.33
3,3-Dimethylpentane	2.27
2,2,3-Trimethylbutane	2.92

* For the estimated uncertainties in these values, see Prosen and Rossini (32).

4. HEATS OF ISOMERIZATION

Differences in the heats of formation, which are the heats of isomerization, of some representative isomeric hydrocarbons of several classes are given in Tables III, IV, V, and VI. These values are taken from the "w" tables (18) of the American Petroleum Institute Research Project 44. Values for other isomeric hydrocarbons, including diolefin and acetylene hydrocarbons, may be obtained from the above tables (18). See also Rossini (30, 31), Prosen and Rossini (32, 33), and Prosen et al. (29, 34, 45).

With regard to the energy content of isomeric hydrocarbons, the following points are to be noted:

(a) Among given paraffin isomers, that isomer is most stable with regard to energy (lowest energy content) which has the most compact carbon skeleton with, at the same time, a minimum of steric hindrance or con-

TABLE IV

HEATS OF ISOMERIZATION* OF SOME MONOOLEFIN HYDROCARBONS IN THE GASEOUS STATE AT 0°K.

Compound	H(1-alkene) $-$ H(isomer)
	kcal./mole
1-Butene...	0.00
cis-2-Butene...	1.364
trans-2-Butene...	2.652
Isobutene..	3.482
1-Pentene..	0.00
cis-2-Pentene..	1.197
trans-2-Pentene..	2.381
2-Methyl-1-butene.....................................	3.322
2-Methyl-2-butene.....................................	4.696
3-Methyl-1-butene.....................................	1.700

* For the estimated uncertainties in these values, see Prosen and Rossini (33).

TABLE V

HEATS OF ISOMERIZATION* OF SOME ALKYL BENZENE HYDROCARBONS IN THE GASEOUS STATE AT 0°K.

Compound	H(n-alkyl benzene) $-$ H(isomer)
	kcal./mole
Ethylbenzene..	0.00
1,2-Dimethylbenzene..................................	2.821
1,3-Dimethylbenzene..................................	2.991
1,4-Dimethylbenzene..................................	2.853
n-Propylbenzene......................................	0.00
Isopropylbenzene......................................	0.560
1-Methyl-2-ethylbenzene..............................	1.718
1-Methyl-3-ethylbenzene..............................	2.217
1-Methyl-4-ethylbenzene..............................	2.569
1,2,3-Trimethylbenzene...............................	4.283
1,2,4-Trimethylbenzene...............................	5.342
1,3,5-Trimethylbenzene...............................	5.569

* For the estimated uncertainties in these values, see Prosen, Johnson, and Rossini (34).

straint in the molecule (as produced by space interference of neighboring parts of the molecule).

(b) Among the monoolefin hydrocarbons, that isomer is most stable with regard to energy content which has the double bond most centralized in the molecule, with a maximum number of substituent alkyl groups on the carbon atoms forming the double bond. This is probably also true of acetylene hydrocarbons having one triple carbon-carbon bond.

(c) Among the alkyl benzene hydrocarbons, relatively little change is produced in the energy content on shifting the relative position of alkyl groups attached to the benzene ring. In general, for the same total number of carbon atoms in the substituent alkyl groups, greater stability with regard to energy content is found in the isomers with the greater number of substituent groups. Thus, with regard to energy content, the trimethylbenzenes are more stable than the methylethylbenzenes, which are more stable than the propylbenzenes. Among given dialkyl benzenes, those with

TABLE VI

HEATS OF ISOMERIZATION* OF SOME ALKYL CYCLOHEXANE HYDROCARBONS IN THE GASEOUS STATE AT 0°K.

Compound	$H(n$-alkyl cyclohexane) $-H$(isomer)
	kcal./mole
Ethylcyclohexane...............................	0.00
1,1-Dimethylcyclohexane.........................	1.990
cis-1,2-Dimethylcyclohexane.....................	.01
trans-1,2-Dimethylcyclohexane...................	1.97
cis-1,3-Dimethylcyclohexane.....................	3.08
trans-1,3-Dimethylcyclohexane...................	1.12
cis-1,4-Dimethylcyclohexane.....................	1.14
trans-1,4-Dimethylcyclohexane...................	3.05

* For the estimated uncertainties in these values, see Prosen, Johnson, and Rossini (29,45).

1,3-substitution are more stable, and, among the trialkyl benzenes, those with 1,3,5-substitution are more stable with regard to energy, in the gaseous state at low temperatures.

(d) Among the diolefins, conjugation of the double bonds produces greatly increased stability with regard to energy content.

IV. EVALUATION OF FREE ENERGIES OF FORMATION

The free energy function, $(F - E_0)/T$, is the easiest thermodynamic property to calculate statistically because it involves only the simple partition function. For a gas in its standard state one has

$$(F° - E_0°)/T = (F° - H_0°)/T = R(1 - \ln \sum A_i). \qquad (107)$$

Furthermore, for any given reaction, one can calculate $\Delta(F° - H_0°)/T$ as the sum of the values of the free energy function for the products of the reaction less the sum of the values of the free energy function for the reactants:

$$\Delta\left(\frac{F^\circ - H_\circ^\circ}{T}\right) = \sum_{\text{products}} \left(\frac{F^\circ - H_\circ^\circ}{T}\right) - \sum_{\text{reactants}} \left(\frac{F^\circ - H_\circ^\circ}{T}\right). \tag{108}$$

Further, it is seen that

$$\Delta\left(\frac{F^\circ - H_\circ^\circ}{T}\right) = \frac{\Delta F^\circ}{T} - \frac{\Delta H_\circ^\circ}{T}. \tag{109}$$

Combination of equations 48 and 109 gives

$$\frac{\Delta F^\circ}{T} = -R \ln K = \frac{\Delta H_\circ^\circ}{T} + \Delta\left(\frac{F^\circ - H_\circ^\circ}{T}\right). \tag{110}$$

The value of $\Delta H_\circ^\circ/T$ for any reaction is obtained from the value of ΔH° for 25°C. corrected to 0°K. by means of values for the heat content at 25°C. referred to 0°K. for the several molecules involved:

$$\Delta H_\circ^\circ = \Delta H^\circ{}_{298.16} - \Delta(H^\circ{}_{298.16} - H_\circ^\circ) \tag{111}$$

where, as usual,

$$\Delta(H_{298.16}^\circ - H_\circ^\circ) = \sum_{\text{products}} (H_{298.16}^\circ - H_\circ^\circ) - \sum_{\text{reactants}} (H_{298.16}^\circ - H_\circ^\circ). \tag{112}$$

V. Tables of Chemical Thermodynamic Data

In the tables of Selected Values of Properties of Hydrocarbons (18, 35) issued by the American Petroleum Institute Research Project 44 values are given for the following thermodynamic functions:

$(H^\circ - H_\circ^\circ)/T$, the heat content function

$(F^\circ - H_\circ^\circ)/T$, the free energy function

S°, the entropy

$H^\circ - H_\circ^\circ$, the heat content

C_p°, the heat capacity

ΔHf°, the heat of formation from the elements

ΔFf°, the free energy of formation from the elements

$\log Kf$, the logarithm of the equilibrium constant of formation from the elements.

In the tables cited, values for the foregoing functions are given as a function of temperature, usually 0° to 1500°K., for the following hydrocarbons in the gaseous state, as of October 31, 1948:

Paraffins, C_1 to C_8, all isomers.

Monoolefins, C_2 to C_6, all isomers.

Diolefins, C_3 to C_5, all isomers.
Acetylenes, C_2 to C_5, all isomers.
Alkyl cyclohexanes, C_6 to C_8, all isomers.
Alkyl benzenes, C_6 to C_9, all isomers.
Styrenes, C_8 and C_9, all isomers.
Cyclopentene and cyclohexene.
Normal paraffins, C_1 to C_{20}.
Normal monoolefins (1-alkenes), C_2 to C_{20}.
Normal acetylenes (1-alkynes), C_2 to C_{20}.
Normal alkyl cyclopentanes, C_5 to C_{21}.
Normal alkyl cyclohexanes, C_6 to C_{22}.
Normal alkyl benzenes, C_6 to C_{22}.

In addition to values of the properties listed above, the tables of the American Petroleum Institute Research Project 44 also give values for the following properties, for most of the same compounds:

Heat of formation, free energy of formation, and entropy, of the liquid, at 25°C.

Heat and entropy of fusion.

Heat and entropy of vaporization.

Standard heat, entropy, and free energy of vaporization at 25°C.

Heat of combustion, of the gas and the liquid, at 25°C.

VI. CHEMICAL EQUILIBRIUM AMONG HYDROCARBONS AND RELATED COMPOUNDS

1. REACTIONS INVOLVING O_2, H_2, H_2O, C, CO, CO_2, AND CH_4.

Wagman et al. (36) calculated values for the increment in heat content, the increment in free energy, the logarithm of the equilibrium constant, and the equilibrium constant, to 1500°K., for the following reactions:

C (solid, graphite) + CO_2 (gas) = 2CO (gas)   (113)

C (solid, graphite) + H_2O (gas) = CO (gas) + H_2 (gas)   (114)

CO (gas) + $1/2 O_2$ (gas) = CO_2 (gas)   (115)

CO (gas) + H_2O (gas) = CO_2 (gas) + H_2 (gas)   (116)

CH_4 (gas) + $1/2 O_2$ (gas) = CO (gas) + $2H_2$ (gas)   (117)

CH_4 (gas) + CO_2 (gas) = 2CO (gas) + $2H_2$ (gas)   (118)

CH_4 (gas) + H_2O (gas) = CO (gas) + $3H_2$ (gas)   (119)

CH_4 (gas) + $2H_2O$ (gas) = CO_2 (gas) + $4H_2$ (gas).   (120)

In Fig. 1 are plotted the values of the logarithm of the equilibrium constant for these reactions (except 117) and for the following reaction:

$$C \text{ (solid, graphite)} + 2H_2 \text{ (gas)} = CH_4 \text{ (gas)}. \tag{121}$$

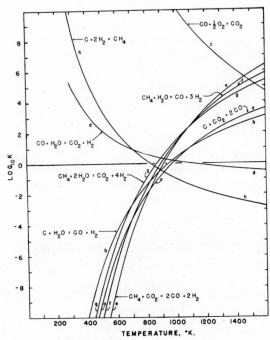

FIG. 1. Plot of the logarithm of the equilibrium constant for eight reactions involving O_2, H_2, H_2O, C (graphite), CO, CO_2, and CH_4

The scale of ordinates gives the logarithm (to the base 10) of the equilibrum constant, $\log_{10} K$, for the given reaction. The scale of abscissas gives the temperature in degrees Kelvin. The curves apply to the following reactions:

    (a) C (solid, graphite) + CO_2 (gas) = 2 CO (gas)
    (b) C (solid, graphite) + H_2O (gas) = CO (gas) + H_2 (gas)
    (c) CO (gas) + 1/2 O_2 (gas) = CO_2 (gas)
    (d) CO (gas) + H_2O (gas) = CO_2 (gas) + H_2 (gas)
    (e) CH_4 (gas) + CO_2 (gas) = 2 CO (gas) + $2H_2$ (gas)
    (f) CH_4 (gas) + H_2O (gas) = CO (gas) + $3H_2$ (gas)
    (g) CH_4 (gas) + $2H_2O$ (gas) = CO_2 (gas) + $4H_2$ (gas)
    (h) C (solid, graphite) + $2H_2$ (gas) = CH_4 (gas).

(From D. D. Wagman, J. E. Kilpatrick, W. J. Taylor, K. S. Pitzer, and F. D. Rossini J. Research Natl. Bur. Standards **34**, 143 (1945)).

2. PARAFFINS

Prosen and Rossini (32), Prosen et al. (37, 38) and Pitzer and Kilpatrick (39) have summarized the results on the thermodynamic properties of the paraffin hydrocarbons.

Figure 2 gives a plot which shows the thermodynamic stability, per

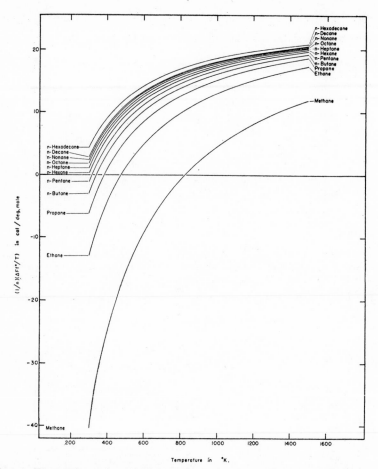

Temperature in °K.

FIG. 2. Thermodynamic stability of the normal paraffin hydrocarbons in the gaseous state as a function of temperature.

The scale of ordinates gives the value of $(1/n)\ (\Delta Ff°/T)$ in cal./ deg. mole, where n is the number of carbon atoms per molecule, T is the absolute temperature in °K., and $\Delta Ff°$ is the standard free energy of formation of the hydrocarbon from the elements, solid carbon (graphite) and gaseous hydrogen. The scale of abscissas gives the temperature in degrees Kelvin.

This plot shows the thermodynamic stability, per carbon atom, with respect to the elements, of the normal paraffin hydrocarbons in the gaseous state. Points below the zero line indicate that the gaseous hydrocarbon in its standard state has a thermodynamic tendency to be formed from solid (graphite) and gaseous hydrogen in their respective standard states.

(From E. J. Prosen, K. S. Pitzer, and F D. Rossini. *J. Research Natl. Bur. Standards* **34,** 403 (1945)).

carbon atom and with respect to the elements solid carbon (graphite) and gaseous hydrogen, of the normal paraffin hydrocarbons in the gaseous state as a function of the temperature

In Figs. 3, 4, 5, 6, and 7 are plotted, respectively for the two butanes, the three pentanes, the five hexanes, the nine heptanes, and the eighteen

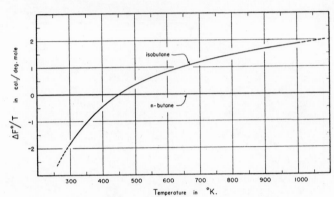

FIG. 3. Free energy of isomerization of the two butanes.
The scale of ordinates gives the value of $\Delta F^{\circ}/T$, in cal./deg.mole, for the isomerization, $n\text{-}C_4H_{10}$ (gas) = $i\text{-}C_4H_{10}$ (gas). The scale of abscissas gives the temperature in degrees Kelvin.
(From E. J. Prosen, K. S. Pitzer, and F. D. Rossini, *J. Research Natl. Bur. Standards* **34**, 403 (1945)).

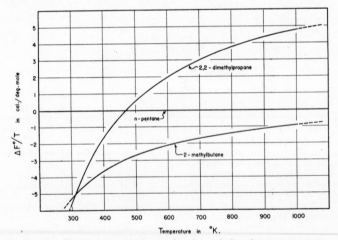

FIG. 4. Free energy of isomerization of the three pentanes.
The scale of ordinates gives the value of $\Delta F^{\circ}/T$, in cal./deg.mole, for the isomerization, $n\text{-}C_5H_{12}$ (gas) = $i\text{-}C_5H_{12}$ (gas). The scale of abscissas gives the temperature in degrees Kelvin.
(From E. J. Prosen, K. S. Pitzer, and F. D. Rossini, *J. Research Natl. Bur. Standards* **34**, 403 (1945)).

octanes, the values of $\Delta F^{\circ}/T$, as a function of the temperature T, for the reaction of isomerization in the gaseous state:

$$n\text{-Paraffin(gas)} = \text{Isoparaffin(gas)}. \tag{122}$$

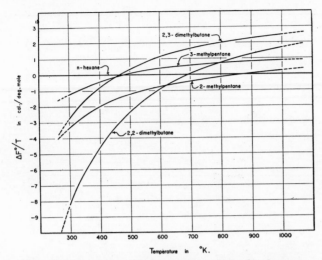

FIG. 5. Free energy of isomerization of the five hexanes.
The scale of ordinates gives the value of $\Delta F^\circ/T$, in cal./deg. mole, for the isomerization, $n\text{-}C_6H_{14}$ (gas) $= i\text{-}C_6H_{14}$ (gas). The scale of abscissas gives the temperature in degrees Kelvin.
(From E. J. Prosen, K. S. Pitzer, and F. D. Rossini, *J. Research Natl. Bur. Standards*
34, 403 (1945)).

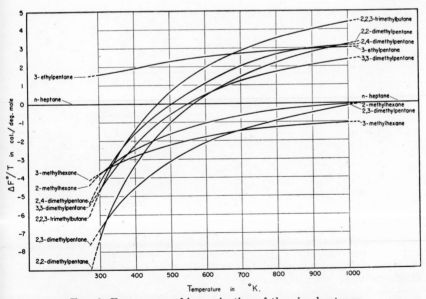

FIG. 6. Free energy of isomerization of the nine heptanes
The scale of ordinates gives the value of $\Delta F^\circ/T$, in cal./deg. mole, for the isomerization, $n\text{-}C_7H_{16}$ (gas) $= i\text{-}C_7H_{16}$ (gas). The scale of abscissas gives the temperature in degrees Kelvin.
(From E. J. Prosen, K. S. Pitzer, and F. D. Rossini, *J. Research Natl. Bur. Standards*
34, 403 (1945)).

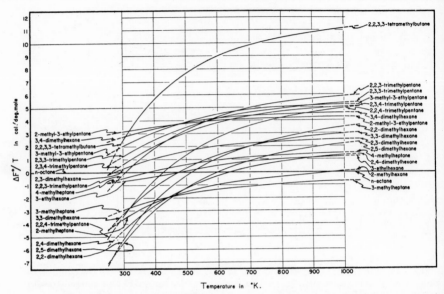

Temperature in °K.

FIG. 7. Free energy of isomerization of the eighteen octanes.
The scale of ordinates gives the value of $\Delta F°/T$, in cal./deg. mole, for the isomerization, $n\text{-}C_8H_{18}$ (gas) $= i\text{-}C_8H_{18}$ (gas). The scale of abscissas gives the temperature in degrees Kelvin.
(From E. J. Prosen, K. S. Pitzer, and F. D. Rossini, *J. Research Natl. Bur. Standards* **34**, 255 (1945)).

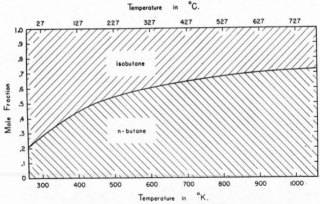

FIG. 8. Equilibrium concentrations of the two butanes
The scale of ordinates measures the amount in mole fraction, and the scale of abscissas gives the temperature in degrees Kelvin and degrees centigrade. The vertical width of a band at a given temperature measures the mole fraction of the given isomer present at equilibrium with all of its other isomers, in the gas phase.
(From E. J. Prosen, K. S. Pitzer, and F. D. Rossini, *J. Research Natl. Bur. Standards* **34**, 403 (1945)).

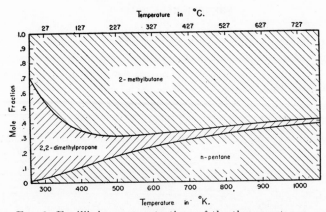

FIG. 9. Equilibrium concentrations of the three pentanes.
The scale of ordinates measures the amount in mole fraction, and the scale of
abscissas gives the temperature in degrees Kelvin and degrees centigrade. The
vertical width of a band at a given temperature measures the mole fraction of the
given isomer present at equilibrium with all of its other isomers, in the gas phase.
From E. J. Prosen, K. S. Pitzer, and F. D. Rossini, *J. Research Natl. Bur. Standards*
34, 403 (1945)).

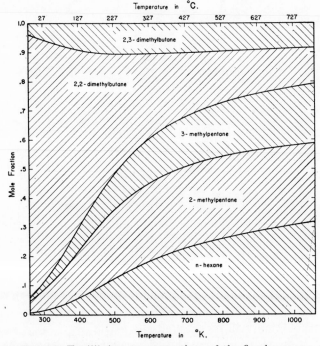

FIG. 10. Equilibrium concentrations of the five hexanes.
The scale of ordinates measures the amount in mole fraction, and the scale of
abscissas gives the temperature in degrees Kelvin and degrees centigrade. The
vertical width of a band at a given temperature measures the mole fraction of the
given isomer present at equilibrium with all of its isomers, in the gas phase.
(From E. J. Prosen, K. S. Pitzer, and F. D. Rossini, *J. Research Natl. Bur. Standards*
34, 403 (1945)).

From these charts, one may see at a glance, for any temperature in the given range and within the limits of uncertainty of the present calculations, which of the isomers, for any given number of carbon atoms, is thermodynamically the most stable (lowest value of $\Delta F^\circ/T$), which is the least stable (highest value of $\Delta F^\circ/T$), and the order of stability of the other isomers. From the assigned uncertainties (37, 38) it follows that those isomers having at some given temperature values of $\Delta F^\circ/T$ that differ

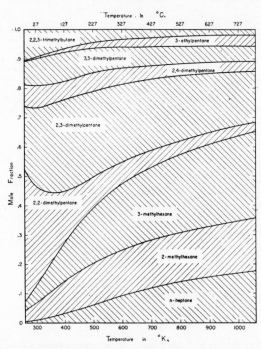

FIG. 11. Equilibrium concentrations of the nine heptanes.
The scale of ordinates measures the amount in mole fraction, and the scale of abscissas gives the temperature in degrees Kelvin and degrees centigrade. The vertical width of a band at a given temperature measures the mole fraction of the given isomer present at equilibrium with all of its other isomers, in the gas phase. (From E. J. Prosen, K. S. Pitzer, and F. D. Rossini, *J. Research Natl. Bur. Standards* **34**, 403 (1945)).

by less than the uncertainty are ones for which the exact order of stability cannot be stated since the values overlap. In such cases, the amounts present at equilibrium will be substantially equal.

In Figs. 8, 9, 10, 11, and 12, are plotted, as a function of the temperature, the amounts, in mole fraction, of each of the isomers present at equilibrium with all its other isomers in the gas phase, respectively for the two butanes, the three pentanes, the five hexanes, the nine heptanes, and the eighteen octanes. The vertical width of each band gives the mole fraction for that isomer at the selected temperature. The mole fractions of the several isomers are plotted additively, so that their sum is unity at all temperatures.

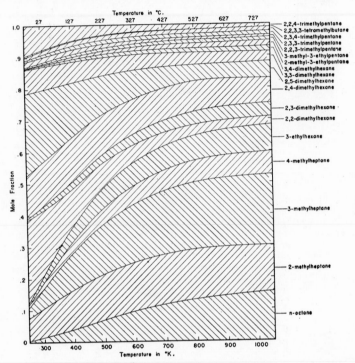

FIG. 12. Equilibrium concentrations of the eighteen octanes.
The scale of ordinates measures the amount in mole fraction, and the scale of abscissas gives the temperature in degrees Kelvin and degrees centigrade. The vertical width of a band at a given temperature measures the mole fraction of the given isomer present at equilibrium with all of its other isomers, in the gas phase. (From E. J. Prosen, K. S. Pitzer, and F. D. Rossini, *J. Research Natl. Bur. Standards* **34**, 255 (1945)).

With regard to the thermodynamic stability of the isomers, among the butanes, pentanes, hexanes, heptanes, and octanes, respectively, the following general conclusions may be drawn:

At 25°C., the normal isomer is among the isomers of lesser stability. Relative to the other isomers, the normal isomer increases in stability with increase in temperature, and at 1000°K. is among the most stable of the isomers.

(b) At 25°C., the 2,2-dimethyl isomer is among the most stable of the isomers, but it rapidly becomes less stable with increasing temperature and at 1000°K. is among the least stable of the isomers.

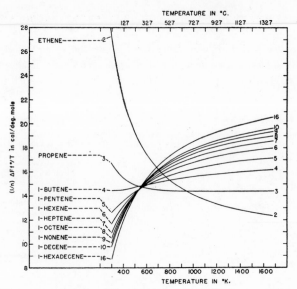

FIG. 13. Thermodynamic stability of the 1-alkene hydrocarbons in the gaseous state as a function of temperature.

The scale of ordinates gives the value of $(1/n)\,(\Delta Ff^\circ/T)$ in cal./deg. mole, where n is the number of carbon atoms per molecule, T is the absolute temperature in degrees Kelvin, and ΔFf° is the standard free energy of formation of the hydrocarbon from the elements, solid carbon (graphite) and gaseous hydrogen. The scale of abscissas gives the temperature in degrees Kelvin.

(From J. E. Kilpatrick, E. J. Prosen, K. S. Pitzer, and F. D. Rossini, *J. Research Natl. Bur. Standards* **36**, 559 (1946)).

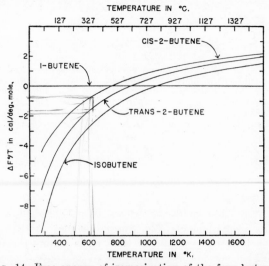

FIG. 14. Free energy of isomerization of the four butenes.

The scale of ordinates gives the value of $\Delta F^\circ/T$, in cal./deg. mole, for the isomerization of 1-butene into the other isomers, in the gaseous state, as indicated. The scale of abscissas gives the temperature in degrees Kelvin.

(From J. E. Kilpatrick, E. J. Prosen, K. S. Pitzer, and F. D. Rossini, *J. Research Natl. Bur. Standards* **36**, 559 (1946)).

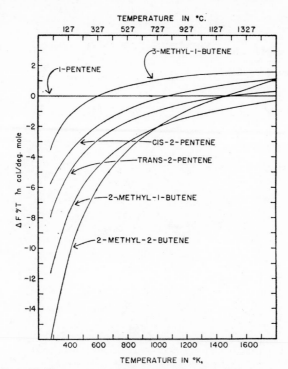

FIG. 15. Free energy of isomerization of the six pentenes.
The scale of ordinates gives the value of $\Delta F°/T$; in cal./deg. mole, for the isomerization of 1-pentene into the other isomers, in the gaseous state, as indicated. The scale of abscissas gives the temperature in degrees Kelvin.
(From J. E. Kilpatrick, E. J. Prosen, K. S. Pitzer, and F. D. Rossini, *J. Research Natl. Bur. Standards* **36,** 559 (1946).

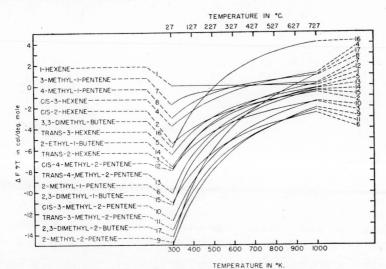

FIG. 16. Free energy of isomerization of the seventeen hexenes.
The scale of ordinates gives the value of $\Delta F°/T$, in cal./deg. mole, for the isomerization of 1-hexene into the other isomers, in the gaseous state, as indicated. The scale of abscissas gives the temperature in degrees Kelvin.
(From J. E. Kilpatrick, E. J. Prosen, K. S. Pitzer, and F. D. Rossini, *J. Research Natl. Bur. Standards* **36,** 559 (1946)).

(c) The more highly-branched isomers are among the least stable at the higher temperatures.

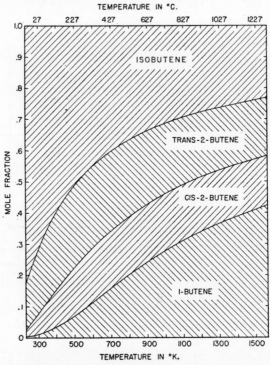

FIG. 17. Equilibrium concentrations of the four butenes.
The scale of ordinates measures the amount in mole fraction, and the scale of abscissas gives the temperature in degrees Kelvin and degrees centigrade. The vertical width of a band at a given temperature measures the mole fraction of the given isomer present when at equilibrium with all of its other isomers, in the gas phase. (From J. E. Kilpatrick, E. J. Prosen, K. S. Pitzer, and F. D. Rossini, J. Research Natl. Bur. Standards **36**, 559 (1946)).

3. MONOOLEFINS

Kilpatrick *et al.* (40), Prosen and Rossini (33), and Kilpatrick and Pitzer (41) have summarized the results on the thermodynamic properties of the monoolefin hydrocarbons.

Figure 13 shows the thermodynamic stability of the 1-alkenes in the gaseous state as a function of temperature, per carbon atom and with respect to the elements solid carbon (graphite) and gaseous hydrogen. This plot for the 1-alkenes may be compared to the corresponding one for the normal paraffins.

In Figs. 14, 15, and 16 are plotted, as a function of the temperature T, respectively for the four butenes, the six pentenes, and the seventeen hexenes, the values of $\Delta F°/T$ for the reaction of isomerization in the gaseous state:

$$1\text{-Alkene, normal (gas)} = \text{Isomeric Alkene (gas).} \qquad (123)$$

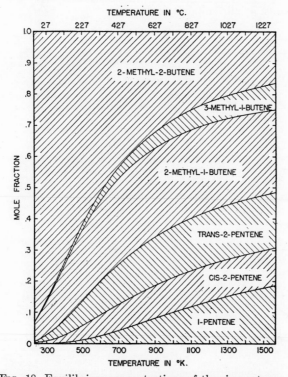

FIG. 18. Equilibrium concentrations of the six pentenes.
The scale of ordinates measures the amount in mole fraction, and the scale of abscissas gives the temperature in degrees Kelvin and degrees centigrade. The vertical width of a band at a given temperature measures the mole fraction of the given isomer present when at equilibrium with all of its other isomers, in the gas phase.
(From J. E. Kilpatrick, E. J. Prosen, K. S. Pitzer, and F. D. Rossini, *J. Research Natl. Bur. Standards* **36**, 559 (1946)).

From these charts, one may see at a glance, for any temperature in the given range and within the limits of uncertainty of the calculations, which of the isomers is thermodynamically most stable (lowest value of $\Delta F°/T$) and which is the least stable (highest value of $\Delta F°/T$). These plots may be compared with the corresponding ones for the butanes, pentanes, hexanes, heptanes, and octanes.

In Figs. 17, 18, and 19 are plotted, as a function of temperature, respectively for the four butenes, six pentenes, and seventeen hexenes, the amounts, in mole fraction, of each of the isomers present at equilibrium with its other alkene isomers in the gas phase. The vertical width of each band gives the mole fraction for that isomer at the selected temperature. The mole fractions of the several isomers are plotted additively, so that their sum is unity at all temperatures.

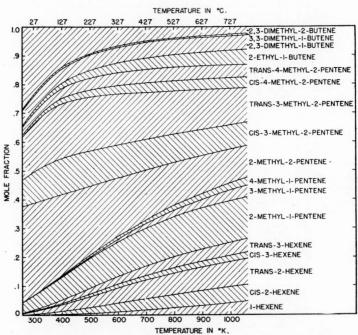

FIG. 19. Equilibrium concentrations of the seventeen hexenes.
The scale of ordinates measures the amount in mole fraction, and the scale of abscissas gives the temperature in degrees Kelvin and degrees centigrade. The vertical width of a band at a given temperature measures the mole fraction of the given isomer present when at equilibrium with all of its other isomers, in the gas phase.
(From J. E. Kilpatrick, E. J. Prosen, K. S. Pitzer, and F. D. Rossini, *J. Research Natl. Bur. Standards* **36**, 559 (1946)).

In Fig. 20 are plotted, as a function of the temperature, values of the logarithm of the equilibrium constant for the reaction of hydrogenation of a given 1-alkene to the corresponding normal paraffin, in the gaseous state:

$$1\text{-Alkene(gas)} + H_2\text{(gas)} = n\text{-Paraffin(gas)} \qquad (124)$$

The curves show the change in the value of the logarithm of the equiibrium constant of hydrogenation with increase in the number of carbon atoms in the molecule.

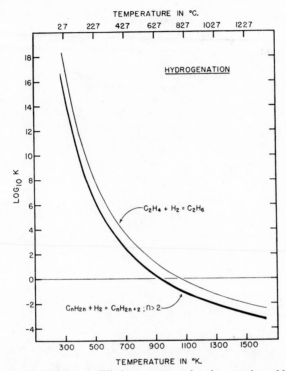

FIG. 20. Logarithm of the equilibrium constant for the reaction of hydrogenation of 1-alkenes to n-paraffins.

The scale of ordinates gives the value of the logarithm (to the base 10) of the equilibrium constant for the reaction of hydrogenation of a given 1-alkene to the corresponding normal paraffin, in the gaseous state. The scale of abscissas gives the temperature in degrees Kelvin. The values calculated for propylene, 1-butene, and the higher 1-alkenes all fall within the width of the heavy line indicated.
(From J. E. Kilpatrick, E. J. Prosen, K. S. Pitzer, and F. D. Rossini, *J. Research Natl. Bur. Standards* **36**, 559 (1946)).

In Fig. 21 are plotted, as a function of temperature, values of the logarithm of the equilibrium constant for the following reactions of dimerization:

$$2C_2H_4 \text{ (ethylene, gas)} = C_4H_8 \text{ (1-butene, gas)} \qquad (125)$$

$$2C_3H_6 \text{ (propylene, gas)} = C_6H_{12} \text{ (1-hexene, gas)} \qquad (126)$$

$$2C_4H_8 \text{ (1-butene, gas)} = C_8H_{16} \text{ (1-octene, gas)} \qquad (127)$$

$$2C_5H_{10} \text{ (1-pentene, gas)} = C_{10}H_{20} \text{ (1-decene, gas)} \qquad (128)$$

$2C_nH_{2n}$ (1-alkene, normal, gas) = $C_{2n}H_{4n}$ (1-alk ne, normal, gas);
$n > 5$. (129)

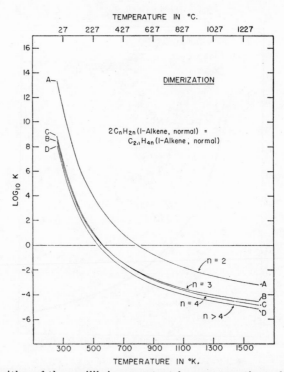

Fig. 21. Logarithm of the equilibrium constant for some reactions of dimerization. The scale of ordinates gives the value of the logarithm (to the base 10) of the equilibrium constant for some reactions of dimerization of 1-alkenes to 1-alkenes, in the gaseous state. The scale of abscissas gives the temperature in degrees Kelvin. The lowest curve shown is that for 1-pentene and higher 1-alkenes.
(From J. E. Kilpatrick, E. J. Prosen, K. S. Pitzer, and F. D. Rossini, *J. Research Natl. Bur. Standards* **36,** 559 (1946)).

In Fig. 22 are plotted, as a function of temperature, values of the logarithm of the equilibrium constant for the following reactions of alkylation, involving the addition of a paraffin to a monoolefin:

Ethylene (gas) + Isobutane (gas) = 2,3-Dimethylbutane (gas) (130)

Propylene (gas) + Isobutane (gas) = 2,3-Dimethylpentane (gas) (131)

Isobutene (gas) + Isobutane (gas) = 2,2,4-Trimethylpentane (gas) (132)

2-Methyl-2-butene (gas) + Isobutane (gas) = 2,2,5-Trimethyl-
hexane (gas). (133)

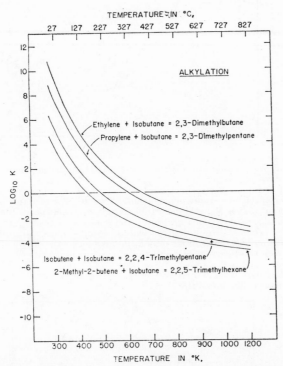

FIG. 22. Logarithm of the equilibrium constant for some reactions of alkylation.
The scale of ordinates gives the value of the logarithm (to the base 10) of the equilibrium constant for some reactions of alkylation (addition of an olefin to a paraffin to form a paraffin), in the gaseous state. The scale of abscissas gives the temperature in degrees Kelvin.
(From J. E. Kilpatrick, E. J. Prosen, K. S. Pitzer, and F. D. Rossini, *J. Research Natl. Bur. Standards* **36**, 559 (1946)).

4. ACETYLENES

Wagman *et al.* (42) have summarized the results on the thermodynamic properties of the acetylene hydrocarbons.

Figure 23 shows the thermodynamic stability of the 1-alkynes in the gaseous state as a function of the temperature, in the form of a plot of the standard free energy of formation, per carbon atom, divided by the absolute temperature. This plot may be compared with the corresponding ones for the normal paraffins and the 1-alkene monoolefins.

In Figs. 24 and 25 are plotted, as a function of the temperature, the

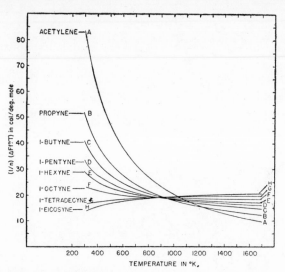

Fig. 23. Thermodynamic stability of the 1-alkyne hydrocarbons in the gaseous state as a function of temperature.

The scale of ordinates gives the value of $(1/n)$ $(\Delta Ff^\circ/T)$ in cal./deg. mole, where n is the number of carbon atoms per molecule, T is the absolute temperature in degrees Kelvin, and ΔFf° is the standard free energy of formation of the hydrocarbon from the elements, solid carbon (graphite) and gaseous hydrogen. The scale of abscissas gives the temperature in degrees Kelvin. Points below the zero line indicate that the gaseous hydrocarbon in its standard state has a thermodynamic tendency to be formed from solid carbon (graphite) and gaseous hydrogen in their respective standard states.

(From D. D. Wagman, J. E. Kilpatrick, K. S. Pitzer, and F. D. Rossini, *J. Research Natl. Bur. Standards* **35,** 467 (1945)).

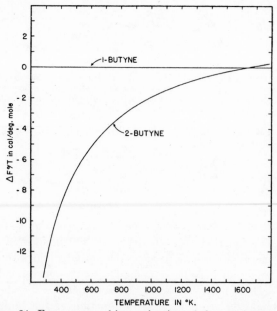

Fig. 24. Free energy of isomerization of the two butynes.

The scale of ordinates gives the value of $\Delta F^\circ/T$, in cal./deg. mole, for the isomerization of 1-butyne (gas) into 2-butyne (gas). The scale of abscissas gives the temperature in degrees Kelvin.

(From D. D. Wagman, J. E. Kilpatrick, K. S. Pitzer, and F. D. Rossini, *J. Research Natl. Bur. Standards* **35,** 467 (1945)).

values of $\Delta F^\circ/T$ for the isomerization of the two butynes and the three pentynes, respectively, according to the reaction:

$$\text{1-Alkyne, normal (gas)} = \text{Isomeric alkyne (gas)}. \qquad (134)$$

From these charts, one may see at a glance, for any temperature in the given range, and within the assigned limits of uncertainty, which of the

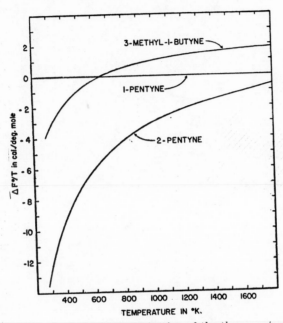

FIG. 25. Free energy of isomerization of the three pentynes.
The scale of ordinates gives the value of $\Delta F^\circ/T$, in cal/deg. mole, for the isomerization of 1-pentyne (gas) into the appropriate isomeric pentyne (gas). The scale of abscissas gives the temperature in degrees Kelvin.
(From D. D. Wagman, J. E. Kilpatrick, K. S. Pitzer, and F. D. Rossini, *J. Research Natl. Bur. Standards* **35**, 467 (1945)).

isomers is thermodynamically most stable (lowest value of $\Delta F^\circ/T$) and which is the least stable (highest value of $\Delta F^\circ/T$).

In Figs. 26 and 27 are plotted, as a function of temperature, for the butynes and pentynes, respectively, the amounts, in mole fraction, of each of the isomers present when at equilibrium with its other acetylene isomers in the gas phase. The vertical width of each band gives the mole fraction for that isomer at the selected temperature. The mole fractions of the several isomers are plotted additively, so that their sum is unity at all temperatures.

In Figs. 28, 29, 30 and 31 are plotted as a function of temperature, for

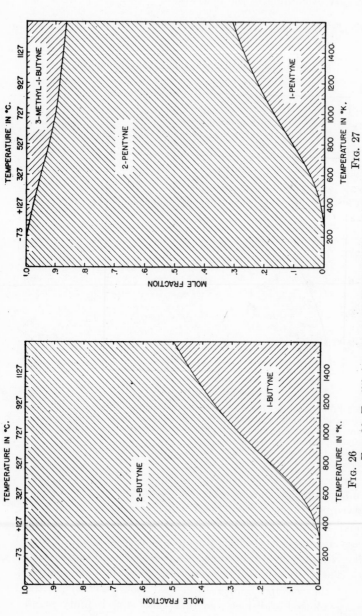

Fig. 26. Equilibrium concentrations of the two butynes.

The scale of ordinates measures the amount in mole fraction, and the scale of abscissas gives the temperature in degrees Kelvin and degrees centigrade. The vertical width of a band at a given temperature measures the mole fraction of the given isomer present when at equilibrium with all of its other isomers, in the gas phase. (From D. D. Wagman, J. E. Kilpatrick, K. S. Pitzer, and F. D. Rossini, *J. Research Natl. Bur. Standards* **35**, 467 (1945)).

Fig. 27. Equilibrium concentrations of the three pentynes.

The scale of ordinates measures the amount in mole fraction, and the scale of abscissas gives the temperature in degrees Kelvin and degrees centigrade. The vertical width of a band at a given temperature measures the mole fraction of the given isomer present when at equilibrium with all of its other isomers, in the gas phase.

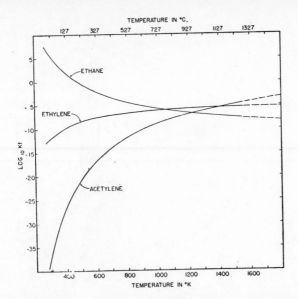

Fig. 28. Logarithm of the equilibrium constant of formation of ethane, ethylene, and acetylene.
The scale of ordinates gives the logarithm (to the base 10) of the equilibrium constant of formation of the hydrocarbons in the gaseous state from the elements solid carbon (graphite) and gaseous hydrogen, with each substance in its thermodynamic standard state. The scale of abscissas gives the temperature in degrees Kelvin and degrees centigrade.
(From D. D. Wagman, J. E. Kilpatrick, K. S. Pitzer, and F. D. Rossini, *J. Research Natl. Bur. Standards* **35**, 467 (1945)).

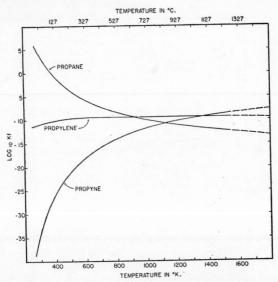

Fig. 29. Logarithm of the equilibrium constant of formation of propane, propylene, and propyne.
The scale of ordinates gives the logarithm (to the base 10) of the equilibrium constant of formation of the hydrocarbons from the elements solid carbon (graphite) and gaseous hydrogen, with each substance in its thermodynamic standard state. The scale of abscissas gives the temperature in degrees Kelvin and degrees centigrade.
(From D. D. Wagman, J. E. Kilpatrick, K. S. Pitzer, and F. D. Rossini, *J. Research Natl. Bur. Standards* **35**, 467 (1945)).

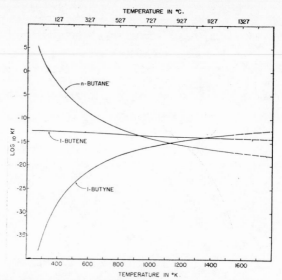

FIG. 30. Logarithm of the equilibrium constant of formation of n-butane, 1 butene, and 1-butyne.

The scale of ordinates gives the logarithm (to the base 10) of the equilibrium constant of formation of the hydrocarbons from the elements solid carbon (graphite) and gaseous hydrogen, with each substance in its thermodynamic standard state The scale of abscissas gives the temperature in degrees Kelvin and degrees centigrade.

(From D. D. Wagman, J. E. Kilpatrick, K. S. Pitzer, and F. D. Rossini, *J. Research Natl. Bur. Standards* **35,** 467 (1945)).

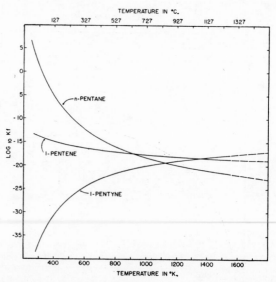

FIG. 31. Logarithm of the equilibrium constant of formation of n-pentane, 1-pentene, and 1-pentyne.

The scale of ordinates gives the logarithm (to the base 10) of the equilibrium constant of formation of the hydrocarbons from the elements solid carbon (graphite) and gaseous hydrogen, with each substance in its thermodynamic standard state. The scale of abscissas gives the temperature in degrees Kelvin and degrees centigrade.

(From D. D. Wagman, J. E. Kilpatrick, K. S. Pitzer, and F. D. Rossini, *J. Research Natl. Bur. Standards* **35,** 467 (1945)).

the C_2, C_3, C_4, and C_5 hydrocarbons, respectively, values of $\log_{10} Kf$, the logarithm (to the base 10) of the equilibrium constant, of the reaction of forming the given hydrocarbon in its standard gaseous state from the elements solid carbon (graphite) and gaseous hydrogen according to the

TABLE VII

RANGES OF TEMPERATURE IN WHICH, FOR MOLECULES OF THE SAME NUMBER OF CARBON ATOMS, THE NORMAL PARAFFIN, 1-ALKENE, AND 1-ALKYNE HYDROCARBONS, C_2 TO C_5, ARE RELATIVELY MOST STABLE IN THE PRESENCE OF HYDROGEN, WITH EACH SUBSTANCE IN ITS THERMODYNAMIC STANDARD STATE.

Number of C atoms	n-Paraffin		1-Alkene		1-Alkyne	
	Range of temperature*					
	°K.	°C.	°K.	°C.	°K.	°C.
	Below		Between		Above	
C_2	1065	792	1065–1390	792–1117	1390	1117
C_3	930	657	930–1350	657–1077	1350	1077
C_4	935	662	935–1350	662–1077	1350	1077
C_5	915	642	915–1350	642–1077	1350	1077

*Temperatures rounded to the nearest 5°K.

following equations, for the paraffin, olefin, and acetylene series, respectively:

$$nC \text{ (solid, graphite)} + (n + 1) \text{ H}_2\text{(gas)} = C_nH_{2n+2} \text{ (gas, normal paraffin)} \tag{135}$$

$$nC \text{ (solid, graphite)} + n \text{ H}_2\text{(gas)} = C_nH_{2n} \text{ (gas, 1-alkene)} \tag{136}$$

$$nC \text{ (solid, graphite)} + (n - 1) \text{ H}_2\text{(gas)} = C_nH_{2n-2} \text{ (gas, 1-alkyne).} \tag{137}$$

The differences in the values of the ordinates of any given pair of curves in Figs. 28, 29, 30, and 31 give the value of the logarithm of the equilibrium constant for the appropriate reaction of hydrogenation or dehydrogenation.

The plots in Figs. 28, 29, 30, and 31 show, for molecules of the same number of carbon atoms, the ranges of temperature in which the normal paraffin, 1-alkene, and 1-alkyne hydrocarbons are relatively most stable (highest value of log Kf) in the presence of hydrogen, with each substance (including the hydrogen) in its thermodynamic standard state of unit fugacity of 1 atmosphere. These ranges of temperature are given in Table VII in degrees Kelvin and Centigrade, and are important in the analysis of any process involving hydrogenation or dehydrogenation of these molecules.

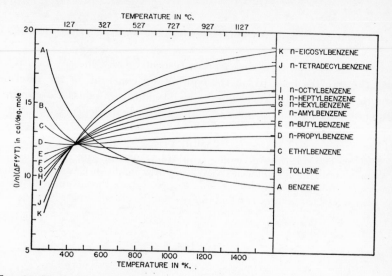

FIG. 32. Thermodynamic stability of the normal alkyl benzenes in the gaseous state as a function of temperature.

The scale of ordinates gives the value of $(1/n)(\Delta Ff°/T)$ in cal./deg. mole, where n is the number of carbon atoms per molecule, T is the absolute temperature in degrees Kelvin, and $\Delta Ff°$ is the standard free energy of formation of the hydrocarbon from the elements, solid carbon (graphite) and gaseous hydrogen, all at the given temperature. The scale of abscissas gives the temperature in degrees Kelvin.
(From W. J. Taylor, D. D. Wagman, M. G. Williams, K. S. Pitzer, and F. D. Rossini, *J. Research Natl. Bur. Standards* **37**, 95 (1946)).

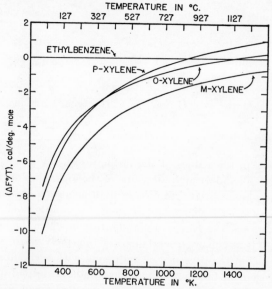

FIG. 33. Free energy of isomerization of the C_8H_{10} alkyl benzenes.

The scale of ordinates gives the value of $\Delta F°/T$, in cal./deg. mole, for the isomerization of ethylbenzene into the other isomers, in the gaseous state, as indicated. The scale of abscissas gives the temperature in degrees Kelvin.
(From W. J. Taylor, D. D. Wagman, M. G. Williams, K. S. Pitzer, and F. D. Rossini, *J. Research Natl. Bur. Standards* **37**, 95 (1946)).

5. ALKYL BENZENES

Taylor *et al.* (43) and Prosen *et al.* (34) have summarized the results on
he thermodynamic properties of the alkyl benzenes.

Figure 32 shows the thermodynamic stability of the normal alkyl ben-
nes in the gaseous state as a function of the temperature, in the form of a
ot of the standard free energy of formation, per carbon atom, divided by
he absolute temperature. This plot may be compared with the correspond-

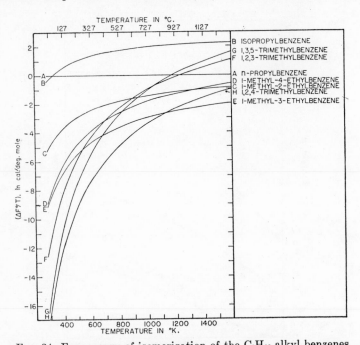

FIG. 34. Free energy of isomerization of the C_9H_{12} alkyl benzenes.
The scale of ordinates gives the value of $\Delta F^\circ/T$, in cal./deg. mole, for the isomer-
zation of *n*-propylbenzene into the other isomers, in the gaseous state, as indicated.
The scale of abscissas gives the temperature in degrees Kelvin.
(From W. J. Taylor, D. D. Wagman, M. G. Williams, K. S. Pitzer, and F. D. Rossini,
J. *Research Natl. Bur. Standards* **37**, 95 (1946)).

ing ones for the normal paraffins, the 1-alkene monoolefins, and the 1-alkyne
acetylenes.

In Figs. 33 and 34 are plotted, as a function of the temperature, the
values of $\Delta F^\circ/T$ for the isomerization of the C_8H_{10} and C_9H_{12} alkyl benzenes,
according to the reactions:

Ethylbenzene (gas) = Isomeric alkyl benzene (gas)   (138)

n-Propylbenzene (gas) = Isomeric alkyl benzene (gas).   (139)

From these plots, one may see at a glance, for any temperature in the given range, and within the assigned limits of uncertainty, which of the isomers is thermodynamically most stable (lowest value of $\Delta F°/T$) and which is the least stable (highest value of $\Delta F°/T$).

In Figs. 35 and 36 are plotted, as a function of temperature, for the C_8H_{10} and the C_9H_{12} alkyl benzenes, respectively, the amounts, in mole

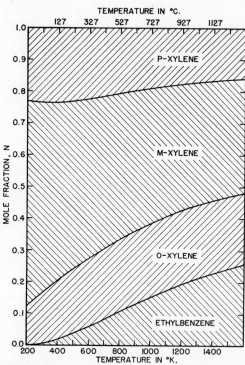

FIG. 35. Equilibrium concentrations of the C_8H_{10} alkyl benzenes.

The scale of ordinates measures the amount in mole fraction, and the scale of abscissas gives the temperature in degrees Kelvin and degrees centigrade. The vertical width of a band at a given temperature measures the mole fraction of the given isomer present when at equilibrium with all of its other isomers, in the gas phase.

(From W. J. Taylor, D. D. Wagman, M. G. Williams, K. S. Pitzer, and F. D. Rossini, *J. Research Natl. Bur. Standards* **37**, 95 (1946)).

fraction, of each of the isomers present at equilibrium with its other isomers in the gas phase. The vertical width of each band gives the mole fraction for that isomer at the selected temperature. The mole fractions of the several isomers are plotted additively so that their sum is unity at all temperatures.

In Figs. 37, 38, and 39, are plotted as a function of temperature, values

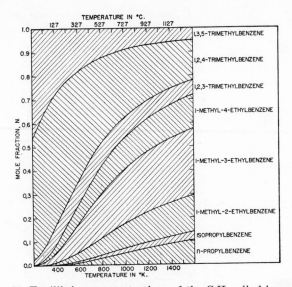

FIG. 36. Equilibrium concentrations of the C_9H_{12} alkyl benzenes.
The scale of ordinates measures the amount in mole fraction, and the scale of abscissas gives the temperature in degrees Kelvin and degrees centigrade. The vertical width of a band at a given temperature measures the mole fraction of the given isomer present when at equilibrium with all of its other isomers, in the gas phase. (From W. J. Taylor, D. D. Wagman, M G. Williams, K. S. Pitzer, and F. D. Rossini, *J. Research Natl. Bur. Standards* **37,** 95 (1946)).

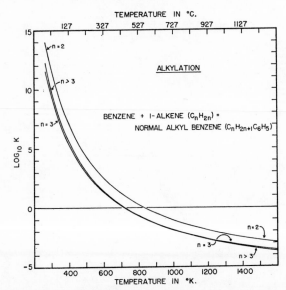

FIG. 37. Logarithm of the equilibrium constant for some reactions of alkylation.
The scale of ordinates gives the value of the logarithm (to the base 10) of the equilibrium constant for some reactions of alkylation (addition of an olefin to benzene to form an alkyl benzene), in the gaseous state. The scale of abscissas gives the temperature in degrees Kelvin and degrees centigrade. (From W. J. Taylor, D. D. Wagman, M. G. Williams, K. S. Pitzer, and F. D. Rossini, *J. Research Natl. Bur. Standards* **37,** 95 (1946)).

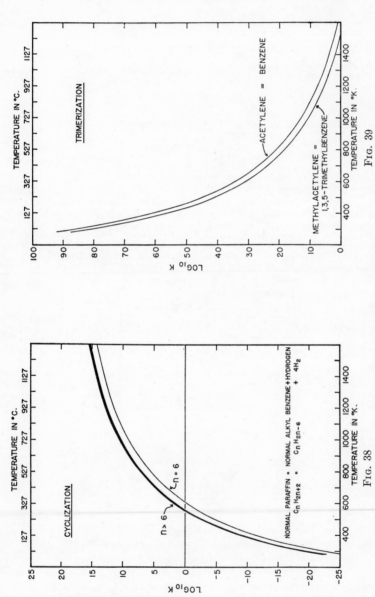

FIG. 38. Logarithm of the equilibrium constant for some reactions of cyclization. The scale of ordinates gives the value of the logarithm (to the base 10) of the equilibrium constant for the reaction of cyclization of a normal paraffin to form a normal alkyl benzene, in the gaseous state. The scale of abscissas gives the temperature in degrees Kelvin and degrees centigrade. The values calculated for n-heptane and higher paraffins fall within the width of the heavy line indicated.

(From W. J. Taylor, D. D. Wagman, M. G. Williams, K. S. Pitzer, and F. D. Rossini, *J. Research Natl. Bur. Standards* **37**, 95 (1946)).

FIG. 39. Logarithm of the equilibrium constant for some reactions of trimerization.

The scale of ordinates gives the value of the logarithm (to the base 10) of the equilibrium constant for some reactions of trimerization of alkynes to alkyl benzenes in the gaseous state. The scale of abscissas gives the temperature in degrees Kelvin.

of the logarithm of the equilibrium constant for some reactions of alkylation (addition of an olefin to benzene to form an alkyl benzene), cyclization (conversion of normal paraffin to alkyl benzene plus hydrogen), and trimerization (of acetylene to benzene and of methylacetylene to 1,3,5-trimethylbenzene), for the following reactions:

Alkylation

Benzene (gas) + Ethylene (gas) = Ethylbenzene (gas) (140)

Benzene (gas) + Propylene (gas) = n-Propylbenzene (gas) (141)

Benzene (gas) + Propylene (gas) = Isopropylbenzene (gas) (142)

Benzene (gas) + C_nH_{2n} (1-alkene, normal, gas) =
n-Alkyl benzene (gas); $n > 3$ (143)

Cyclization

n-Hexane (gas) = Benzene (gas) + Hydrogen (gas) (144)

n-Heptane (gas) = Toluene (gas) + Hydrogen (gas) (145)

n-Octane (gas) = Ethylbenzene (gas) + Hydrogen (gas) (146)

n-Nonane (gas) = n-Propylbenzene (gas) + Hydrogen (gas) (147)

n-Paraffin (gas) = n-Alkyl benzene (gas) + Hydrogen (gas);
above nonane (148)

Trimerization

Acetylene (gas) = Benzene (gas) (149)

Methylacetylene (gas) = 1,3,5-Trimethylbenzene (gas). (150)

6. ALKYL CYCLOPENTANES

Kilpatrick *et al.* (44) and Prosen *et al.* (29) have summarized the results on the thermodynamic properties of the alkyl cyclopentane hydrocarbons.

Figure 40 shows the thermodynamic stability of the normal alkyl cyclopentanes in the gaseous state as a function of the temperature, in the form of a plot of the standard free energy of formation, per carbon atom, divided by the absolute temperature. This plot may be compared with the corresponding ones for the normal paraffins, the 1-alkene monoolefins, 1-alkyne acetylenes, and the normal alkyl benzenes.

Figure 41 gives a plot of the logarithm of the equilibrium constant, as a

function of the temperature, for the following reactions of cyclization of normal paraffins to normal alkyl cyclopentanes:

n-Pentane (gas) = Cyclopentane (gas) + Hydrogen (gas)   (151)

n-Hexane (gas) = Methylcyclopentane (gas) + Hydrogen (gas)   (152)

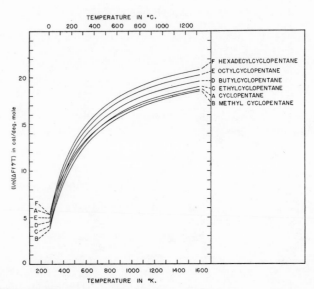

FIG. 40. Thermodynamic stability of the normal alkyl cyclopentanes in the gaseous state as a function of temperature.
The scale of ordinates gives the value of $(1/n)$ $(\Delta Ff^\circ/T)$ in cal./deg. mole, where n is the number of carbon atoms per molecule, T is the absolute temperature in degrees Kelvin, and ΔFf° is the standard free energy of formation of the hydrocarbon from the elements, solid carbon (graphite) and gaseous hydrogen. The scale of abscissas gives the temperature in degrees Kelvin. Points below the zero line indicate that the gaseous hydrocarbon in its standard state has a thermodynamic tendency to be formed from solid carbon (graphite) and gaseous hydrogen in their respective standard states.
(From J. E. Kilpatrick, H. G. Werner, C. W. Beckett, K. S. Pitzer, and F. D. Rossini, *J. Research Natl. Bur. Standards* **39**, 523 (1947)).

n-Heptane (gas) = Ethylcyclopentane (gas) + Hydrogen (gas)   (153)

n-Paraffin (gas) = n-Alkyl cyclopentane (gas) + Hydrogen (gas):
    for n-Octane and higher.   (154)

Figure 42 gives a plot of the logarithm of the equilibrium constant, as a function of the temperature, for the following reactions of hydrogenation of normal alkyl benzenes to normal alkyl cyclopentanes:

Benzene (gas) + Hydrogen (gas) = Methylcyclopentane (gas)   (155)

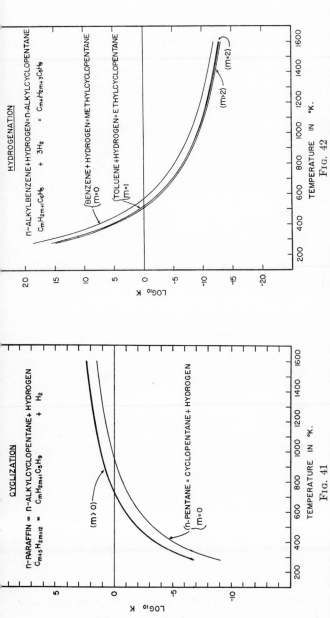

Fig. 41. Logarithm of the equilibrium constant for the reaction of cyclization of normal paraffins to normal alkyl cyclopentanes.
The scale of ordinates gives the value of the logarithm (to the base 10) of the equilibrium constant for the reaction of cyclization of a given normal paraffin to the corresponding normal alkyl cyclopentane, in the gaseous state. The scale of abscissas gives the temperature in degrees Kelvin. The values for the cyclization to methylcyclopentane, ethylcyclopentane, and the higher normal alkyl cyclopentanes all fall within the width of the heavy line indicated.
(From J. E. Kilpatrick, H. G. Werner, C. W. Beckett, K. S. Pitzer, and F. D. Rossini, *J. Research Natl. Bur. Standards* **39**, 523 (1947)).

Fig. 42. Logarithm of the equilibrium constant for the reaction of hydrogenation of normal alkyl benzenes to normal alkyl cyclopentanes.
The scale of ordinates gives the value of the logarithm (to the base 10) of the equilibrium constant for the reaction of hydrogenation of a given normal alkyl benzene to the corresponding normal alkyl cyclopentane, in the gaseous state. The scale of abscissas gives the temperature in degrees Kelvin.
(From J. E. Kilpatrick, H. G. Werner, C. W. Beckett, K. S. Pitzer, and F. D. Rossini, *J. Research Natl. Bur. Standards* **39**, 523 (1947)).

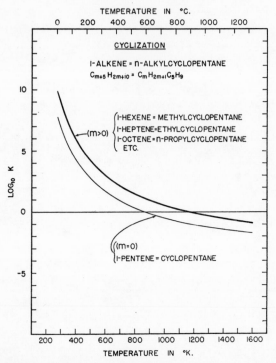

FIG. 43. Logarithm of the equilibrium constant for the reaction of cyclization of 1-alkene monoolefins to normal alkyl cyclopentanes.

The scale of ordinates gives the value of the logarithm (to the base 10) of the equilibrium constant for the reaction of cyclization of a given 1-alkene monoolefin to the corresponding normal alkyl cyclopentane, in the gaseous state. The scale of abscissas gives the temperature in degrees Kelvin. The values for the formation of methylcyclopentane, ethylcyclopentane, and higher normal alkyl cyclopentanes all fall within the width of the heavy line.

(From J. E. Kilpatrick, H. G. Werner, C. W. Beckett, K. S. Pitzer, and F. D. Rossini, *J. Research Natl. Bur. Standards* **39**, 523 (1947)).

Toluene (gas) + Hydrogen (gas) = Ethylcyclopentane (gas) (156)

Ethylbenzene (gas) + Hydrogen (gas) = *n*-Propylcyclopentane (gas) (157)

n-Propylbenzene (gas) + Hydrogen (gas) = *n*-Butylcyclopentane (gas) (158)

n-Alkyl benzene (gas) + Hydrogen (gas) = *n*-Alkyl cyclopentane (gas); for *n*-Butylbenzene and higher. (159)

Figure 43 gives a plot of the logarithm of the equilibrium constant, as a

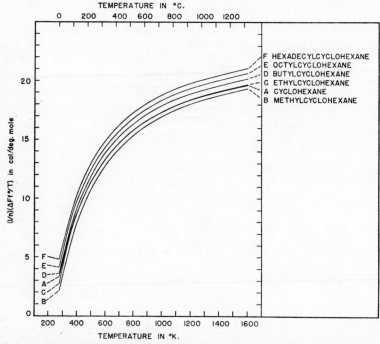

TEMPERATURE IN °C.

F HEXADECYLCYCLOHEXANE
E OCTYLCYCLOHEXANE
D BUTYLCYCLOHEXANE
C ETHYLCYCLOHEXANE
A CYCLOHEXANE
B METHYLCYCLOHEXANE

TEMPERATURE IN °K.

FIG. 44. Thermodynamic stability of the normal alkyl cyclohexanes in the gaseous state as a function of temperature.

The scale of ordinates gives the value of $(1/n)\,(\Delta Ff^{\circ}/T)$ in cal./deg. mole, where n is the number of carbon atoms per molecule, T is the absolute temperature in degrees Kelvin, and ΔFf° is the standard free energy of formation of the hydrocarbon from the elements, solid carbon (graphite) and gaseous hydrogen. The scale of abscissas gives the temperature in degrees Kelvin. Points below the zero line indicate that the gaseous hydrocarbon in its standard state has a thermodynamic tendency to be formed from solid carbon (graphite) and gaseous hydrogen in their respective standard states.

(From J. E. Kilpatrick, H. G. Werner, C. W. Beckett, K. S. Pitzer, and F. D. Rossini, *J. Research Natl. Bur. Standards* **39**, 523 (1947)).

function of the temperature, for the following reactions of cyclization of 1-alkene monoolefins to normal alkyl cyclopentanes:

1-Pentene (gas) = Cyclopentane (gas)   (160)

1-Hexene (gas) = Methylcyclopentane (gas)   (161)

1-Heptene (gas) = Ethylcyclopentane (gas)   (162)

1-Alkene (gas) = n-Alkyl cyclopentane (gas); for 1-octene and
    higher.   (163)

7. ALKYL CYCLOHEXANES

Kilpatrick *et al.* (44) and Prosen *et al.* (29, 45) have summarized the results on the thermodynamic properties of the alkyl cyclohexane hydrocarbons.

Figure 44 shows the thermodynamic stability of the normal alkyl cyclohexanes in the gaseous state as a function of the temperature, in the form of a plot of the standard free energy of formation, per carbon atom, divided

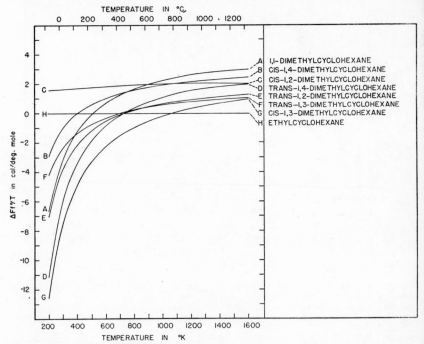

FIG. 45. Free energy of isomerization of the eight C_8H_{16} alkyl cyclohexanes. The scale of ordinates gives the value of $\Delta F°/T$, in cal./deg. mole, for the isomerization of ethylcyclohexane into the other isomers, in the gaseous state, as indicated. The scale of abscissas gives the temperature in degrees Kelvin.
(From J. E. Kilpatrick, H. G. Werner, C. W. Beckett, K. S. Pitzer, and F. D. Rossini, *J. Research Natl. Bur. Standards* **39**, 523 (1947)).

by the absolute temperature. This plot may be compared with the corresponding ones for the normal paraffins, the 1-alkene monoolefins, the 1-alkyne acetylenes, the normal alkyl benzenes, and the normal alkyl cyclopentanes.

In Fig. 45 is plotted, as a function of the temperature, the values of $\Delta F°/T$ for the isomerization of the C_8H_{16} alkyl cyclohexanes, according to the reaction

$$\text{Ethylcyclohexane (gas)} = \text{Dimethylcyclohexane (gas).} \qquad (164)$$

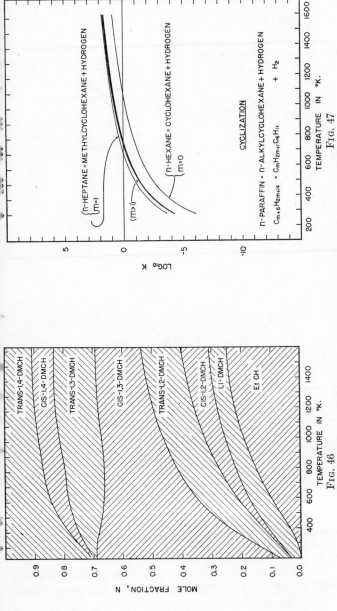

FIG. 47

FIG. 46

FIG. 46. Equilibrium concentrations of the eight C_8H_{16} alkyl cyclohexanes. The scale of ordinates measures the amount in mole fraction, and the scale of abscissas gives the temperature in degrees Kelvin and degrees centigrade. The vertical width of a band at a given temperature measures the mole fraction of the given isomer present when at equilibrium with all of its other isomers, in the gas phase. (From J. E. Kilpatrick, H. G. Werner, C. W. Beckett, K. S. Pitzer, and F. D. Rossini, *J. Research Natl. Bur. Standards* **39**, 523 (1947)).

FIG. 47. Logarithm of the equilibrium constant for the reaction of cyclization of normal paraffins to normal alkyl cyclohexanes. The scale of ordinates gives the value of the logarithm (to the base 10) of the equilibrium constant for the reaction of cyclization of a given normal paraffin to the corresponding normal alkyl cyclohexane, in the gaseous state. The scale of abscissas gives the temperature in degrees Kelvin. The values calculated for ethylcyclohexane, *n*-propylcyclohexane, and the higher normal alkyl cyclohexanes all fall within the width of the heavy line. (From J. E. Kilpatrick, H. G. Werner, C. W. Beckett, K. S. Pitzer, and F. D. Rossini, *J. Research Natl. Bur. Standards* **39**, 523 (1947)).

From this plot, one may see at a glance, for any temperature in the given range, and within the assigned limits of uncertainty, which of the isomers is thermodynamically most stable (lowest value of $\Delta F^\circ / T$) and which is the least stable (highest value of $\Delta F^\circ / T$).

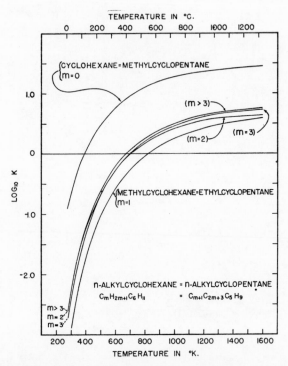

FIG. 48. Logarithm of the equilibrium constant for the reaction of conversion of normal alkyl cyclohexanes to normal alkyl cyclopentanes.

The scale of ordinates gives the value of the logarithm (to the base 10) of the equilibrium constant for the reaction of conversion of a given normal alkyl cyclohexane to the corresponding normal alkyl cyclopentane, in the gaseous state. The scale of abscissas gives the temperature in degrees Kelvin.

(From J. E. Kilpatrick, H. G. Werner, C. W. Beckett, K. S. Pitzer, and F. D. Rossini, *J. Research Natl. Bur. Standards* **39**, 523 (1947)).

In Fig. 46 is plotted, as a function of the temperature, for the C_8H_{16} alkyl cyclohexanes, the amounts, in mole fraction, of each of the isomers present at equilibrium with its other isomers in the gas phase. The vertical width of each band gives the mole fraction for that isomer at the selected temperature. The mole fractions of the several isomers are plotted additively, so that their sum is unity at all temperatures.

Figure 47 gives a plot of the logarithm of the equilibrium constant, as a

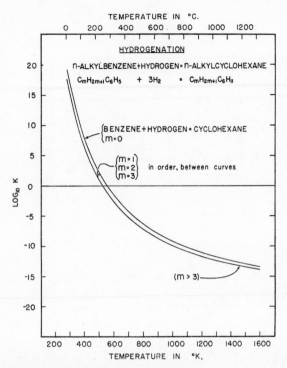

Fig. 49. Logarithm of the equilibrium constant for the reaction of hydrogenation of normal alkyl benzenes to normal alkyl cyclohexanes.

The scale of ordinates gives the value of the logarithm (to the base 10) of the equilibrium constant for the reaction of hydrogenation of a given normal alkyl benzene to the corresponding normal alkyl cyclohexane in the gaseous state. The scale of abscissas gives the temperature in degrees Kelvin. The upper curve is that for the hydrogenation of benzene and the lower curve is for the hydrogenation of n-butylbenzene, n-pentylbenzene, and the higher normal alkyl benzenes. The curves for toluene, ethylbenzene, and n-propylbenzene are, in order, between the two curves. (From J. E. Kilpatrick, H. G. Werner, C. W. Beckett, K. S. Pitzer, and F. D. Rossini, *J. Research Natl. Bur. Standards* **39**, 523 (1947)).

function of the temperature, for the following reactions of cyclization of normal paraffins to normal alkyl cyclohexanes:

$$n\text{-Hexane (gas)} = \text{Cyclohexane (gas)} + \text{Hydrogen (gas)} \qquad (165)$$

$$n\text{-Heptane (gas)} = \text{Methylcyclohexane (gas)} + \text{Hydrogen (gas)} \qquad (166)$$

$$n\text{-Octane (gas)} = \text{Ethylcyclohexane (gas)} + \text{Hydrogen (gas)} \qquad (167)$$

$$n\text{-Paraffin (gas)} = n\text{-Alkyl cyclohexane (gas)} + \text{Hydrogen (gas)};$$
$$\text{for } n\text{-Nonane and higher.} \qquad (168)$$

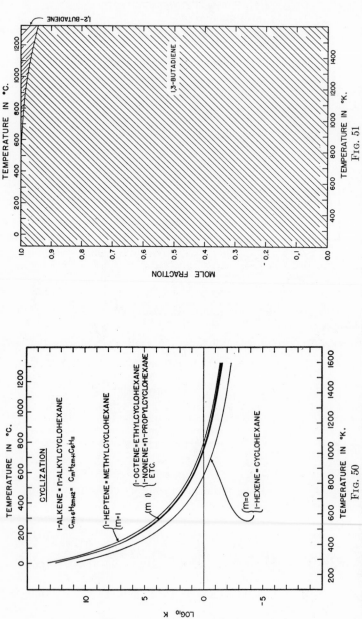

FIG. 50. Logarithm of the equilibrium constant for the reaction of cyclization of 1-alkene monoolefins to normal alkyl cyclohexanes. The scale of ordinates gives the value of the logarithm (to the base 10) of the equilibrium constant for the reaction of cyclization of a given 1-alkene monoolefin to the corresponding normal alkyl cyclohexane, in the gaseous state. The scale of abscissas gives the temperature in degrees Kelvin. The value for the formation of ethylcyclohexane, n-propylcyclohexane, and the higher normal alkyl cyclohexanes all fall within the width of the heavy line. (From J. E. Kilpatrick, H. G. Werner, C. W. Beckett, K. S. Pitzer, and F. D. Rossini, *J. Research Natl. Bur. Standards* **39**, 523 (1947)).

FIG. 51. Equilibrium concentrations of the two butadienes.

The scale of ordinates measures the amount in mole fraction, and the scale of abscissas gives the temperature in degrees Kelvin and degrees centigrade. The vertical width of a band at a given temperature measures the mole fraction of the given

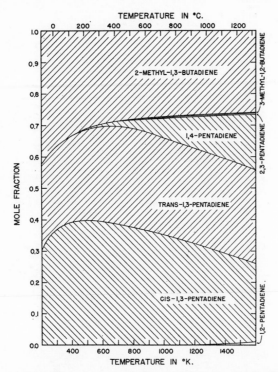

Fig. 52. Equilibrium concentrations of the seven pentadienes.
The scale of ordinates measures the amount in mole fraction, and the scale of abscissas gives the temperature in degrees Kelvin and degrees centigrade. The vertical width of a band at a given temperature measures the mole fraction of the given isomer present at equilibrium with all of its other isomers in the gaseous state. (From J. E. Kilpatrick, C. W. Beckett, E. J. Prosen, K. S. Pitzer, and F. D. Rossini, *J. Research Natl. Bur. Standards* **42**, 225 (1949)).

Figure 48 gives a plot of the logarithm of the equilibrium constant, as a function of the temperature, for the following reactions of conversion of normal alkyl cyclohexanes to normal alkyl cyclopentanes:

Cyclohexane (gas) = Methylcyclopentane (gas)   (169)

Methylcyclohexane (gas) = Ethylcyclopentane (gas)   (170)

Ethylcyclohexane (gas) = n-Propylcyclopentane (gas)   (171)

n-Propylcyclohexane (gas) = n-Butylcyclopentane (gas)   (172)

n-Alkyl cyclohexane (gas) = n-Alkyl cyclopentane (gas); for
n-Butylcyclohexane and higher.   (173)

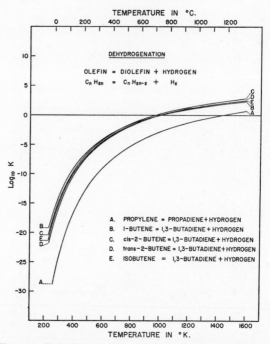

FIG. 53. Dehydrogenation of monoolefins to diolefins.

The scale of ordinates gives the value of the logarithm (to the base 10) of the equilibrium constant for the reaction of dehydrogenating a given monoolefin to a given diolefin, in the gaseous state. The scale of abscissas gives the temperature in degrees Kelvin.

The several curves refer to the following reactions in the gaseous state:

(A) propylene = propadiene + hydrogen
(B) 1-butene = 1,3-butadiene + hydrogen
(C) cis-2-butene = 1,3-butadiene + hydrogen
(D) trans-2-butene = 1,3-butadiene + hydrogen
(E) isobutene = 1,3-butadiene + hydrogen

(From J. E. Kilpatrick, C. W. Beckett, E. J. Prosen, K. S. Pitzer, and F. D. Rossini, J. Research Natl. Bur. Standards **42**, 225 (1949)).

Figure 49 gives a plot of the logarithm of the equilibrium constant, as a function of the temperature, for the following reactions of hydrogenation of normal alkyl benzenes to normal alkyl cyclohexanes:

Benzene (gas) + Hydrogen (gas) = Cyclohexane (gas)   (174)

Toluene (gas) + Hydrogen (gas) = Methylcyclohexane (gas)   (175)

Ethylbenzene (gas) + Hydrogen (gas) = Ethylcyclohexane (gas)   (176)

n-Propylbenzene (gas) + Hydrogen (gas) = n-Propylcyclohexane
    (gas)   (177)

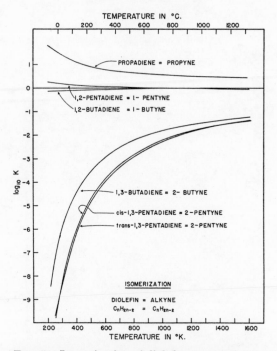

FIG. 54. Isomerization of diolefins to acetylenes.

The scale of ordinates gives the value of the logarithm (to the base 10) of the equilibrium constant for the reaction of isomerization of a given diolefin to a given acetylene hydrocarbon, in the gaseous state. The scale of abscissas gives the temperature in degrees Kelvin.

The several curves are for the following reactions in the gaseous state, as indicated:

propadiene = propyne
1,2-butadiene = 1-butyne
1,2-pentadiene = 1-pentyne
1,3-butadiene = 2-butyne
cis-1,3-pentadiene = 2-pentyne
trans-1,3-pentadiene = 2-pentyne

(From J. E. Kilpatrick, C. W. Beckett, E. J. Prosen, K. S. Pitzer, and F. D. Rossini, J. Research Natl. Bur. Standards **42**, 225 (1949)).

n-Alkyl benzene (gas) + Hydrogen (gas) = n-Alkyl cyclohexane
(gas); for n-Butylbenzene and higher.   (178)

Figure 50 gives a plot of the logarithm of the equilibrium constant, as a function of the temperature, for the following reactions of cyclization of 1-alkene monoolefins to normal alkyl cyclohexanes:

1-Hexene (gas) = Cyclohexane (gas)   (179)

1-Heptene (gas) = Methylcyclohexane (gas)   (180)

1-Octene (gas) = Ethylcyclohexane (gas)   (181)

1-Alkene$_{\underline{\ }}^{w}$(gas) = n-Alkyl cyclohexane (gas); for 1-Nonene and
higher.   (182)

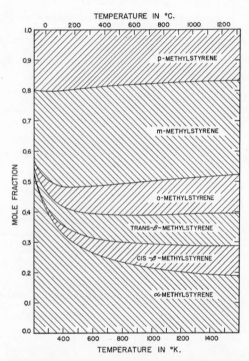

FIG. 55. Equilibrium concentrations of the six methylstyrenes.
The scale of ordinates measures the amount in mole fraction, and the scale of abscissas gives the temperature in degrees Kelvin and degrees centigrade. The vertical width of a band at a given temperature measures the mole fraction of the given isomer present at equilibrium with all of its other isomers in the gaseous state. (From J. E. Kilpatrick, C. W. Beckett, E. J. Prosen, K. S. Pitzer, and F. D. Rossini, *J. Research Natl. Bur. Standards* **42,** 225 (1949)).

8. DIOLEFINS

Kilpatrick *et al.* (46) have summarized the results on the thermodynamic properties of the diolefins C_3 to C_5.

In Fig. 51 are plotted, as a function of temperature, for the two butadienes, the amounts, in mole fraction, of each of the isomers present at equilibrium with the other isomer in the gaseous state.

In Fig. 52 are plotted, as a function of temperature, for the seven pentadienes, the amounts, in mole fraction, of each of the isomers present at equilibrium with the other isomers in the gaseous state.

In Fig. 53 are plotted, as a function of temperature, values of the logarithm of the equilibrium constant for the reactions of dehydrogenation of propylene to propadiene and of each of the four butenes to 1,3-butadiene.

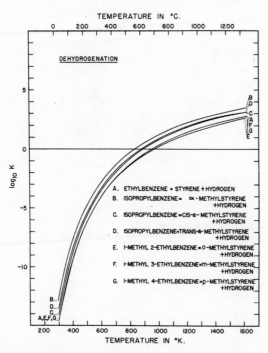

FIG. 56. Dehydrogenation of alkyl benzenes to corresponding styrenes.

The scale of ordinates gives the value of the logarithm (to the base 10) of the equilibrium constant for the reaction of dehydrogenating a given alkyl benzene to a corresponding styrene, in the gaseous state. The scale of abscissas gives the temperature in degrees Kelvin.

The several curves refer to the following reactions in the gaseous state:

(A) ethylbenzene = styrene + hydrogen
(B) isopropylbenzene = α-methylstyrene + hydrogen
(C) isopropylbenzene = cis-β-methylstyrene + hydrogen
(D) isopropylbenzene = $trans$-β-methylstyrene + hydrogen
(E) 1-methyl-2-ethylbenzene = o-methylstyrene + hydrogen
(F) 1-methyl-3-ethylbenzene = m-methylstyrene + hydrogen
(G) 1-methyl-4-ethylbenzene = p-methylstyrene + hydrogen

(From J. E. Kilpatrick, C. W. Beckett, E. J. Prosen, K. S. Pitzer, and F. D. Rossini, *J. Research Natl. Bur. Standards* **42**, 225 (1949)).

In Fig. 54 are plotted, as a function of temperature, values of the logarithm of the equilibrium constant for the reactions of isomerization of propadiene to propyne, 1,2-butadiene to 1-butyne, 1,2-pentadiene to 1-pentyne, 1,3-butadiene to 2-butyne, cis-1,3-pentadiene to 2-pentyne, and $trans$-1,3-pentadiene to 2-pentyne.

9. STYRENE AND METHYLSTYRENES

Kilpatrick *et al.* (46) have summarized the results on the thermodynamic properties of styrene and the methylstyrenes.

In Fig. 55 are plotted, as a function of temperature, for the six methyl-

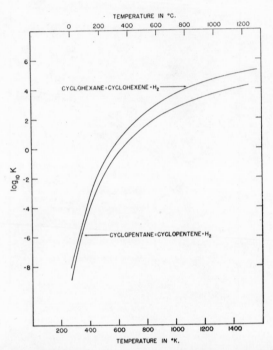

FIG. 57. Dehydrogenation of cycloparaffins to cycloolefins.

The scale of ordinates gives the value of the logarithm (to the base 10) of the equilibrium constant for the reaction of dehydrogenating the given cycloparaffin to the corresponding cycloolefin, in the gaseous state. The scale of abscissas gives the temperature in degrees Kelvin.

The curves refer to the following reactions in the gaseous state:

C_5H_{10} (gas, cyclopentane) = C_5H_8 (gas, cyclopentene) + H_2 (gas)

C_6H_{12} (gas, cyclohexane) = C_6H_{10} (gas, cyclohexene) + H_2 (gas)

(From M. B. Epstein, K. S. Pitzer, and F. D. Rossini, *J. Research Natl. Bur. Standards* **42**, 379 (1949)).

styrenes, the amounts, in mole fraction, of each of the isomers present at equilibrium with the other isomers in the gaseous state.

In Fig. 56 are plotted, as a function of temperature, values of the logarithm of the equilibrium constant for the reactions of dehydrogenation of ethylbenzene to styrene, isopropylbenzene to α-methylstyrene, isopropylbenzene to *cis*-β-methylstyrene, isopropylbenzene to *trans*-β-methylstyrene,

1-methyl-2-ethylbenzene to o-methylstyrene, 1-methyl-3-ethylbenzene to m-methylstyrene, and 1-methyl-4-ethylbenzene to p-methylstryene.

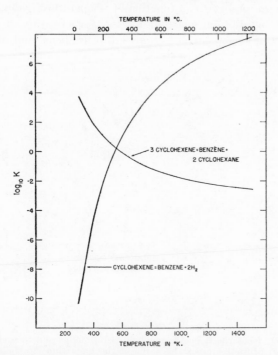

FIG. 58. Dehydrogenation of cyclohexene to benzene and disproportionation of cyclohexene to benzene and cyclohexane.

The scale of ordinates gives the value of the logarithm (to the base 10) of the equilibrium constant for the given reaction, in the gaseous state. The scale of abscissas gives the temperature in degrees Kelvin.

The curves refer to the following reactions in the gaseous state:

$$C_6H_{10} \text{ (gas, cyclohexene)} = C_6H_6 \text{ (gas, benzene)} + 2H_2 \text{ (gas)}$$
$$3C_6H_{10} \text{ (gas, cyclohexene)} = C_6H_6 \text{ (gas, benzene)} + 2C_6H_{12} \text{ (gas, cyclohexane)}.$$

(From M. B. Epstein, K. S. Pitzer, and F. D. Rossini, *J. Research Natl. Bur. Standards* **42**, 379 (1949)).

10. CYCLOPENTENE AND CYCLOHEXENE

Epstein *et al.* (47) and Beckett *et al.* (48) have summarized the results on the thermodynamic properties of cyclopentene and cyclohexene.

In Fig. 57 are plotted, as a function of temperature, values of the logarithm of the equilibrium constant for the reactions of dehydrogenation of cyclopentane to cyclopentene and of cyclohexane to cyclohexene.

In Fig. 58 are plotted, as a function of temperature, values of the logarithm of the equilibrium constant for the dehydrogenation of cyclohexene to benzene and for the disproportionation of cyclohexene to cyclohexane and benzene.

In Fig. 59 are plotted, as a function of temperature, values of the logarithm of the equilibrium constant for the isomerization of cyclopentene to 1-pentyne, of cyclopentene to *trans*-1,3-pentadiene, and of cyclohexene to 1-hexyne.

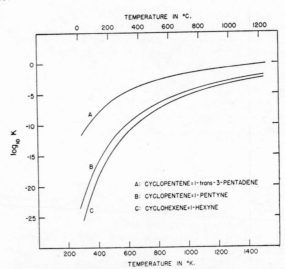

FIG. 59. Isomerization of cycloolefins to diolefins and to acetylenes.
The scale of ordinates gives the value of the logarithm (to the base 10) of the equilibrium constant for the given reaction, in the gaseous state. The scale of abscissas gives the temperature in degrees Kelvin.
The curves refer to the following reactions in the gaseous state:
  (A) C_5H_8 (gas, cyclopentene) = C_5H_8 (gas, *trans*-1,3-pentadiene)
  (B) C_5H_8 (gas, cyclopentene) = C_5H_8 (gas, 1-pentyne)
  (C) C_6H_{10} (gas, cyclohexene) = C_6H_{10} (gas, 1-hexyne)
(From M. B. Epstein, K. S. Pitzer, and F. D. Rossini, *J. Research Natl. Bur. Standards* **42**, 379 (1949)).

REFERENCES

1. G. N. Lewis, *Proc. Am. Acad. Arts. Sci.* **37**, 49 (1901).
2. G. N. Lewis and M. Randall, Thermodynamics and the Free Energy of Chemical Substances. McGraw-Hill Book Company, New York, 1923.
3. R. H. Newton, *Ind. Eng. Chem.* **27**, 302 (1935).
4. W. C. Edmister, *Petroleum Refiner* **27**, 104 (1948).
5. O. A. Hougen and K. M. Watson, Chemical Process Principles. Part Two. Wiley, New York, 1947.
6. K. M. Watson, Process Engineering Data. National Petroleum Publishing Company, Cleveland, 1944.
7. W. F. Giauque, *J. Am. Chem. Soc.* **52**, 4816 (1930).
8. L. Pauling, *J. Am. Chem. Soc.* **57**, 2680 (1935).
9. J. O. Clayton and W. F. Giauque, *J. Am. Chem. Soc.* **54**, 2610 (1932).

10. J. O. Clayton and W. F. Giauque, *J. Am. Chem. Soc.* **55**, 5071 (1933).
11. J. O. Clayton and W. F. Giauque, *J. Am. Chem. Soc.* **55**, 4875 (1933).
12. R. W. Blue and W. F. Giauque, *J. Am. Chem. Soc.* **57**, 991 (1935).
13. E. D. Eastman, *Chem. Revs.* **18**, 257 (1936).
14. L. Pauling and E. D. Eastman, *J. Chem. Phys.* **4**, 393 (1936).
15. H. L. Johnston and A. T. Chapman, *J. Am. Chem. Soc.* **55**, 153 (1933).
16. R. C. Tolman, The Principles of Statistical Mechanics. Oxford University Press, Oxford, 1938.
17. J. E. Mayer and M. G. Mayer, Statistical Mechanics. Wiley, New York, 1940.
18. Selected Values of Properties of Hydrocarbons. American Petroleum Institute Research Project 44. National Bureau of Standards, Washington, 1948.
19. J. D. Kemp and K. S. Pitzer, *J. Am. Chem. Soc.* **59**, 276 (1937).
20. E. B. Wilson, Jr., *Chem. Revs.* **27**, 17 (1940).
21. K. S. Pitzer, *J. Chem. Phys.* **5**, 469, 473 (1937).
22. B. L. Crawford, *J. Chem. Phys.* **8**, 273 (1940).
23. K. S. Pitzer and W. D. Gwinn, *J. Chem. Phys.* **9**, 485 (1941).
24. W. D. Gwinn and K. S. Pitzer, *J. Chem. Phys.* **16**, 303 (1948).
25. G. B. Kistiakowsky, J. R. Lacher, and F. Stitt, *J. Chem. Phys.* **7**, 289 (1939).
26. J. D. Kemp and C. J. Egan, *J. Am. Chem. Soc.* **60**, 1521 (1938).
27. G. B. Kistiakowsky, J. R. Lacher, and W. W. Ransom, *J. Chem. Phys.* **6**, 900 (1938).
28. F. D. Rossini, *Chem. Revs.* **18**, 233 (1936).
29. E. J. Prosen, W. H. Johnson, and F. D. Rossini, *J. Research Natl. Bur. Standards* **37**, 51 (1946).
30. F. D. Rossini, *J. Research Natl. Bur. Standards* **13**, 21 (1934).
31. F. D. Rossini, *Chem. Revs.* **27**, 1 (1940).
32. E. J. Prosen and F. D. Rossini, *J. Research Natl. Bur. Standards* **34**, 263 (1945).
33. E. J. Prosen and F. D. Rossini, *J. Research Natl. Bur. Standards* **36**, 269 (1946).
34. E. J. Prosen, W. H. Johnson, and F. D. Rossini, *J. Research Natl. Bur. Standards* **36**, 455 (1946).
35. F. D. Rossini, K. S. Pitzer, W. J. Taylor, J. E. Kilpatrick, J. P. Ebert, C. W. Beckett, M. G. Williams, and H. G. Werner, Selected Values of Properties of Hydrocarbons. National Bureau of Standards Circular 461. U.S. Government Printing Office, 1947.
36. D. D. Wagman, J. E. Kilpatrick, W. J. Taylor, K. S. Pitzer, and F. D. Rossini, *J. Research Natl. Bur. Standards* **34**, 143 (1945).
37. E. J. Prosen, K. S. Pitzer, and F. D. Rossini, *J. Research Natl. Bur. Standards* **34**, 255 (1945).
38. E. J. Prosen, K. S. Pitzer, and F. D. Rossini, *J. Research Natl. Bur. Standards* **34**, 403 (1945).
39. K. S. Pitzer and J. E. Kilpatrick, *Chem. Revs.* **39**, 435 (1946).
40. J. E. Kilpatrick, E. J. Prosen, and K. S. Pitzer, *J. Research Natl. Bur. Standards* **36**, 559 (1946).
41. J. E. Kilpatrick and K. S. Pitzer, *J. Research Natl. Bur. Standards* **37**, 163 (1946).
42. D. D. Wagman, J. E. Kilpatrick, K. S. Pitzer, and F. D. Rossini, *J. Research Natl. Bur. Standards* **35**, 467 (1945).
43. W. J. Taylor, D. D. Wagman, M. G. Williams, K. S. Pitzer, and F. D. Rossini, *J. Research Natl. Bur. Standards* **37**, 95 (1946).
44. J. E. Kilpatrick, C. W. Beckett, H. G. Werner, K. S. Pitzer, and F. D. Rossini, *J. Research Natl. Bur. Standards* **39**, 523 (1947).

45. E. J. Prosen, W. H. Johnson, and F. D. Rossini, *J. Research Natl. Bur. Standards* **39,** 173 (1947).
46. J. E. Kilpatrick, C. W. Beckett, E. J. Prosen, K. S. Pitzer, and F. D. Rossini, *J. Research Natl. Bur. Standards* **42,** 225 (1949).
47. M. B. Epstein, K. S. Pitzer, and F. D. Rossini, *J. Research Natl. Bur. Standards* **42,** 379 (1949).
48. C. W. Beckett, N. K. Freeman, and K. S. Pitzer, *J. Am. Chem. Soc.,* **70,** 4227 (1948).
49. E. B. Wilson, Jr., *J. Chem. Phys.* **4,** 526 (1936).
50. C. C. Stephenson and H. O. McMahon, *J. Chem. Phys.* **7,** 614 (1939).
51. J. Sherman and R. B. Ewell, *J. Phys. Chem.* **46,** 641 (1942).

AUTHOR INDEX

The numbers in parentheses are reference numbers; those in italics
refer to the pages on which references are listed in bibliographies at
the end of each article.
Example: Alberty, R. A., 259 (1) means that reference number 1 is
mentioned on page 259, without the author's name.

435

Subject Index

NOTE: The compounds listed alphabetically in the tables on pages 259–264 and 273–300 are not indexed unless mentioned elsewhere in the book.

A

Absorption cells, 116
  fabrication of, 189
Absorption currents, 217, 222
Acetic acid, 242, 247, 251, 256, 270
Acetic anhydride, 267, 268, 303
Acetone 305
Acetylene, 38, 39, 77, 78, 150, 151, 174, 403ff.
  trimerization of, 414, 415
Acetylenes, free energy of isomerization, 404, 405
  stability of, 404
Adiabatic calorimetry, 338
Aldol, 268
Alcohols, 250
Alkanes, see Paraffins
Alkenes, see Olefins
Alkylates, 107
Alkylation, 402, 403
  of benzene, 413, 415
Alkylbenzenes, 201, 284, 411ff.
  free energy of isomerization of n-, 411
  hydrogenation of n-, 423
  isomeriztion of, 410
  stability of n-, 410, 411, 413
n-Alkylcyclohexanes, conversion to n-alkylcyclopentanes, 422, 425
Alkylcyclohexanes, free energy of isomerization, 420
  stability of, 419
Alkylcyclopentanes, 415
  conversion to n-alkylcyclohexanes, 422, 425
  stability of, 416
Alkylnaphthenes, 325
Alkynes, see Acetylenes
Allene, 77
Amine, 235
Ammonia, 270
Ammonium hydroxide, 257
n-Amyl alcohol, 249
n-Amylbenzene, 410
Angular momentum quantum number, 138
Anharmonicity, 123
Aniline, 244, 257, 267, 268, 269, 272, 301, 304, 305
Aniline point, 275, 301
Aniline points, mixed, 304
Anthracene, 65, 157, 212, 327, 351
Appearance potentials, 100
Aromatic compounds, 66, 199, 201
Artificial conductivity, 225
Asphalt, 302, 303

Atomic polarization, 236
Atomic structure factor, 60
Attenuation factor, 177
Automatic recording unit, 178

B

Beer's law, 157, 168, 169, 171, 173, 174, 183, 201
Bending vibration, 124
Benzene, 47, 64, 66, 69, 77, 78, 154, 210, 203, 204, 205, 237, 243, 248, 250, 265, 171, 301, 317, 327, 410, 417, 426
Benzyl alcohol, 184, 304
Beta-radiation, 229
Binding energy, 21
Binodal curves, 244, 248, 253
Black body radiator, 118
Boltzmann distribution law, 374
Bond, covalent, 2
Bond angles, 30, 64, 77
  energy, 4, 21
  lengths, 64, 77
  refractions, 237
Bragg's law, 59
Breakdown, of hydrocarbons, 238
Broadening, pressure, 169
n-Butane, 77, 93, 94, 96, 109, 171, 172, 173, 328, 390, 392, 408
1,3-Butadiene, 42, 47, 48, 77, 78, 160, 172, 206, 424, 426, 427
1,2-Butadienes, 424
tert-Butanol, 249
1-Butene, 77, 171, 172, 384, 396, 398, 401, 408, 426
2-Butene, cis and trans, 77, 101, 106, 171, 172, 173, 358, 396, 398, 426
Butenes, free energy of isomerization of, 396
n-Butylbenzene, 410
tert-Butylbenzene, 200
n-Butylcyclohexane, 419
n-Butylcyclopentane, 158, 423
Butylene, see Butene
Butylphenols, 164
1-Butyne, 406, 404, 408, 427, 429
2-Butyne, 404, 406, 427, 429

C

Calcium fluoride, 116
Calorimeter, 339, 340, 357
  triple point, 343
Calorimetric method, 335, 346
  technique, 338, 339, 343
Calorimetry, adiabatic, 338

446